2 2 95/32

D1595792

THE MANAGEMENT OF INNOVATIVE
TECHNOLOGICAL CORPORATIONS

THE MANAGEMENT OF INNOVATIVE TECHNOLOGICAL CORPORATIONS

SIMON RAMO

Director, TRW Inc.
and
Visiting Professor, Management Sciences
California Institute of Technology

A WILEY–INTERSCIENCE
PUBLICATION

JOHN WILEY & SONS

New York Chichester
Brisbane Toronto

Library of Congress Cataloging in Publication Data:

Ramo, Simon.
 The management of innovative technological corporations.

 "A Wiley-Interscience publication."

 Includes index.
 1. Industrial management. I. Title. II. Title:
Technological corporations.
HD31.R26   658'.04'5   79-19460
ISBN 0-471-04436-9

PREFACE

This book is the result of two sets of the author's experiences. One stemmed from the creating and general management of technological corporations, some small—at least in the beginning—and others very large. The other is founded in teaching Business Administration and Engineering and Science students in universities.

Successful general management of technological corporations requires a serious interest in the recruiting of personnel who have the potential to be competent managers and in the extended training of managers. Also important is ensuring an adequate appreciation of management patterns by the professional employees engaged in specialized functional activities. They need to know why certain policies, controls, decision-making procedures, organizational concepts, and other management approaches are used. Furthermore, in technological corporations, many engineers and scientists often are required to move into management without the basic management tools that they could have received with a typical formal business school education. Of course, they can pick up accounting, finance, investment analysis and most established business fundamentals by reading and part-time courses. But it is not easy for them to find what they need efficiently presented in the context of a technological corporation.

For engineers and scientists arriving fresh into technological industry from college, it remains true today that only a fraction (even those long appreciative of the high probability their future employment would be in industry) come with some completed management courses. Quite often even those who have had a bit of business education are likely only to have been exposed to techniques which, though valuable, are not well connected with the *technological* corporation. Thus, although some of the young engineers may come to industry with an appreciation of the idea of a return on investment and be able to read a balance sheet with ease, many still hold to myths such as that newness in technology equates to profitability, or that the world will indeed beat a path to the door of the corporation with a better mousetrap. They particularly are likely to lack a feel for the integration and interrelationship of all of the functions—marketing, manufacturing, financing, product design and the rest. It usually takes longer than is desirable for the new engineer in technological industry to understand the management decision process and many such other important factors as the impact of government, the way inflation affects the R & D budget, and the need to study the competition.

In the best business schools of American universities, the typical graduate, through case studies and specialized courses in sophisticated analytical techniques, will have had an exposure to intellectual disciplines often beyond what the average experienced manager actually uses. Some of the leading academics and some creative analysts within technological corporations are together engaged in exploring new frontiers of management concepts and new tools, particularly those using available high capacity computers that can handle complex programs and modeling. Still there is a shortage of courses, and certainly of textbooks that have this book's objective of setting down the important basics particularly pertinent in the managing of a *technological* corporation. Both the student preparing to enter industry and the manager seeking to broaden his outlook must come to see successful technological corporation management as the competent relating of the technological aspects, such as engineering and manufacturing, with market, government, international and personnel aspects. In this text a considerable effort is made to explain how the separate pieces operate in the framework of the integrated whole.

There is a big difference between what the specialized operations analyst needs and what every professional employee of a technological corporation should understand. In this book, I have tried to create a useful balance between theory and practice, the quantitative and the qualitative. I have limited its scope to highly practical theory and theoretically sound practice. By this latter I mean practices most solidly credible. The aim has been to establish considerations—from goals, marketing strategies and organization principles, to quantitative analyses of performance and investment decisions—that appear worthwhile for all technical and business graduates to understand well if they plan to work in a technological corporation.

The book has already been used for these purposes, in various stages of notes and drafts. The text proper has many examples, and each chapter includes a number of additional problems at the end. In college classroom work these were assigned as homework, and the students' solutions were discussed in class. Most of the quantitative problems have proved to be readily solvable by the students who have read the text and text examples carefully. A few of the problems involve some subtle points that extend the text material, but the better students have always been able to handle these problems as well. The qualitative problems offer an opportunity for the professor to elaborate. For practicing managers in technological industry, or for those who are in training to be managers, working these added problems need not be considered essential, since the text incorporates an adequate number of illustrative examples. However, some time spent with the chapter-end problems might be advantageous.

The book requires no severe prerequisites. No mathematics beyond algebra is used. Only elementary knowledge is assumed of accounting, law, economics, business, and government.

I would like to acknowledge the benefit in revising drafts obtained from the suggestions of many students, faculty members, and associates at TRW, particularly from Mr. Ron Orr, who at the University of Southern California and the California Institute of Technology served as a deputy in teaching and working with students.

Redondo Beach, California   SIMON RAMO
September 1979

CONTENTS

THE MANAGEMENT OF INNOVATIVE TECHNOLOGICAL CORPORATIONS

1

GOALS AND OBJECTIVES

The Many Kinds of Objectives and Their Variability

Scientists would tell us that the collection of matter and beings constituting the universe is too vast and complex for us ever to describe all its detailed characteristics and laws of behavior. Nevertheless, the universe is here. We must live with it. What we know about it already is considerable, and that partial knowledge can be used to benefit the world's society.

A manager of a corporation would tell us that the piece of the universe comprising his company, though a tiny segment of the whole of creation, is nevertheless complex enough and sufficiently unmonitorable and uncontrollable in all its aspects that we cannot expect to cite intellectual disciplines and rules completely governing that business entity's performance. Nevertheless, much accumulated wisdom and many tried and true approaches are available for directing a corporation's affairs. An understanding and a skillful application of these can go far to ensure the success of the corporate endeavor.

A corporation is an intricate system of people, machines and facilities. It is a marvelous network of flow of information, money, material and products. It has myriad connections with the outside world through which a pattern of (some cooperative and some contesting) influences are communicated. If it is, moreover, a *technological* corporation, then it is even more marvelous and complex and also more dynamic and puzzling. Its laws and nature are even more intriguing and challenging to observe and understand. Now the very heart of the corporation's activity—the development, production and marketing of

1

technological products—is in constant disturbance as a result of scientific discovery and technological advance.

Every corporation is only a part of a huge worldwide activity to whose shifting economic, social and cultural interfaces the corporation must adapt. The altering of the scientific and technological base of the world creates both added difficulties and attractive opportunities for a technological corporation. No matter how large and competent, no corporation can expect its advances of the technological frontiers to be more than a small fraction of all that the world's fraternity of scientists and engineers will discover, invent and develop. A technological corporation's foundation floats on a rough sea of the world's churning science with new technological waves in constant formation.

The complexity and challenge of operating successfully with only partial knowledge and understanding, and the remarkable interactions of people with the system inside and outside the company, make the task of managing a technological corporation a fascinating one. This comment is not made to persuade the reader that of all the things he or she can choose to do in life the role of corporate manager is the one to aspire to. Being a successful corporation executive depends on possessing the right assortment of intellectual qualities and talents, high motivation, a practical sense of values and the opportunity. Ideally, a manager should have analytical and creative powers, aptitudes for directing people, and a balanced mixture of prudence, gambling instinct, wisdom and entrepreneurial flair. The reader may or may not possess or be able to develop these characteristics. Rather, these statements about the job of corporate management are made merely because they are true. Since they are fundamental, they are appropriate for starting our discussion.

Why a Corporation?

Let's begin this first chapter on the management of technological corporations with a conspicuously obvious question. What are or should be a corporation's goals and objectives. We are compelled to introduce one other issue just ahead. Why do we appear to assume that a business organization engaged in producing and marketing technological products is necessarily a corporation, a particular kind of legal entity that has many shareholders who constitute the owners? Certainly, a technological enterprise may well be a not-for-profit activity, such as a foundation or a technical university. Even if it is profit motivated, it may be owned by one person or a partnership of a group of individuals. It does not have to be a corporation.

This textbook is written around the corporation approach because that is the most common and important form in which profit-seeking technological activity exists. Many reasons have developed for the corporation to be the preferred business structure. Technological operations, to have the best chance for long-term success, typically must and do become quite large. Very substantial amounts of capital must be invested in them. The practical way to raise this capital is from a large number of investors. The technological activity sooner or later will become considerably diversified. Also, the company must be in a position to market its products widely, often internationally, and provide a staff for numerous supporting functions, such as application engineering with the customers, field maintenance and plentiful research and development both to ensure the position of the company's existing products in a competitive market and to develop new products. As the full potential of the company is realized, the capital invested in the entity grows.

Of course, many of the considerations taken up in this chapter, as well as the various management principles and tools discussed in the rest of the book, will apply to a proprietorship or a partnership (and even to the management of a nonprofit entity, such as a university research laboratory or a technical government agency). However, such applicabilities are incidental; this text was not written with the idea of covering such other situations. Rather, the point of view we take is deliberately chosen for pertinence to those prevalent, profit-seeking, industrial business organizations whose products and services are highly dependent upon science and technology.

Quantitative Objectives*

In tennis the professional player has in mind winning as the goal. The tactical, short-term objective during the play is to hit the ball in the court and so hard or so well-placed, that the opponent is unable to return it. Can we state a simple concept that defines what the chief executive of a corporation has to do? Asking even more, can we recite the goal or objective quantitatively? The "name of the game" in running a corporation may be treated quantitatively in at least two ways.

One approach recognizes that the management has been entrusted with some resources, more specifically, let us say, some capital. A cost

---

* In this chapter we shall often informally use the words "goal" and "objective" as synonymous, but most often we shall prefer "objective" for short-range "goal" and "goal" for long-range "objective."

goes with the use of this capital. The management must seek to maximize the return on this capital and to cause the difference between the return and the cost of capital to be as large as possible.

With this quantitative and simple concept in mind, we are equipped at least with a guide on how to proceed to study management. We must study the costs of capital and learn how to acquire the necessary capital for the activity at minimum cost. Then we must find out how to obtain a return on that capital, how to measure it and know we have it, and how to maximize it.

The other quantitative concept is to think of the task of management as that of maximizing the market value of a share of common stock. The price at which a shareholder is able to sell that share is a measure of the success of management. The higher the price the better the report card on management performance.

In principle, of course, these two quantitative concepts should amount to the same thing, and if it were not for the presence of a host of qualitative factors, then they would. In the long run, disregarding short-term ups and downs, steadily maximizing the difference between the return on managed capital and the cost of it would, at the same time, maximize the average market value of a share of ownership of the corporation.

Success in management, and the judging and proving of it, involves a combination of these quantitative concepts and numerous other qualitative ones, factors that do not lend themselves to quantitative evaluation. These all interplay in so complex a fashion that no easy rules exist for sorting them out and analyzing them. Good management means somehow achieving a practical balance in using as guides the measurable and quantitative parameters along with the less definite but equally important qualitative ones.

Qualitative Objectives

To provide one quick example of a qualitative objective for the management of a technological corporation, none is more conspicuous than that of strength in the pertinent science and technology. A well justified fear of management is being surpassed on the dynamic technological front by the superior technology of a competitor. Management must aspire to be capable of adjusting to general technological advance that may make obsolete the corporation's products. Conversely such advances may offer new applications and opportunities to capitalize on the technological strengths of the company. The permanent goal of possessing a sound technological position translates itself into such near-term objectives as ensuring adequate size and quality of the research and development effort, acquiring and holding enough technical experts, and maintaining broad liaison with technology advance outside the company.

A way to discuss further the qualitative goals and objectives and also describe another useful concept to serve as a guide for management as it sets goals is to recognize that the management of a corporation has many constituents. The goal of management tends to become that of satisfying these constituents. They include, in addition to the shareholders, the bankers or creditors to whom the corporation owes money, the general employees, the members of management, the customers, the suppliers, the governments of the nations, counties, and cities involved, the community in which the corporation lives and the general public. These groups have varying goals and objectives. They have different amounts of experience and sophistication. Their value judgments are only partially predictable (which means they are partially unpredictable) and are not necessarily correct ones. The constituents vary in the amount of information they possess concerning both the corporation and the outside world to which the corporation must relate. They interpret available facts differently, and they do not employ the same criteria. As a result, a very large spread exists in their measures of satisfactory or unsatisfactory results. We shall shortly examine the range of these measures.

Some objectives are short-range and temporary, merely a step toward long-time goals that might be regarded as permanent. No business with any degree of complexity goes along totally smoothly. Ups and downs are everywhere. There is a need for quick reactions to crises and for skill to prevent such crises by sensing their buildup ahead of time. Frequent occasions arise for changing organization, financing, product lines, or management personnel, and these alterations will involve objectives which,, although preferably consistent with a long-time goal, may be temporary. Growth and stability must be in proper balance. Objectives concerning both of these corporate characteristics are not entirely expressible or measurable in numbers. Risk is generally present in every aspect of a business and often both short-term objectives and long-term goals explicitly include an attempt to achieve compatibility between the risk-taking inherent in seeking a profit and the profit the risky effort might bring. Risk-taking, to a proper degree, goes hand in hand with the objectives of the management. Increased risk is sometimes deliberately accepted if it is presumed proper in relation to the anticipated improved corporate performance.

There is no simple, single goal or set of goals for the long term, nor a like set of objectives for the short, that will be wholly consistent with the long term. Instead, a broad spectrum of objectives exists, and it is always changing. The goals and objectives of a corporation must be continually articulated and reviewed, challenged and restructured. When it examines and selects alternatives, management must strive for a practical degree of harmony and compromise about goals and objectives. What is desired (or to be settled for) is completeness (never complete), measurability (never completely quantitatively describable), consistency (tolerable inconsistencies to be lived with) and flexibility (never totally flexible).

Satisfying the Constituents

The Shareholder

As stated earlier, one way that management can satisfy the wishes of the holders of the equity stock of the company, the corporations's real owners, is to manage in such a way that the market price of their stock is maximized. The real worth at any moment of what the shareholder owns in a share of stock is what he can sell it for. He may believe it is worth a great deal more than the market price (and on rare occasions a shareholder may feel it is worth considerably less than the market price), but it is what he can realize in a sale of his share that counts as the true value at that moment. However, it is a great oversimplification to imagine that this kind of thinking will adequately cover what shareholders expect from management. Most of them have in mind a lot of things beyond the present market price of the shares.

Some shareholders will have purchased the shares with the idea of holding them for a long time. To them the value ought to be reckoned by the "present value"* of the stream of dividends they hope to receive over the years. They are also interested in today's market price, of course, because their plans may have to change, and they may wish to turn their shares into cash. If, in the long term, the stock is expected to provide an excellent return through steady or increasing dividends, some shareholders will be only mildly concerned if the stock's market price slips temporarily below where they think it should be. In fact,

---

* Later we shall be more precise about this term. We mean by it that future dividends are discounted to an appropriate value today to compensate for the later date of their actual receipt and the earning power of the funds in the interim.

a purist might say that the market price for a share of stock should always be precisely equal to the present value of the stream of future dividends out to eternity. But even if everyone who bought a share of stock or sold one were impressed with this way of judging the price, a wide range of estimates would exist of the size of those accumulated dividends.

Some will buy the shares of a technological corporation in anticipation of technological breakthroughs by the company, or at least of announcements that would be convincing enough to cause the market price to go up rapidly in the short term. If shares were purchased with the idea that the market price might double in the next year, the purchasers would then be annoyed with management if it does not do so. In new technological corporations, there usually is a substantial period from the founding of the company until it pays or is expected to pay regular dividends. For those companies, it might be better to reinvest earnings in further product development and market penetration and not pay out needed cash in dividends. The image or the substantive evidence of growth and technological advance may figure heavily into the market price of a share of stock in a technological corporation. A company with modest earnings, or one still in a start-up or loss position as regards earnings, may have a higher market price per share than another corporation whose products are more mature, even though the latter has good earnings and a strong dividend paying record.

If the product line of a technological corporation is believed to be in danger of technological obsolescence, or if the company generally appears not to be holding its own in technological advance, then it may find the demand for its shares disappointingly low, even though it's operations are presently profitable. Thus, the relation between the true long-term worth of a corporation and its momentary stock value is difficult to predict.

It is tempting to recommend that for goals and objectives the management of a technological corporation should ignore the market price of its stock and concentrate on providing sound management. Such a focus, it could be argued, would automatically result in the value of the shares being maximized in the long run, even though the market value at any particular moment might be off severely from that value. Unfortunately, the immediate market value of the shares has to be of importance to management, because it bears on the ability of management to raise further capital at that time by the sale of more stock. It also affects management's ability to arrange beneficial mergers and acquisitions using newly issued shares in a trade for companies to be acquired. It influences management and general employee morale. It affects indirectly the general confidence in the company, bearing on its success in marketing its products and in recruiting top personnel. For these reasons stock price figures into the priorities for the use of management energy, a precious corporate resource.

Thus what the shareholders want and think and the market price of equity securities, both figure into the goals and objectives of management.

The Creditors

When it sets objectives, management has to consider the banks, bond-holders and other creditors from whom the corporation borrows funds. To obtain these funds requires a satisfactory financial condition and enough earnings to provide ample evidence that the loan will be repaid as promised. For a going corporation that does not even remotely expect to be threatened by bankruptcy (or by a tight money situation so extreme the ability to pay back loans may be endangered) it is still important that the corporation be strong financially, because then it will merit a low interest rate on its loans. The less the corporation needs to borrow and the more certain it is that in the future it will no longer need the sum borrowed or more, the lower will be the interest rate and hence the cost of the capital obtained. Generally, the creditor wants to see an earnings stream sufficient to cover the interest charges, all of the fixed burdens of the corporation, and the dividends it plans to pay (or ought to pay) with a substantial cushion left over. The creditor looks, in other words, for a healthy coverage, a wide safety margin between cash in-flow and cash out-flow and thus a strong ability to pay back the loan.

The use of borrowed money is important to the manager of the corporation. Most often, optimum financing means a mixture of funds raised by the selling of shares and funds borrowed. Good management involves arranging the right ratio of debt to equity capital. Aside from this it is important to the manager to have a favorable overall image with the sources of borrowed funds. Banks are sources of information valuable to management and can provide counseling on financial matters, leads to acquisition and merger possibilities and judgments about timing for expansion and the location of such expansion. They provide independent and objective analyses of the overall financial performance of the corporation. It has to be one of the goals of a corporation to merit credit.

The Employee

It is beyond discussion that the general employees, in their motivation, productivity, skills and cooperation, are key factors in the success of a corporation. In a technological corporation it is very important that the environment of the corporation be attractive to outstanding technical personnel. The different functions of the total personnel—engineering, marketing, production, field maintenance, accounting, public relations—all require specialized attention, because to some extent what makes for the most outstanding employee performance and morale will vary from one category to another. However, a good manager knows that all employees are interested in their take-home pay, overall benefits, job security, opportunities for growth, the environment in which they work and the overall image of the company.

Management employees of course are interested in these same things. In addition, the opportunity and challenge of the job, the stability and growth opportunities, and the perquisites and prestige of the position are almost as important as salary.

When it looks at either long-term goals or short-term objectives, top management has to be constantly aware of the importance of the general and management employee structure of the company. Although the long-range goal is relatively easy to state in general terms—to have outstandingly well satisfied, enthusiastically contributing, competent employees at competitive costs—the proper management of personnel involves numerous and changing short-term objectives. These may range from the appropriate handling of a single negotiation with a workers union to modification of the top executive salary structure.

The Customer

We shall devote considerable attention in this text to that constituency of management known as the customer. Some managers would simply put the customer at the top of the list—no customer, no income. Management must have as a goal a satisfied customer. Intermediate objectives may be to increase the number of customers in the short term, attract a new group of them for certain product endeavors, offer them additional inducement, or eliminate a bad customer situation immediately by a concerted attack. But, in general, in setting goals and objectives the management must cater to the desire of the customer for a dependable product that is cost and price competitive and does what the customer expects of it.

Short-term sales objectives with customers are very likely to fail in the face of a long-term low reputation of the company, if the company's apparent stability and overall image in providing customer satisfaction is tarnished. Particularly when offering technological products, a need exists for a goal of a healthy reputation with the customer. On many simple nontechnological products customers will buy from the supplier with the lowest price. But in a technological product the customer will look at more than price. The description of the product is more complex, and confidence by the customer that the performance will be as he anticipates is often based on respect for the depth of the technological effort by the selling corporation. The buyer will expect expertise in providing him with a product suited to his technical task.

Management of a technological corporation must be prepared to include a long-term goal of close relationship with the customer during a product's inception, development, and production design and in application, service and repair even after the sale is completed.

The Supplier

All corporations must develop sound relations with suppliers who furnish them with materials, components and supporting services. This is especially important for a technological corporation. No company is sufficient unto itself, and a technological corporation depends upon technological ideas from specialized expertise beyond those it breeds internally. For technological corporations it is important to have a cooperative group of suppliers with whom there is a long-term, close relationship, including a considerable amount of interchange of technological information. The corporation's products depend in part on the suppliers' products, and effective coordination is required if the most harmonious and cost-effective performance is to result. A supplier in turn will be motivated to work closely with a technological corporation that appears to him to have financial stability and a strong enough marketing and product development program to hold its place in the competitive world.

Accordingly, part of framing the objectives and goals of a technological corporation includes a suitable meshing with the goals and objectives of its suppliers.

The Government

The government is more than a small factor in the running of any corporation. The management of a technological corporation particularly must always have the government in mind. For technical products, the federal government is the largest customer, regulator, rule maker and influence on the overall environment for technological advance. It is the most important sponsor of research and development. The government is often a partner and sometimes a competitor.

The corporate management must figure out the relationship it seeks with government. It must harmonize the corporation's plans with the plans of government, and adjust its goals and objectives to allow for the impact and influence of government.

The Public

The general public—beyond the fact that included among that body are customers, voters who influence government actions and attitudes, and shareholders—judges a corporation and creates the environment within which the corporation must live. The goals of a corporation must take into account community relations in all of the geographical locations where the corporation operates. The company's actions and image in those communities have a great deal to do with the success of the corporation because such community influences directly affect the employees and may affect the regulation of the actions of the corporation. The corporation must plan to have the image of a responsible member of the community.

The corporation's goals and objectives should encompass excellent communications between the corporation and the public at large as well as the citizens of the specific communities in which the corporation operates. Most of the information about the benefits provided by the company, or claimed harm it may do, to the community in the short or long term reaches the community through the communications media, that is, through newspapers, radio and television. Thus the company must have as one goal effective communication links with these media.

Corporate management must recognize that it has a communications need with many dimensions and perhaps some communications problems and opportunities. It is not enough to have good goals and objectives for all the constituencies that management knows demand satisfaction. It is necessary also that a communications program exist to reach all these constituencies effectively.

Financial Condition Objectives

What kind of goals should a corporation have for its financial condition? To be strong financially, yes, but can we be more specific?

The Balance Sheet

Table 1–A is a simplified balance sheet listing the assets and liabilities of a well run technological corporation in sound financial condition. We could say that this is a good balance sheet. By looking at the ratios of the various numbers on this sheet, an experienced analyst might be inclined to regard the company as probably in reasonably strong shape financially, although at the same time his confidence about that tentative opinion would be limited. He would want to know a lot more about the company, see more figures describing the operation and learn much qualitative information about the company's present and future product and market situation.

To help us see why, even superficially, we should have a beginning confidence in the financial condition of this company, it will be helpful to revise* the balance sheet into Table 1–B where we have subtracted the current liabilities from both sides to get working capital, the difference between current assets and current liabilities. Having done this, we now see total assets of $1100 million, with the shareholders' equity (the sum of proceeds from sale of stock and the cumulative retained earnings) making up $800 million, against a total debt of $300 million. The debt to equity ratio is 3 to 8 (.375) and the ratio of debt to total assets defined in Table 1–B is 3 to 11 (.273).

If this company is profitable within the par range of the meaning of that term for good technological corporations, then its earnings will be substantially greater than the interest on the debt. If it had not borrowed funds, it would either have less assets at work to produce earnings or it would have had to issue more shares, diluting the earnings per share. At this point, without further analysis, we are biased to believe that the company may be using debt properly. Of course, it is much too early to say for sure. In following chapters we shall go into this matter with reasonable thoroughness. At this point suffice it to say that a .375 debt-to-equity ratio, although a bit high, is in the region where sound technical corporations often operate.† Of course, some companies, outstanding from the standpoint of the quality of their balance sheet, have no debt at all. They may not be using sufficient leverage, that is, debt added to equity, to fatten earnings by employing more assets, or they may have good reasons to resist doing

---

* Both approaches to the balance sheet are commonly employed, the choice depending on the details to be emphasized. See Appendix A for a short elaboration of balance sheet presentation alternatives.

† See Appendix B.

Table 1-A

Assets (millions $)			Liabilities (millions $)		
Current Assets			Current Liabilities		560
Cash	20		Debt		
Receivables	400		Current	30	
Inventories	500		Long-term	270	
Prepaids	40				
Total		960	Total		300
Fixed Assets		550	Shareholders' Equity		
Intangibles		100	Common Stock	50	
Marketable Securities		50	Retained Earnings	750	
			Total		800
Total Assets		1660	Total Liabilities		1660

part of their financing by borrowing. We shall also say more about this later on.

Accepted accounting guidelines require that many leases be capitalized. If a corporation has obligated itself to a long-term lease of a facility, for example, then the rules say this is the same as if it had obligated itself for a loan, because even if the company finds its business falling off so drastically it no longer needs the facility, it must go on paying for it according to the terms of the lease. It would be misleading to fail to recognize this real obligation on the balance sheet. A way to show it there is to consider the lease obligation as a part of long-term debt. A technological corporation that is growing rapidly, particularly one in its infancy, can stretch available capital by leasing rather than buying much of the assets required in its business. When it does so, this is basically no different from borrowing operating funds in more direct ways. In this text, where we think of

Table 1-B

Assets (millions $)		Liabilities (millions $)	
Working Capital	400	Debt	300
Fixed Assets	550	Shareholders' Equity	800
Intangibles	100		
Marketable Securities	50		
Total Assets	1100	Total Liabilities	1100

assets (A) as balancing equity (Q) plus debt (D), D should be understood to include the lease obligation.

We note that the corporation has marketable securities of $50 million. Our confidence is greater in the financial condition of the company when we see this excess cash listed in the assets column. Of course, these funds could have been used to pay off some of the debt. So the corporation really has the financial strength and option to select a smaller debt-to-equity ratio than was previously mentioned.

Working Capital

What of the working capital? First, we are glad to note from Table 1–A that the current assets substantially exceed the current liabilities. Also from Table 1–B we see that if the company had to be shut down and only the liquid assets could be turned into cash (the fixed assets and intangibles, let us say, being essentially worthless for instant conversion) we would realize the working capital, $400 million, plus the marketable securities of $50 million, for a total of $450 million, which exceeds all debt. There would appear to be very little chance this company could be bankrupt in the near future.

If we knew more about the company and its products we would be able to ponder the individual items making up the working capital. We would know, for instance, whether the receivables of $400 million are high, indicating that the company does not do a good job of getting its customers to pay their bills, and whether the current liabilities are too large, suggesting the company itself is a slow payer. Similarly we would know whether the inventories being carried are out of line. Depending upon the kind of product being manufactured and the length of time that product must be in manufacture, there can be substantial and justified variations in the amount invested in partially completed products on their way through the factory. It may or may not be desirable to carry a large inventory of parts and raw materials. This would be judged in part on what appears to be happening to, or is in prospect for, the price structure, whether materials are going to be in short supply at some later time, or whether a strike is believed to impend in industries supplying critical items to the company.

Thus, we cannot engage in a critical analysis of this corporation's financial condition from the sparse items listed in Tables 1–A and 1–B. However, we still put this forward as a typical balance sheet configuration of a sound technological corporation, which most corporation directors wish their company to be. The ratios of the various items shown are in the range which management might well set down as a goal. (See Appendix B.)

Intangibles

A substantial intangible figure on the balance sheet is generally considered a negative when analyzing the quality of a balance sheet. However, in Table 1–B this figure is less than 10 percent of the total assets, so this is not a vital issue. These intangibles probably resulted from purchases in the past by the corporation of other companies. Presumably the assets of those companies were purchased for cash, but at a price greater than the stated (book) value on the balance sheet of the acquired corporation. The reason why it was sound for our corporation to have paid more than the acquired corporation's book value was because of the anticipated stream of future earnings of the purchased company. If the intangibles item on the balance sheet properly belongs there, and is not to be written off as worthless, it means we really expect the corporation to enjoy an earnings flow from the purchased asset that will turn out to be the equivalent of the stated intangible. Usually the plan is to decrease the stated value, writing it down gradually, that is, amortizing it, in 30 to 40 years. Some of the earnings thus are given up to cover this loss of book assets each year. Eventually, the specific intangible item so amortized will disappear from the balance sheet. Of course, for justified reasons, new intangibles may appear. For instance, the company may pay millions for a valuable patent.

Earnings Objectives; The Profit and Loss Statement

What should be the goals of a corporation for earnings? To maximize them, at least in the long run? True. But that is too simple and not very helpful. First of all there is a time element. A technological corporation's management may decide to sacrifice near-term earnings and take on high added expenses to do more research and development. This would be done to increase earnings later. The company would hope by such a strategy to earn a lot more for the shareholders by the time the whole history of events is recorded. Of course, some constituencies, perhaps the shareholders, may not be happy with this decision in the short term, and this would have to be considered by the management as it sets up its goals.

Cash Flow and Earnings

A sensible objective for earnings has to be related in substantial part to cash requirements, to the amount of funds needed (to be acquired either from retained earnings, from sale of more equity stock or by borrowing) to invest in expansion to attain growth of earnings. Suppose a corporation happens at a given time to have very little debt, a substantial amount of excess cash, and earnings sufficient to pay an acceptable dividend and replace depreciated assets with plenty left over for reinvestment that will provide the financial backing for all the growth the market demand creates in the particular product line the corporation is selling. Under such circumstances the immediate earnings objective for management is quite different from that of a corporation hard pressed to find the cash it needs to expand and hold its market position in a product line that is expanding and where competitors would be very happy to take away the corporation's customers.

Management usually has the goal to increase earnings. Among other ways, earnings can be enhanced in the short term quite often by simply putting more assets to work and acquiring these assets by using borrowed funds. So objectives concerning earnings are tied into objectives concerning debt-equity ratios, as well as with objectives for cash flow, funds available for investment, and growth. But there is more.

Goals for Return on Investment

Recall the basic quantitative objective of management we stated earlier, that of seeking the highest return on the capital entrusted to management compared with the cost of that capital. Surely the earnings objectives of a corporation must be consistent with maximizing this difference. But this aim is implemented by setting an objective for the return on each incremental investment. The management is constantly engaged in investment decisions—a new plant, a new machine, a new R & D project, a start up of a new product. Each time management invests funds it usually seeks a return that is greater than the cost of capital, and the bigger the expected difference, the better the decision will appear to be. However, the good cash return may be accumulated gradually over a substantial period of time, not necessarily during the year for which earnings are being reported. The performance of the corporation during any one period consists of the contributions during that period of pieces of histories unfolding over many years on a large number of individual investment decisions. What happens to the corporation during a year is the integrated sum of what is happening to these many projects on many fronts, all presumably the result of decisions made at various times—some that year, but most in years before. It is sensible for management to have goals for each incremental investment it makes, mindful that it will not know whether it has realized the goal until that whole project is complete. This may take years. The reported earnings of a corporation for a period is related to, albeit in a complicated way, the incremental return on the active investment projects.

Later we shall study the relationships among such important parameters as reported earnings for a period, debt-equity ratio, cash flow and returns on individual investments. Then earnings goals and objectives will become clearer. However, to continue this introduction to the matter of goals and objectives as it relates to earnings performance, we shall find it useful to introduce a number of symbols and quantitative relationships.

Nomenclature for Financial Performance

Table 1–C lists nomenclature we shall use throughout the text. We assume that balance sheets will be in the form of Table 1–B so that A

Table 1–C   Definitions of Operating Parameters

S = Sales or Revenues
C = Costs
$E = S - C$ = Earnings
D = Debt
Q = Equity (shareholders' original investments plus retained earnings)
A = Assets Employed = $D + Q$
T = Depreciation
W = Working Capital = Current Assets − Current Liabilities
F = Cash Flow = $E + T$
V = Dividends
i = Interest Rate
R_{ES} = Sales Margin = E/S
R_{SA} = Turnover = S/A
R_{DQ} = Debt-Equity Ratio = D/Q
R_{DA} = Debt-Assets Ratio = D/A
R_{EA} = Return on Assets Employed = E/A
R_A = Return on Assets Employed Before Interest Charges = $(E + iD)/A$
R_{EQ} = Return on Equity = E/Q
R_V = Dividend Ratio = V/E
N = Number of Common Shares Outstanding
Q_S = Book Value of Common Share = Q/N
P = Market Value of Common Shares Outstanding
P_S = Market Value of Common Share = P/N
E_S = Earnings per Common Share = E/N
M = Price-Earnings Multiple = P_s/E_s

and D are defined consistent with that form. A is total assets as shown on the assets side and D is the long term debt. In some instances we shall wish to express quantities in per (common) share amounts. This will be done by adding the subscript "s" to the symbol for the quantity. Thus with E standing for the earnings of the corporation and N the number of common shares outstanding $E_s = E/N$.

Most often we shall use E to represent the net earnings of the corporation, that is, the differences between sales, S, and costs, C, with C comprising *all* costs, including depreciation, interest and taxes. Sometimes we shall want to discuss a gross earnings figure, a figure before taxes or even before interest, and so forth. Then, unless we slip up, we shall always so indicate. Usually the specifics of the discussion will make clear which earnings, gross or net, are meant. Similarly, the interest rate, i, will be generally understood to mean after taxes, unless specifically stated in a discussion as being before taxes.

T, the depreciation, is the amount of cash set aside (from the total cash received in the sale of products and services) to cover the replacement costs of the facilities and other capital items that are depreciating. Since the calculated and reported earnings, E, are net after subtracting this depreciation cost item, T, we must add T back to E to obtain the positive cash being generated, F. Now, it may be argued that F is not all actually available for discretionary use, and, in fact, an amount, T, must actually be committed and spent to buy replacements for the depreciating plant assets. To be even more accurate, during inflation, funds greater than T are required to maintain the working assets in top condition. This is because the Internal Revenue Service (IRS) only allows a depreciation expense related to the original (historical) costs of the depreciating asset, not its replacement cost. However, when we ask about the cash being *produced*, not that which is being *spent* or *dispensed*, then $F = E + T$ is the correct relation.

The Ratio R_A

The various ratios introduced are straight forward except R_A, which is extremely important to the question of goals and objectives and for gauging financial performance. It deserves further comment at this point.

R_A measures the ability of the corporation to generate earnings by employing the assets of the corporation. If R_A is to perform this measurement for us, it must ignore the method the corporation used to finance and acquire these assets in the first place, whether by selling equity shares, accumulating earnings or borrowing money. Accordingly, since the calculated and reported E is after paying interest charges (iD), the real earning power of the assets is $E + iD$. This figure truly represents the earnings generated before we lowered them to include recognition of the fact that some of our assets were paid for by borrowed funds. We shall sometime refer loosely to R_A as the return on assets employed. We say loosely because R_A is really that return *before interest charges*. This distinguishes R_A from R_{EA} which is the return on assets employed after interest charges.

In setting financial objectives, management will pay close attention to R_A. In fact, no objective is more important than a target for R_A. To illustrate why and give an introduction to the relationships among R_{DA}, R_V and growth, let us derive an expression for the growth rate, g, of the earnings, E, of a corporation.

(We have chosen to use a simple balance sheet, a correspondingly simple definition of the total assets A, and an equally simplified definition of R_A, the return on assets employed before interest charges. By doing this, we have made it easier for us to demonstrate certain fundamental principles without getting into accounting details. For instance, in computing R_A, an annual financial ratio, the earnings for the given year will be compared with the assets at the beginning of that year. Admittedly, this procedure is not admirable, if the assets change radically during the year. Many companies, in calculating R_A, generate monthly asset figures by taking the average of the assets at the beginning and ending of each month and also annualize monthly earnings. Then the annual R_A is the average of the twelve ratios computed monthly.)

Growth Rate of Earnings

From the definition of R_A

$$E = R_A A - iD \tag{1}$$

This says that the net earnings are a result of the basic working of the assets to produce R_A, less the interest charges that are paid. Or

$$E = (R_A - iR_{DA})A \tag{2}$$

The cash flow is

$$F = E + T \tag{3}$$

Suppose some of the cash is used to pay dividends (V) and some is employed to provide replacement of depreciating assets (T). Then the cash left, the retained earnings that will add to shareholders' equity (Q), is

$$\Delta Q = (E + T) - T - V = E(1 - R_V) \qquad [4]$$

If the equity (Q) grows, so will the earnings in the period ahead (assuming R_{EQ} remains constant) in the ratio

$$\Delta E = R_{EQ}\Delta Q \qquad [5]$$

or, from Equation 4

$$\Delta E = R_{EQ}(1 - R_V)E \qquad [6]$$

from which the rate of growth in earnings, g, is

$$g = \frac{\Delta E}{E} = (1 - R_V)R_{EQ} \qquad [7]$$

Let us look at this another way. Suppose that, keeping R_{DA} constant, we borrow an amount, ΔD, so that the total assets available to be employed in the period ahead will now be $A + \Delta A$ where

$$\Delta A = \Delta Q + \Delta D$$

which, from Eq. 4 and the definition of R_{DA} is

$$\Delta A = E(1 - R_V) + R_{DA}\Delta A \qquad [8]$$

Rearranging Equation 8 yields

$$\Delta A = E\,\frac{1 - R_V}{1 - R_{DA}} \qquad [9]$$

Employing this added increment of assets with the same effectiveness as in the last period, that is, assuming R_A, which measures this effectiveness, remains constant, we shall realize an increment to earnings above the previous E (see Equation 2) of

$$\Delta E = (R_A - iR_{DA})\Delta A$$

$$= \frac{1 - R_V}{1 - R_{DA}} (R_A - iR_{DA})E \qquad [10]$$

Comparing delta E with E gives the growth rate of earnings,

$$g = (R_A - iR_{DA})(1 - R_V)/(1 - R_{DA}) \qquad [11]$$

For a company with no debt

$$g = R_A(1 - R_V) \qquad [12]$$

and for one with no dividends

$$g = (R_A - iR_{DA})/(1 - R_{DA}) \qquad [13]$$

while with neither

$$g = R_A \qquad [14]$$

As a check, note from the definitions of Table 1–C,

$$R_{EQ} = E/Q = \frac{R_A A - iR_{DA}A}{A(1 - R_{DA})} = \frac{R_A - iR_{DA}}{1 - R_{DA}} \qquad [15]$$

This, if substituted into Equation 7, yields Equation 11.

If all of the key operating ratios (R_A, R_V, R_{DA} and i) stay constant then g is the growth rate not only for earnings but also for equity, assets and debt.

From these equations we can say that a company with a specific set of values of these operating parameters should not announce a growth rate goal greater than that given by Equation 11 unless the management is also prepared to claim it is able to improve the operating ratios and make that claim credible.

Generally, but not always, corporations are expected to pay dividends on the common shares, if not now then in the not too distant future. Of course, particularly for a corporation involved in new exciting technology, the management may be able to justify a goal for many years of no dividends and, instead, a maximum reinvestment of earnings to back growth. An R_V of 20 to 30 percent is common for highly regarded, large, well established technological corporations. Hence, a management goal to provide such a dividend ratio is equally common. (See Appendix B.)

A technological corporation generally can be said to need growth for success and, if successful, it will attain a steady growth. A g of 10 percent or higher is a reasonably ambitious long-time goal for a technological corporation. If this range of growth is to occur with a dividend ratio of 25 percent and a debt of no more than 25 percent, both typical goals, then from Equation 11 (assuming $i = .05$)

$$.1 = (R_A - .05 \times .25)(1 - .25)/(1 - .25)$$

or

$$R_A = .1 + .0125 = .1125$$

which says a goal to attain an R_A of greater than 11.25 percent is incumbent on management for consistency with its g, R_{DA} and R_V goals.

A "Good" P & L Statement

With these relationships established, let us now look at a typical Profit and Loss Statement for an established technological corporation. Table 1–D is a simplified report of a year's operating results. In addition to

**Table 1–D   A Good P & L Statement
(millions of $)**

Sales	100.0
Costs (except taxes and interest)	78.0
Earnings (before taxes and interest)	22.0
Interest Paid (before tax deductions)	0.8
Earnings (after interest)	21.2
Taxes (at 50 percent)	10.6
Earnings (after tax)	10.6
Depreciation	4.0
Cash Flow	14.6
Dividends Paid	3.3
Investment to Replace Depreciating Facilities	4.0
Investment for Growth	7.3

the figures shown, let us assume the balance sheet for this company would show the assets as $40 million and R_{DA} = .20, meaning that the equity, Q, is $32 million and the debt, D, $8 million. Using this and the after-tax earnings (Table 1–D) of $10.6 million, R_A (the return on assets employed before interest charges) is seen to be

$$R_A = \frac{E + iD}{A} = \frac{10.6 + .05 \times 8}{40} = 11/40 = .275$$

(where after tax quantities, at 50 percent tax, have been used).

This is an outstanding return, greatly exceeding the recent average cost of capital figures, as we shall see in the next chapter. An R_A of over 20 percent is a difficult long-term steady value for most technological companies to attain. (See Appendix B.)

From the figures given in Table 1–D, we have also

$$R_V = 3.3/10.6 = .31$$

Thus the growth rate, g, assuming all operating ratios can and will be maintained in the period ahead, is given by Equation 11 as

$$g = (.275 - .05 \times .2)\frac{1 - .31}{1 - .2} = .228$$

From the table, E = $10.6 million on sales of $100 million for a sales margin of

$$R_{ES} = 10.6/100 = .106$$

Another reason for calling the profit and loss statement a good one is that the corporation appears to be earning enough not only to dwarf the interest expense on its debt but also to finance a more than satisfactory growth rate. Of course, we do not know if the earnings can be maintained long at the level reported in this earnings statement which reports one year of activity. Again, as with our quick look at a typical good balance sheet earlier, we have not sufficient information to judge confidently whether the company is going to be successful in the long run. However, we can say that this P & L statement is outstanding and almost any technological corporation could well aspire to it as either a long-term goal or a short-term one.

Most technological corporations do not attain the sales margin shown in this example, the general level of return on assets employed, the ability to pay dividends, interest charges and taxes, and at the same time have so much left over to plow back for adequate replacement of its plant and facilities and for continued growth. A corporation's P & L performance could be much poorer than that described in Table 1–D and the corporation still be properly judged as in satisfactory condition. (See Appendix B.)

Suppose, for instance, that a company has invested heavily in new products still in the start-up stage and the sales volume has not yet reached the levels required to show profits. The important issue becomes then whether the sales will continue rising to reach a profit phase in the not too distant future. Or perhaps the corporation has elected to broaden its marketing greatly. Because it is paying the extra marketing costs for a year or two, earnings are hurt. It if appears to be laying the groundwork for superior earnings and a stronger overall position in the market for a substantial period into the future, then the temporary low profit condition can be tolerated.

Generally speaking, if the P & L statement for a given year meets the objectives of most of the constituencies, then the constituencies' next question will be, "Can the corporation keep it up?" On the other hand, if the P & L statement is disappointing in one respect or another, the constituencies will expect management to explain what is being done to change the situation. Thus, the annual earnings performance has to figure heavily into the goals and objectives of the corporation, just as does the overall financial condition of the corporation shown by the makeup of its assets and liabilities.

Sales and Market Position Objectives

Generally a corporation has the long-term goal of a strong marketing position for its product vis-a-vis competitors for a long period in which the customers will find the product, at the least, acceptable, and, preferably, extremely cost-effective and attractive. Usually a technological corporation tends to become diversified, and its product mix in any case includes some old and some new products, some satisfactory ones and some less so in terms of their position against competitors and their cost-effectiveness for the customer. The management seeks as a sales goal that it sell the right products for that company, products close to unique, that it maintain a head start over competitors, and that its technology be current. It wants its market share to be high compared with competitors, with continued market growth, and a high return on assets employed.

If these conditions are not met, management must alter them, perhaps even liquidating the product line or selling it to some other corporation. Of course, we can imagine other realistic possibilities. Perhaps the product line could be extended by further development, or further risk investment should be made in a quest for higher sales volume to cut costs through volume. Maybe the manufacturing technology could be improved to cut the cost of manufacture, or technological development could be pushed to better the performance of the product and extend its life.

Consider a corporation, for example, for whom the main operating parameters are as indicated in Table 1–E. The company's performance as judged by R_A at .105 is only fair, as is the sales margin (R_{ES}) at .032. The debt appears too high at $R_{DA} = .5$, although the turnover, at $R_{SA} = 2.5$, is in the range of most successful technological corporations.

Suppose now that the management decides to give up the unsatisfactory product lines, even though this will entail temporary losses and cause the company to be smaller in terms of sales and employees. The strategy is to cause the modified corporation to be in a stronger posture. Specifically, the company sells for $15 million the division producing the unsatisfactory products, to which it now has $20 million of assets committed, for a loss of $5 million. (At some future time,

Table 1–E   End of Year Balance Sheet (millions of $)

Assets		Liabilities	
Satisfactory Products	80	Debt	50
Unsatisfactory Products	20	Equity	50
Total	100	Total	100

Last Year's P & L (millions of $)

Sales	250
Earnings	8
Dividends	5
Interest Rate (after tax)	0.05

$R_A = (E + iD)/A = (8 + .05 \times 50)/100 = .105$
$R_{ES} = 8/250 = .032$
$R_{DA} = 50/100 = .5$
$R_{SA} = 250/100 = 2.5$

when and if the company posts some capital gains on the sale of assets, it might recover some of this loss by putting it against the gain and cutting its capital gain income taxes. We will not count on this now.) Also, the operating results for the year ahead are hurt with a one-time loss of another $5 million after tax as the company is readjusted. Some customers are compensated for their dislocations as the product lines are transferred, termination costs are paid to some employees, and so forth, all the result of dropping product lines. However, $10 million after tax is earned for the year on the retained product lines. The net earnings from operations of $5 million is sufficient to continue the dividend at $5 million. It leaves no cash to list as retained earnings and be used for reinvestment in growth, although depreciation of the existing assets is covered in the net earnings.

The new results for the year are shown in Table 1–F. In it we imagine the sale of the division is made as the new year starts, giving us this balance sheet as a revision of the end of year previous balance sheet of Table 1–E. Also, the cash obtained in the sale is used imme-

Table 1–F   New End of Year Balance Sheet (millions of $)

Assets		Liabilities	
Assets Employed in Retained Products	80	Debt	50
Cash from sale of a division	15	Equity	45
Total	95	Total	95

Revised Balance Sheet After Repayment of $15 Million of Debt

Assets		Liabilities	
Retained Products	80	Debt	35
		Equity	45
Total	80	Total	80

Next Year's P & L (millions of $)

Sales	200
Earnings	5
Earnings on Retained Products	10
Dividends	5

$R_A = (10 + .05 \times 35)/80 = .147$ on retained products
$R_{ES} = 10/200 = .05$ on retained products
$R_{DA} = 35/80 = .4375$
$R_{SA} = 200/80 = 2.5$

diately to pay off $15 million of the debt, leading to the further revised balance sheet shown. Since no contribution to retained earnings is made, the debt and equity remain the same in the year ahead, that is, this is also the next end of year balance sheet.

We note that the R_A and R_{ES} have improved, if the company is judged now only by the retained products. If the performance of the corporation keeps up (the one-time losses now behind it), its earnings will make possible reinvestment after dividends are paid in new product endeavors or expansion of the existing ones. The price per share of the common stock on the market will probably rise. It is a smaller but better company after the changes and the temporary losses.

Summary About Goals and Objectives

We have in this chapter introduced the matter of the quantitative and qualitative considerations that must figure into management's goals and objectives. There are very many such considerations, and the full complement of goals and objectives of a company constitute a detailed list of what the management must try to do in every area of its endeavor, from engineering to marketing, from production to distribution, from arranging financing to keeping the community happy. In discussing some corporate goals and objectives in this chapter we were really engaged in trying to meet two objectives of this book. First, we wanted to introduce the idea that a certain amount of clarity about goals and objectives is an essential aspect of management. We wanted to get that thought in early. We also wanted to begin, though only to begin, the process of seeing how goals and objectives relate to the procedures, the art and the tools of management.

There is not too much point in having an objective if you have no way of deciding whether you have reached it, no way to measure where you stand, and vagueness about what you are observing. Trying to set up goals and objectives is a way of trying to be clear about what you are up to in managing the corporation. If you do not know what you are trying to do, then you are handicapped. At the least you should know that you must try to do something about the handicap. As a manager begins to be specific about a preferred effort, he will be led to practical means to follow what is happening because he will be motivated to see if his goals and objectives are being met. In a very important way, then, goals will lead him to the disciplines of sound management. Thus, the subject of goals and objectives also has been a suitable way to commence this text and introduce the rest of it.

Problems

1–1. Study the annual and 10-K reports of a leading technological corporation and summarize what you believe might be that company's short- and long-term goals. Why are the managers not clearer in stating their goals in these reports? Could it be they fear giving an advantage to their competitors through such publicly stated information? Do they believe the information uninteresting to their shareholders? Or do they think it may disclose weakness in their market position or overall management?

1–2. Using the balance sheet and profit & loss figures in the annual report of the technological corporation you studied in the previous problem, estimate a credible growth rate of earnings per share that would be consistent with the company's continuing its recent performance.

1–3. A corporation in recent years has performed approximately as follows: R_A = 17 percent, R_{DA} = 50 percent, R_V = 50 percent, i = .04. If these ratios are held constant as the company reinvests available gererated earnings to finance further market penetration, what will be its sales and earnings growth? Assume annual depreciation expense just equals annual capital investment to replete depreciating assets.

1–4. A company with a new high technology product operating profitably has the goal of capturing as large a share of the market as possible. It risks operating with high debt to equity ratio. For the period ahead it expects an R_A of 12 percent. The bank is willing to loan it money at 10 percent up to an R_{DA} of 50 percent; from 50 percent to 70 percent (the maximum that the bank will go), the interest rate x, will rise according to the formula:

$$x = .1[1 + .5(R_{DA} - .5)] = .075 + .05R_{DA}$$

Compare the earnings after taxes and interest when (1) operating with R_{DA} = .5 and (2) operating with R_{DA} = .7. Assume that R_A is not altered by the change in volume implied by the variation in total assets employed between the two alternatives, that no dividends are paid, all earnings are plowed back and the tax rate is 50 percent.

1–5. A company has been growing rapidly, has been highly leveraged and has not paid dividends. Looking ahead it sees a more modest sales growth rate of 7 percent per year as a steady condition for many years. It plans a dividend payout ratio of 25 percent, pays interest charges after taxes at the rate of 5 percent and expects a constant return on assets employed of 16 percent before interest charges for the foreseeable future. Its debt at the present time is equal to shareholder's equity. It plans to use the excess cash generated each year, above the requirement for payment of dividends, replacement of depreciating assets and reinvestment for growth, to improve the debt-to-assets ratio. With this plan what approximately will be the value of R_{DA} at the end of five years?

1–6. Redo Tables 1–E and 1–F with the following changes: With the assets remaining $100 million, alter the split between assets employed in satisfactory and unsatisfactory products from $80 to $20 to $75 to $25. Assume the company will sell the unsatisfactory division for $20 million rather than $15 million, for the same $5 million loss on the sale and also, as before, the additional $5 million operating loss. Assume the same $10 million after tax profit on the retained products.

1–7. A company needs a steady growth rate in sales of 10 percent for many years in order to hold its market share against anticipated competition. It expects to be able to maintain a steady R_A of 16 percent and chooses to keep its debt such that R_{DA} = 25 percent. Assuming i = .05 throughout the period, what dividend ratio, R_V, can the company set?

1–8. Plot R_{EQ} against R_A with R_A ranging from 0 to .25 for i = .05 and R_{DA} = .1, .25, and .5.

1–9. Under what conditions relating R_A, R_{DA}, R_V and i would a company have zero growth in earnings, if it depended alone on earnings plow-back to finance the growth?

1–10. From an annual report for a technological corporation, make up a balance sheet with the assets shown as (1) working capital and (2) all other assets, and the liabilities in the form of (1) long term debt and (2) shareholders' equity. This means including any other specific items in one or another of these four categories. State which, if any, items appear to you as possibly inappropriate for such lumping. Also, based on the reported figures, calculate R_A, R_V, R_{DA}, R_{EQ}, and i for this company for the year.

2

THE COST OF CAPITAL

The Corporation as a Converter of Cash Invested to Cash Returned

Early in the previous chapter we cited a useful quantitative simplification of what management should assume it is hired to do. This is to acquire capital and employ it to generate more than the cost of that capital. If a corporation's management accomplishes this, it will be able to compensate the sources of capital for the use of their funds and motivate them to provide more capital as required. It will also have enough funds left over to add to the shareholders' investment and use enhanced assets to expand or strengthen the company.

Management must know the cost of capital and be skilled in arranging for its availability at the lowest cost. Equally, management must be capable of creating the greatest return on the invested capital. These two management talents are related, because the cost of capital to a corporation is not independent of the return it generates on its invested capital. For instance, the interest rate charged a corporation by those who lend money will depend on competitive opportunities for the lenders. If they can lend at the same rate to a corporation whose financial condition appears sounder, they will do so. The less stable the earnings of a corporation appear, the higher will be the interest rate it will have to offer to attract prospective creditors.

The same thing is true when a corporation raises funds by selling equity, shares of the company's ownership. If a corporation seems adequately and safely profitable, with a strong product status in its markets and a conservative balance sheet, an investor will settle for a lower anticipated return than he will seek from another corporation displaying a high risk.

30

To attract its required capital at the lowest cost, whether through debt or equity shares, the corporations's management must choose the right combination of the two sources. Debt financing, as we shall see, is usually cheaper than equity. However, raising capital through debt may not be an available route and may be downright dangerous if the debt-equity ratio gets too high. We introduced this subject superficially in the previous chapter. In this one we shall develop this important balancing issue further.

Figuring the cost of debt is straightforward compared with estimating the cost of equity capital, a less predictable and quantifiable item. There are many reasons for this. Consider first that in taking on a debt, a corporation assumes a fixed contractual obligation to pay a certain rate of interest and to pay off the loan on a committed, clearly stated schedule. A company that defaults on its loans may be thrown into bankruptcy. A lender who conceives of that possibility may refuse to make the loan. Even a slight probability of such a calamity will raise the interest rate. But if the loan is actually made, the management will know the cost of the capital borrowed.

For the issuance of preferred stock, the dividend will be as clearly stated as the interest rate on a debt. The word preferred says that no common shares will receive a dividend until and unless the available funds are used as a first priority to pay the expected preferred dividend. There may also be an understanding that the corporation may choose to call in or buy back the shares at a given price at a stated future time. However, if the company gets into financial difficulties it may suspend the payment of preferred dividends. Suddenly there will be no return for the holder of the preferred.

Of course, the greater the apparent likelihood of an inviolate, steady stream of preferred dividends, the lower the yield (ratio of dividend to share price) the purchaser of a share of preferred will require. The yield and price of the shares will relate to the envisaged quality of the financial performance of the company. If preferred shares are sold, however, at what ever turns out to be the yield, the corporate management will be able to figure readily the cost of the capital raised.

It is in selling common stock (and preferred stock that includes a formula and privilege for converting to common later) that the cost of the capital raised is hardest to gauge, where the deal is vaguest and least binding as to what the purchaser of the shares should expect and what he actually will get back in future returns. The price of the shares, the yield, and the cost of the capital raised are intertwined with the past, present, and anticipated future performance of the company. The relationships are not totally quantifiable and numerous nonpredictable and nonguaranteeable factors enter the picture. Let us consider a few of these.

The return on the investment in common shares may not be in the form of immediate or even early payments of cash dividends to the investor, but of course evidence of the ability to pay those in the future is pertinent to the price of a share. Success for both the corporation and the holder of common means that the cash taken from the holder by the corporation upon the sale of common must be exceeded by the cash paid back to the holder by the corporation with proper allowance for the time that will pass between the two actions. Eventual success must appear credible and probable as the investment is being made, or the purchaser of common shares will not be willing to take the risk. The lower the estimated probability of the payback, and the longer the time before it comes, the greater will be the anticipated yield that the sources of capital will require as their future reward. A case must be presented by management to the prospective investor that shows how funds being raised by selling shares will be employed, and, as time goes on, how the earnings being generated are being reinvested (if they are not being returned to him) to make possible greater returns to him later.

The purchaser of common stock puts up clearly identifiable cash today for possibly more, but not spelled out and promised, cash at some indefinite later time. What then should the investor be willing to pay today in view of this difficulty to assess future benefit? How much should the corporation feel it must charge for a share in view of what cash it will, or may, end up paying out later? Before attempting to answer, let us add more complications.

Technological corporations tend to have the special characteristic that a typical investment in a product endeavor requires years before the generation of enough cash from the manufacture and marketing of the product, beyond the requirement to reinvest, so that the surplus can be paid out in dividends. Time is required for research, product design, development of the market, and building up of a sufficient volume of sales so that the product's price is cost-effective and the costs reduced enough to provide a healthy margin between selling price and cost. In the early years it is important to invest ample funds to design, debug and establish the new product early with a large fraction of the market, thus getting an edge on potential competitors. Also, as new technology becomes available it must be incorporated in the product design to broaden the applications and to improve the techniques of production and distribution. The start-up period for technological products can be long. A mature and successful corporation backs the new products from the profits generated by older ones and still has enough cash flow from successful operations to share the rewards with the investors.

The newer the products, the more attractive is the project to some purchasers of common stock. This is because the new technology probably will bypass and improve on existing techniques or bring entirely new applications into practice and create new markets. The economic benefits of the advanced technology may be exciting in terms of the possible cost effectiveness to a customer. This excitement is in proportion to the degree the endeavor is seen as representing real breakthroughs in science or technology.

At the same time, the newer the technology and the bolder the impact of the introduction of the innovative products, the greater may be the risk of failure. Also increased may be the difficulty of accurately estimating when and how large the eventual return will be. Sources of capital are not unaware of these characteristics of a technological corporation. They are interested in all the information, quantitative and qualitative, emanating from management. The quality of both the information itself and the presentation of it is dependent on the competence of management which then indirectly will affect the cost of capital obtained by selling common stock.

The operation of a mature technological corporation, or one at least well past its inauguration, is certain to consist of numerous scenarios of individual endeavors and investments in many product areas. Some products may have just been started and will not contribute to profits or positive cash flow for years. Others may be in that final period when the product has become somewhat obsolete but still fits a certain market need and does so with good profit and positive cash flow levels. The degree of success of the corporation is judged periodically, typically quarterly, and in more detail, annually. The corporation's sales, revenues, earnings, earnings per share, growth, and especially its return on assets employed and on equity capital are all examined as overall indicators of whether the corporation is succeeding in generating an adequate margin of return over the cost of capital. But the examination is far from simple. Accordingly, the conclusion about the adequacy of the margin is equally difficult.

To add one final point of complexity about the cost of capital raised by selling common stock before we embark on a serious effort to eliminate the confusion consider that some purchasers of common will not be directly interested in the present or even the eventual cash dividends. We already mentioned in Chapter 1 that a shareholder may have bought the shares on the market with the idea of selling them at a higher price only a little later. He plans to get his return by disposing of the shares for an adequately higher price (adequate considering the waiting time and the risk). Looked at in this way, can the corporation that receives the capital from the selling of a share be unconcerned about having eventually to pay out a stream of dividends, a cost for the use of the capital? Or is the problem one solely between the previous shareholder and the new one to whom the former sells his shares? The quick answer is that in order for that sale to be made at all , and particularly for a higher price, the company must be doing well or appearing to have the potential for doing better in the future. That puts an obligation on management. Management is required to operate in such a fashion to make these stock trades possible. If not, the stock price may go down with negative results for management, including difficulties in raising more capital. But how do we translate this into a present and future price and yield, and especially a cost of capital?

We are ready now to take up the principal forms of capital and discuss how management selects and assesses the cost of an optimum pattern of financing.

The Cost of Debt Capital

If a corporation raises funds by borrowing, then the interest charges essentially constitute the cost of capital. It is almost that simple, and the added complications are quite simple. The interest rate is of course a net interest, taking into account that some fees may be used to obtain the borrowed funds. The funds may be in the form of bonds or debentures sold by investment bankers and brokers who are in the business of doing such marketing and charge for it. Usually for a substantial financing of this kind, where the equivalent of long-term IOUs from the company are spread among many individuals and pension funds, trust funds, and the like, one or more investment banking houses on Wall Street will assume the overall burden of arranging the financing. They take a substantial fraction of the total issue themselves, buying it at a wholesale cost and marketing it at a somewhat higher or retail price. The difference is a fee that obviously is paid for by the corporation seeking the funds.

Corporations typically arrange short-term loans from commercial banks. These require early payback, although, for a corporation in good standing such short-term loans are renewed regularly. In addition to the interest rate charged, the bank may require that the corporation keep a substantial average sum in a checking account yielding no interest, a compensating balance. Also, a bank will charge the corporation a fee in return for a promise that the bank will stand ready to make a quick future loan if needed.

For longer term loans from a commercial bank and for longer term bonds or debentures sold more widely through investment banking houses, the payback schedules will vary. The interest rate charged is a function of the time period in which the debentures are expected to remain in the purchasers hands and the various conditions involved in the payback of the loans or the corporation's privilege to call in the debentures for cash. In view of inflation and other dynamics of the economy versus time, the market will assess variously the future values of a debt obligation held for various periods of time.

Those who loan money to a corporation, short-term or long-term, usually insist on some restrictions important to management about operations of the company. The loan's fine print may restrict dividends as a fraction of earnings. It may require that all dividends be halted if earnings fall below a certain amount. The creditor may retain a right to call in the loan, demanding all or part of his funds back, if certain conditions occur in the corporation, usually meaning that matters financial are going badly. The creditors may insist on limitations on management's selling of the company's assets. The corporation may be banned from merging with another company, floating additional shares of stock, or taking on additional loan commitments. All these are intangible, qualitative, and additional costs of debt.

Interest Is Tax Deductible

A major consideration in a decision to raise funds by borrowing is that interest is tax deductible. In recent years and for the foreseeable future, this means the effective interest rate for a profitable corporation is something on the order of one-half of the paid before taxes rate. In addition to basic income tax rates on corporations there are, from time to time, various credits and exemptions, for instance, to encourage investment or export sales. We shall not go into these in any detail in this text. It will serve our goals adequately to use the 50 percent figure as a useful approximation.

We are speaking here of the United States tax rates. Borrowing internationally involves a substantial number of additional factors (which will be discussed more in Chapter 13). As one example, a corporation may borrow overseas, not because it needs to raise funds for the overseas operation but because it wishes to have a hedge against the anticipated higher inflation in the country of that operation compared with United States inflation and the accompanying expectancy that the currency of that nation will be devalued against the American dollar. In other words the international corporation seeks to cover its inadvertent and unavoidable gambles with regard to currency exchange rates.

A technological corporation in a start-up phase without earnings against which it can deduct interest charges for tax purposes, must look upon loans differently from a corporation that is more mature. The United States Internal Revenue Service (IRS) allows a number of years for an averaging out of earnings and losses in the figuring of owed income taxes. If the new corporation can get into a profit position in a few years, then any accumulated losses can be subtracted, at least in part, from the later years' earnings for tax calculations. In such an instance, then, again the charges we shall be interested in are the after tax interest charges.

In summary, the cost of debt capital, expressed as the ratio of the amount paid each year for the use of it to that capital, will be the after-tax interest rate, for which we shall use the symbol i.

Typical Relative Interest Rates

A savings account at a bank is usually considered very safe, if it is within the limits of size of deposit insurable by an agency of the federal government and if the bank qualifies for that insurance. A certificate of deposit at a bank pays a higher rate of interest, is issued only for large sums (say $100,000 or more) and carries more risk. Banks have been known to default on such certificates, though rarely. These two are principle sources of funds available to banks. When a bank loans money to corporations, it must obtain more in interest than the cost of its money. If a guaranteed savings account pays five percent per annum, a bank will charge seven or eight percent as its prime rate, the lowest interest rate that it reserves for (usually big) borrowers considered very safe and sound.

Corporations not so strong financially may be charged one or two percentiles over the prime rate. Corporations in financial difficulties may not be able to borrow at all from a commercial bank, but if they have excellent chances of recovery they may be able to do so at three or four percentiles above the prime.

When a corporation arranges long-term debt financing by selling debentures due ten to twenty years later, in today's inflationary environment, the interest may range from two or three to five percentiles

over the prime or even higher, depending upon the money market's
general guessing at that time about the average inflation over the
long period ahead. A corporation's financial officer tries to plot cash
needs against interest rates and borrows for the future when he thinks
rates are at a low point.

A large corporation in strong financial condition may issue its own
IOUs (called commercial paper) and sell them directly to money
sources looking for safe investments at a higher interest rate than a
savings account with more rapid turnover than long-term debentures.
Corporations may even loan cash to each other. One with temporary
surplus cash buys the commercial paper of the one temporarily needing more cash.

Table 2-A illustrates relative interest rates showing their spread
versus each other and their variation with time.

Cost of Equity Capital

Preferred Stock

The simplest form of preferred, from the standpoint of cost of capital,
is one that also happens to be widely used. It has a specified dividend.
For each share the corporation sells at price P_S it must be prepared to
pay out a dividend each year of V_S. To the original purchaser the yield
is V_S/P_S. The price may vary greatly during the period, which may be
years or decades, during which the stock is outstanding, that is, in the
hands of share owners who expect the dividend. The shares may change
ownership many times and, while the dividend remains constant, the
yield to individual shareholders who purchased stock from others will
vary because of market price variations.

**Table 2–A Yields or Interest Rates on
Selected Securities (percent)**

Security	Jan 1977	Jan 1978
Corporate AAA bonds	7.9	8.25
15–20 year Govt bonds	7.7	8.1
Prime Bank Loan Rate	6.25	7.75
3–5 year Treasury Bills	6.1	7.5
90 day C.D.s	4.7	6.8
Commercial Paper	4.6	6.7
Common Dividend Large, Technological Corp.	4.0	5.0

The cost of capital to the corporation will be determined by the price of a share and the constant dividend. Specifically, for this kind of preferred stock the cost of equity is

$$C_Q = V_S/P_S$$

Of course, to be precise we should include in the price received by the corporation for each share sold, a reduction to cover the expenses of the sale. P_S should then be considered a net figure after all such fees.

The preferred stock dividend is regarded by the corporation as a firm obligation. No self respecting corporation issues preferred shares without the full expectation that it will pay these dividends without fail. However, the purchaser of the shares knows that the corporation may default, if its financial situation turns unfavorable. For this reason, the buyer will be disinterested unless the yield is higher than his safer options. For these (typified by federal government bonds, insured bank savings accounts, and debentures of strong corporations) the chances of the income stream failing are less. Accordingly, the yield to the buyer of preferred shares, and the corporation's cost of equity capital raised through preferred shares, is greater than the interest rate on average loans or debentures. A percent or two (sometimes much more for less well established corporations) separates C_Q for ordinary preferred from the interest rate on loans before taxes. But we recall that interest is tax deductible. Preferred dividends are not. If i is the after-tax interest rate and C_Q the cost of capital for ordinary preferred stock, the difference may be around two to one, that is, approximately,

$$C_Q = 2i$$

If $i = .04$, C_Q might be .07 or .09.

We must be mindful as we compare these two costs of capital that selling preferred shares builds the equity figure on the balance sheet and thus permits carrying more debt within a range of sound debt-equity ratios. Also, sometimes a preferred issue allows the corporation to retire the shares at a later time by paying the shareholder the original price of the shares. If average yields should go down in the market for money in the future, a preferred stock share, with its constant dividend (assuming no perceived default danger), would presumably rise. If a fixed call-in or retirement price applies, this sets a limit to the possible rise in the shares and raises the initial yield requirement to attract purchasers.

It also happens often that the preferred shares are convertible to some stated ratio of the common at the option of the shareholder. This is a sweetener that offers a chance to the preferred holder to receive his dividends, while also gaining further if the company prospers and the common stock's market price rises enough to make the conversion financially advantageous. We shall develop this interesting case further after discussing the relations among cost of capital, share price and yield on common shares.

Common Stock

A purchaser of the common stock of a corporation has no guarantees about either the future market price at which he can sell his shares or the stream of cash dividends he will receive if he holds his shares. The price he is willing to pay rests on some impression or estimate he has as to both of these bases for judging the price. Because of the risk inherent in his estimating the future, the purchaser will set a higher required rate of return with his scenario for the future of a share of common stock than for a similar investment in "sure things." Typically the cost of capital, C_Q, for common shares will be higher than for ordinary preferred. It is often around twice the prime rate for bank loans. If the latter is seven percent, C_Q for common shares may be thirteen or fourteen percent for corporations of high financial standing and higher for companies considered more speculative.

Let us develop some relations among C_Q, P_S, and the dividend and earnings performance of a corporation. We shall start with the simplest case of a corporation we imagine to be rated by the market as a no growth but steady performer. It has paid a constant dividend on its common without fail for years. It holds a strong position in the market for products that appear to be required at a constant rate for the indefinite future. This nongrowth, steady model is not too apt for a technological corporation which, as we shall explain in Chapter 10, generally must establish a pattern of growth. However, the model will still be useful to us as a base for further, broader considerations.

If the corporation is estimated to pay a constant dividend, V_S, at the end of each year, the price of the share a purchaser will pay who is satisfied to receive a rate of return measured by C_Q for this class of investment is given by

$$P_S = V_S/C_Q \qquad [1]$$

where V_S is the dividend received a year after the purchase.

In this model, the corporation's dividend stream, characterized as it is by steadiness and nongrowth, is consistent with a hundred percent dividend payout policy. In other words,

$$V_S = E_S$$

and

$$R_V = 1$$

This is because with no growth, no part of the earnings need be retained to finance it. (Again, we must call attention to this model's idealization. In the present real-life inflationary environment for corporations, the depreciation expenses will not cover replacement costs. For this and other reasons that will be taken up in Chapter 12, an absolutely constant company with no need for asset growth is more for academic discussion, for which it is valuable, rather than for the illustration of actual events.)

The so-called price to earnings multiple, defined as the ratio of market price of a share of stock to earnings per share, can be written as

$$M = P_S/E_S = P_S/V_S = 1/C_Q \qquad [2]$$

Assuming no changes in the general market for money and in the imagined future of the company, then the stock can be resold at a later time for P_S. No stock price stays absolutely constant in actual practice. Either the overall money market swings or the impression of the company changes. Also different potential purchasers will vary in their evaluations of the same company's shares or will use somewhat different values of C_Q. One investor may be full up in holdings in a given risk category and, if he has to consider adding purchases, will do so only at a higher C_Q than another investor who has decided to add holdings in the same risk range. There is a buyer for every seller of stock; obviously they have different situations or see the stock value differently or both.

The Steady Growth Company

Let us shift attention now to another model, much closer to what really happens with technological corporations. Here the corporation's future dividends are seen as increasing each year at a constant rate,

g. If the last previously paid dividend per share was V_{SO}, then the dividend at the end of another year will be

$$V_{S1} = (1 + g)V_{SO} \qquad [3]$$

At the end of the nth year, it will be

$$V_{Sn} = (1 + g)^n V_{SO} \qquad [4]$$

A purchaser of a share who bases his decision on an expected return rate of C_Q should now be willing to pay more than V_{SO}/C_Q, because he is buying a stream of dividends that increase each year. To find the price he should be happy to pay, we need only find the present value of each dividend received over the years and add the sum.

The present value of a cash dividend is obtained by discounting that payment at the rate C_Q for the number of years the purchaser must wait for the payment. Thus, P_S, the sum of the discounted dividends is

$$P_S = \frac{V_{S1}}{1 + C_Q} + \frac{V_{S2}}{(1 + C_Q)^2} + \cdots + \frac{V_{Sn}}{(1 + C_Q)^n} \qquad [5]$$

or

$$P_S = \sum_{n=1}^{n=\text{infinity}} V_{Sn}/(1 + C_Q)^n \qquad [6]$$

and, substituting from [4]

$$P_S = V_{SO} \sum_{n=1}^{n=\text{infinity}} x^n \qquad [7]$$

where

$$x = (1 + g)/(1 + C_Q) \qquad [8]$$

If we look in our algebra books under "series" we shall be reminded that

$$\sum_{n=1}^{n=n} x^n = x(1 - x^n)/(1 - x) \qquad [9]$$

and, if $x < 1$, meaning $C_Q > g$, then

$$\sum_{n=1}^{n=\text{infinity}} x^n = x/(1 - x) \tag{10}$$

so

$$P_S = V_{SO} \frac{1 + g}{1 + C_Q} \frac{1}{1 - (1 + g)/(1 + C_Q)}$$

which simplifies to

$$P_S = V_{SO}(1 + g)/(C_Q - g) \tag{11}$$

and finally to

$$P_S = V_{S1}/(C_Q - g) \tag{12}$$

where V_{S0} is the dividend paid at the end of the first year after purchase. Keeping this definition in mind for the dividend V_S we shall now drop the subscript 1 and write simply

$$P_S = V_S/(C_Q - g) \tag{13}$$

Also, we shall have occasion to use these alternate forms of Equation 13:

$$C_Q - g = V_S/P_S$$
$$C_Q = (V_S/P_S) + g \tag{14}$$

and remembering

$$V_S = R_V E_S$$

and

$$M = P_S/E_S \quad \text{by definition}$$

we also may write

$$C_Q = (R_V/M) + g \tag{15}$$

We can now compare Equation 14 with Equation 1 and see that the purchaser receives his return, C_Q, in part by the expected cash dividend yield at the end of the first year, as though that figure were to be constant, plus the added term, g, to account for the future growth in dividends. This suggests we can derive Equation 14 by another approach. We imagine the purchaser, having paid P_S at the beginning of the year, plans to pocket the dividend, V_S, he will receive at the end of the year, and then immediately sell the share. Since the company, for which we have assumed a steady-growth pattern for its dividends, has made a year of progress on that pattern, he should receive $P_S(1+g)$ on the sale of his share. His total gain or yield therefore will have been $V_S + g P_S$. His rate of return will be this figure divided by the investment he made, P_S, or

$$C_Q = (V_S + gP_S)/P_S$$
$$= (V_S/P_S) + g$$

which is identical to Equation 14.

Finally, it will be useful to have a form of Equation 15 which leads to M when the other parameters are given. Thus, from Equation 15

$$C_Q - g = R_V/M$$

and

$$M = R_V/(C_Q - g) \qquad [16]$$

As an example, a large, mature and successful technological corporation in the late 1970's, when C_Q for such companies envisaged as steady-growth corporations, was around .13, had an $R_V = .3$ and a g = .10. What would have been a reasonable M for that company? From Equation 16

$$M = .3/.03 = 10$$

Actually during this period the value of M for most technological corporations ranged from 5 to 20. Only a small fraction of all the listed technological corporations were, at least at times, below 5 or above 20. The many reasons for this spread in the values of M include: the competitive market for money varies and so C_Q changes; the companies have different R_V values, that is, dividend policies; the earnings of the companies do not follow a simple, steady growth pattern, or, for our purposes, we should say the companies vary to the extent they appear to the stock market as fitting the model of steady growth; their growth rates vary; different shareholders and potential shareholders have varied estimates and each alters his estimate with time about the future progress of the same company and about groups of companies in the different fields.

A Three Phase Model

It will be helpful now to consider the case of a corporation that goes through three phases. This is typical of many high technology companies. In the first, lasting n_1, it pays no dividends, retaining all earnings to reinvest to increase assets and build sales volume. In this beginning phase, the company will likely have losses rather than earnings for the early portion. At the end of this first phase the company pays its first dividend. In the second phase, lasting n_2 years, we assume the dividends grow at a constant rate, g_1. The third phase is one of constant growth, g_2, lower than g_1 and C_Q and, in our model, lasting forever.

We now ask what price a purchaser of a share of common stock should expect to pay on day one, the beginning of phase 1, if he insists on a return C_Q and believes the scenario we have just outlined for the company. We derive P_S as before by adding up the series of properly discounted future dividend payments.

Having just performed the calculation for a steady growth company that goes on forever and derived Equation 13 to quantify the appropriate stock price, let us use that equation to figure out the present value of the dividends received in the third phase. This phase starts $n_1 + n_2$ years after the stock is purchased. Call V_{S1} the first dividend, the one paid at the beginning of phase 2. This will be augmented by n_2 years of growth at rate g_1 during phase 2 to yield $V_{S1}(1 + g_1)^{n_2}$ as phase 3 commences. A year later, the first dividend in phase 3 will be paid, namely, $V_{S1}(1 + g_1)^{n_2} (1 + g_2)$. Substituting into the general formula (Equation 13):

$$P_S = V_S/(C_Q - g)$$

we obtain the value of the future dividend stream *seen at the beginning of the third phase*, namely

$$V_{S1}(1 + g_1)^{n_2}(1 + g_2)/(C_Q - g_2)$$

Next we discount this for the $n_1 + n_2$ years of time at rate C_Q to obtain the contribution to the value of a share from the third phase's dividends seen by a purchaser on day one. Calling this third phase contribution P_{S3} we have

$$P_{S3} = \frac{V_{S1}(1 + g_1)^{n_2}(1 + g_2)}{(C_Q - g_2)(1 + C_Q)^{n_1+n_2}} \qquad [17]$$

From phase 2, the investor will receive a group of dividends, one at the end of each of the n_2 years starting with $V_{S1}(1 + g_1)$ at the end of the first year of phase 2. The dividends will grow at a rate g_1. We recall the formula of Equation 9

$$\sum_{n=1}^{n=n} x^n = x(1 - x^n)/(1 - x)$$

and apply it to the stream of dividends in phase 2 seen at the *beginning* of phase 2. The value of that stream at that moment is

$$\sum_{n=1}^{n=n_2} \frac{V_{S1}(1 + g_1)^n}{(1 + C_Q)^n} = V_{S1} \sum_{n=1}^{n=n_2} x^n$$

where

$$x = (1 + g_1)/(1 + C_Q)$$

Discounting this to bring it back in value n_1 years to day one, we have a contribution from phase 2 to the present value for the purchaser of

$$P_{S2} = \frac{V_{S1}}{(1 + C_Q)^{n_1}} \sum_{n=1}^{n=n_2} x^n = \frac{V_{S1}}{(1 + C_Q)^{n_1}} x \frac{1 - x^{n_2}}{1 - x} \qquad [18]$$

From phase one we have only the single dividend V_{S1} at its period end. This we discount by n_1 years to obtain

$$P_{S1} = V_{S1}/(1 + C_Q)^{n_1} \tag{19}$$

The total present value of all dividends over all three phases is then

$$P_S = P_{S1} + P_{S2} + P_{S3}$$

$$= V_{S1} \left\{ \frac{1}{(1 + C_Q)^{n_1}} + \frac{x(1 - x^{n_2})}{(1 + C_Q)^{n_1}(1 - x)} \right.$$

$$\left. + \frac{(1 + g_1)^{n_2}(1 + g_2)}{(1 + C_Q)^{n_1+n_2}(C_Q - g_2)} \right\}$$

$$= \frac{V_{S1}}{(1 + C_Q)^{n_1}} \left\{ 1 + x \frac{1 - x^{n_2}}{1 - x} + \frac{x^{n_2}(1 + g_2)}{C_Q - g_2} \right\} \tag{20}$$

To illustrate let us take $C_Q = .12$, $g_1 = .25$, $g_2 = .07$, $n_1 = 3$, and $n_2 = 7$. Then

$$x = 1.25/1.12 = 1.12$$

Substituting the numbers in Equation 20 we obtain

$$P_S = 42.43 V_{S1} \tag{21}$$

We might observe that this same company, viewed at different time points (with, however, the history of its progress assumed to be the same and judged the same by shareholders who use the constant C_Q as the return required) will have a varying M with time. Indeed, during the first year or two, with E_S negative or infinitesimal, M can be negative or huge. We belabor this point of the limited value of M as a sign of cost of capital or even of the rating of a corporation, because it is so commonly overrated for these purposes. In fact the formula (Equation 2)

$$M = 1/C_Q$$

which applies to a steady and nongrowth company (and, as we shall see later, to another special case) is very often misapplied to *all* corporations. If a corporation's multiple is very high, it often is assumed erroneously that its cost of capital is very low. Actually, as our analysis has shown, the price of a share is determined by a perception or estimate of what the corporation will do in its future performance with the basic idea that the company had better deliver in time an overall discounted return of C_Q determined by competitive investment opportunities. If a company succeeds in selling shares and it fails to deliver C_Q as anticipated by the investor, or it displays evidence that it will not be able to do so, then the price of the stock will fall. In that sense the corporation would have succeeded, though probably inadvertently, in getting more for its shares than they were worth. The corporation would have taken the investor and obtained the capital at a low price, below the competitive rate C_Q. But the next issuance of stock from that corporation might find the buyers more skeptical, or too few.

Convertible Preferred

To arrive at an approximate relationship among the (1) price of a share of preferred that may be converted to common, (2) the yield (C_Q) and (3) the conversion formula, we need to have available an estimate of the future dividend flow of the company. Then the approach is straightforward. We assume a set preferred dividend paid each year end to the shareholder for a number of years. At some point, if the common pays increasing annual dividends, this flow will stop because the preferred shares will have been turned back into the company in exchange for common shares. From then on it is the future stream of common dividends that adds to the present value of the preferred share.

Reasons other than increased dividends may cause conversion to be interesting to the convertible preferred shareholder. For instance, the holder of a large block of preferred stock of a company that he perceives as being mismanaged may want common stock so as to have a vote in choosing new directors, which voting privilege the preferred shares usually do not possess. He may even be trying to take control.

We shall use as an example one in which the common dividend is growing and the preferred shareholders all choose to convert to common, once the common dividends they would receive after the exchange exceed the preferred dividends. This is a common occurrence but not automatic in every instance. Some preferred holders may choose not to convert, opting to obtain the surer, first priority, steady though lower preferred dividend, thinking that the new higher common dividend may not last, if a recession sets in or a bad competitive situation develops. Many such negative possibilities are available at any time for a pessimistic owner of preferred shares to ponder.

Specifically, let us suppose a new technological corporation is launched totally with equity capital (no debt). A million shares each of common, at $10 per share, and preferred, at $15 per share, are sold. The conversion ratio is 1 to 1. The plan is to pay no common dividends until the total earnings are more than enough to pay twice the preferred dividend of $1.25 per share. Assume that the R_A increases as follows with the years; .02, .06, .10, .12, .14, remaining at .14 indefinitely after the fifth year and that the depreciation costs are equal to replacement charges for depreciating assets.

Let us plot the unveiling history by figuring key per-share figures for the common shares in successive years. (V_{SP} is the preferred dividend and delta Q_S is the retained earnings per common share.)

1st Year $E_{S1} = R_A Q_{S1} = .02 \times (\$10 + \$15) = \$.50$

$$V_{SP} = \$1.25$$

which must be paid out to the holders of the million preferred shares. The rest of the earnings are available to increase Q, the net worth (book value) behind the million common shares, and, more specifically, the cash available for plow back to provide more assets employed. But the first year we do not earn enough to fully cover the preferred dividend, so the delta Q is negative.

$$\Delta Q_S = \$.50 - \$1.25 = -\$.75$$

2nd Year $E_{S2} = R_A Q_{S2} = .06(\$25 - \$.75) = \$1.46$
$\Delta Q_S = \$1.46 - \$1.25 = \$.21$

3rd Year $E_{S3} = R_A Q_{S3} = .10(24.25 + .21) = \$2.45$
$\Delta Q_S = 2.45 - 1.25 = \$1.20$

4th Year $E_{S4} = .12(\$24.46 + \$1.20) = \$3.08$

We should now assume conversion, according to plan. If all the preferred shares convert, this will double the number of shares. Thus, we should modify the above to

$$E_{S4} = \$1.54$$

The common dividend will now be $1.25, and $\Delta Q_S = \$.29$.

Let us now use a C_Q of .15 and calculate the price per share that should have been paid by the common and preferred shareholders who were seeking a return of 15 percent. To do this we need to make a few realistic assumptions about some of the operating parameters not yet specified. First, let us write the 5th year performance and settle on a reasonable R_V and g for the future.

5th Year $E_{S5} = R_A Q_{S5} = .14(25.66/2 + .29) = 1.84$
$V_S = 1.25$ (We retain the 4th year figure.)
$R_V = 1.25/1.84 = .68$

This value of R_V, with an $R_A = .14$, will enable us to finance a growth rate

$$g = (1 - R_V)R_A$$

$$= (1 - .68).14$$

$$= .04$$

Suppose the market opportunity is such that a g of over twice this figure is more suitable, and we must rise to this challenge or lose out to competitors. Still, we do not want to lower the dividend or wait a few years, holding the dividend constant while gradually getting the g up. That, we believe, is too slow. The answer, we decide, is to borrow. Assume $i = .05$, that we borrow at the $R_{DA} = .30$ level, and that we can put the augmented assets to work immediately at the same R_A to increase E_S in the fifth year.

The assets per share we had available for the fifth year were as just calculated

$$Q_S = \$25.66/2 + .29 = \$13.12$$

With an $R_{DA} = .3$, the debt per share compared with equity per share is

$$D_S/Q_S = .30/.70 = .43$$

and the total assets per share now available are thus

$$\$13.12(1.43) = \$18.76$$

This will augment the E_S figure; however, interest charges will eat up some of the gain. The new E_S is

$$E_S = R_A \times 18.76 - i \times \$5.64$$

$$= .14 \times 18.76 - .05 \times \$5.64 = \$2.34$$

Keeping V_S at $1.25 we now have

$$R_V = 1.25/2.34 = .53$$

The steady growth rate that this combination now offers is (using the familiar formula)

$$g = \frac{1 - R_V}{1 - R_{DA}} (R_A - iR_{DA})$$

$$= (.47/.7)(.14 - .05 \times .3)$$

$$= .084$$

which we shall regard as satisfactory, although we could choose to increase the debt somewhat to finance more growth.

At the end of the fifth year, an original holder of the common stock can look at his then present value of the dividend stream ahead (by, with perfect prescience, using the same scenario as we have described) and deduce the quantity (Equation 13)

$$P_{S5} = \frac{\$1.25}{C_Q - g} = \frac{1.25}{.15 - .084} = \$18.94$$

This must now be discounted by five years to see what price should have been paid when the company was being launched. Moreover, we must not overlook the $1.25 dividend received by the common shareholder at the end of the fourth year. The total, discounted to the beginning of year one is:

$$P_{SC} = \frac{\$1.25}{(1 + .15)^4} + \frac{\$18.94}{(1 + .15)^5}$$

$$= \frac{\$1.25}{1.75} + \frac{\$18.94}{2.01} = \$10.14 \qquad [22]$$

The preferred stockholder receives a total cash return with a present value of $10.14 plus three discounted payments of $1.25. Accordingly

$$P_{SP} = \$10.14 + \frac{\$1.25}{1.15} + \frac{\$1.25}{(1.15)^2} + \frac{\$1.25}{(1.15)^3}$$

$$= \$13.00 \qquad [23]$$

Thus the common shareholder, who paid $10.00, so close to $10.14, will realize a return of almost exactly $C_Q = .15$ and the preferred purchaser who paid $15.00 instead of $13.00 will fall a bit short, that is, if the history described in the several previous paragraphs really happen. (A few trial and error attempts would show that a somewhat, but not disastrously lower, C_Q would be realized by the preferred holder.)

Neither the purchasers of the stock nor the corporation's management could tell initially exactly how things would work out. There was no guarantee. The stock purchasers took a risk. The actual unfolding might conceivably have proven more favorable as well as less so. The corporation, it turned out, paid out somewhat less to the shareholders than a C_Q of .15 would have required. Thus, the corporation's cost of equity capital was also less than the value of .15. Sometimes, looked at years later, it can be seen that a corporation actually paid less, or paid more, for its equity capital than was believed to be the going rate at the time the shares were sold and the capital raised. It would hardly be expected that the return would come out right on the nose.

The Overall Cost of Capital

Usually a corporation's capital is raised through a combination of debt and various forms of equity shares, each carrying different costs. When management is guided by the concept that it should strive to earn more return, on the average over time, on the assets it acquires with this capital than the cost of it, it must frequently reassess those costs. Some averaging methods must be used to cover the differing costs of the various segments of the available capital. The costs of acquiring more capital by the available routes will vary with time. During a period when the capital previously raised is being employed to generate earnings, which cost of capital shall we use to compare against the earnings? Should the cost when the capital was obtained be the basis for comparison? If so, what if we find we are obtaining a return greater than that historical cost, but far less than the cost of capital if we had to replace or enhance our debt or equity today? Are we then still to be judged as running a satisfactory operation?

We can change the average cost of capital by changing the mix of debt and equity, and of the various forms of each. A company may be earning at a rate less than its cost of capital and thus rated as performing badly. Yet if it borrows and uses the funds to buy back some of its outstanding equity shares it might so reduce its average cost of capital that the returns will now exceed the cost and the company will be regarded then as a good performer. If the figure can be so readily manipulated, what basis then shall we use to determine the true cost of capital?

Let us add one more dimension of complication to the matter. A large part of the capital structure of a company in business for many years will be the retained earnings. For a corporation established several decades ago or earlier, the latter figure usually will be substantially greater than the original equity raised by selling common stock. When the shares were sold the cost of capital may have been reasonably clear. Does the figure have pertinence today to the whole of the shareholders' equity figure, considering that the large retained earnings part was obtained without any selling of shares or contractual obligations to the outside? Is the cost of the capital represented by the retained earnings zero, that is, having earned and pocketed these funds does not the company have the privilege of using them for nothing?

We shall now tackle these interesting questions.

Debt Versus Equity; Coverage Ratio

Consider a corporation whose annual depreciation charges adequately cover the replacement costs. (This suggests inflation is negligible). Then the positive cash flow remaining, after reinvesting an amount equal to depreciation costs to cover replacement, but before paying either interest charges or dividends, is

$$E + iR_{DA}A = R_AA \qquad [24]$$

An important and common criterion used by commercial banks to describe the financial strength of a company as a prospective recipient of loans is the degree of coverage of obligations. This is measured by a ratio of coverage, R_C, defined by

$$R_C = R_AA/(iR_{DA}A + V) \qquad [25]$$

which relates the cash flow available to pay interest and dividends to the sum of these quantities. This can be written

$$R_C = \frac{R_AA}{iR_{DA}A + R_VE}$$

$$= \frac{R_A}{iR_{DA} + R_V(R_A - iR_{DA})} \qquad [26]$$

in which we have recalled that $E = (R_A - iR_{DA})A$.

Using $i = .04$, $R_{DA} = .25$, $R_V = .3$ and $R_A = .15$ for a specific company example

$$R_C = \frac{.15}{.01 + .3(.15 - .01)}$$

$$= \frac{.15}{.01 + .042} = 2.9$$

Almost three times more cash is being generated than is needed to pay interest charges and dividends.

Continuing with this example, suppose now that a combination of recession and inflation sets in. Costs rise before prices of the final product, and the working capital must be increased to cover the inflated receivables and inventory. (These suppositions will be shown as quite credible in Chapter 12.) Thus R_A falls, more money is borrowed to cover cash requirements and R_{DA} rises even as i increases. Assume R_A now is .05, $i = .06$, $R_{DA} = .5$ and R_V increases to 1.00 as the company tries to keep the dividend from falling too much, although its earnings are dropping. Then, from Equation 26

$$R_C = \frac{.05}{.06 \times .5 + 1.0(.05 - .06 \times .5)}$$

$$= .05/(.03 + .02) = 1.0$$

The R_C of 2.9 was satisfactory to the lender and the corporation was considered as financially sound. An R_C of 1.0 is in the range considered unsatisfactory by most financial sources. The corporation will have difficulty turning over (obtaining renewals on) its loans and will find its i increasing in the future unless it lowers its dividend greatly or increases its R_A or both. This company at this time does not have the option of increasing its debt to lower its cost of capital. In fact, it may have to issue more common stock, increasing its cost of capital to maintain a viable overall capital structure.

Let us now consider a company operating at or near what appears to be the most prudent debt to equity ratio for that company. To use a higher debt might improve the return on equity, R_{EQ}, but it would hurt the coverage ratio, R_C, and the general financial soundness of the company, both its actual and perceived ability to weather any storm or take advantage of any new opportunity that might require a sudden infusion of cash. Suppose this company needs total assets of A in order to operate in a near optimum manner in relationship to is product line position and market opportunities. With a given R_A to represent the company's ability to generate earning on those assets, recall (Equation 15 of Chap. 1) that

$$R_{EQ} = (R_A - iR_{DA})/(1 - R_{DA}) \qquad [27]$$

or

$$R_{EQ} = \frac{R_A(1 - R_{DA}i/R_A)}{1 - R_{DA}} \qquad [28]$$

Thus, if

$$R_A > i$$

then the numerator in Equation 28 will decrease less than the denominator, and R_{EQ} will rise, with a rise in R_{DA}. If not, R_{EQ} will fall.

Accordingly, it is not always true that a company can increase its return on equity by using more borrowed money to leverage the equity. To leverage to advantage for this return R_A must exceed i, just as to minimize cost of capital by use of debt, i must be less than C_Q. If we did not have to consider the need for a strong balance sheet—which need translates into not having too much debt compared with equity—then to make the maximum use of debt we should require only that

$$i < R_A \qquad [29]$$

and

$$i < C_Q \qquad [30]$$

Let us consider debt-equity ratios from still another standpoint. Postulate again a company operating with a sensible R_{DA}. Assume the company needs an increment, ΔA, to enhance its operating capital. It can either borrow ΔA or sell common stock to raise ΔA, each act making a small and presumably acceptable change in R_{DA}, the borrowing raising R_{DA} and the stock sale lowering it. We ask which alternative will yield the largest incremental gain in earnings per share, E_S.

If we borrow ΔA, then the effect on earnings will be

$$\Delta E = (R_A - i)\Delta A \qquad [31]$$

and

$$\Delta E_S = \Delta A (R_A - i)/N \qquad [32]$$

The alternative is to sell ΔN shares at P_S per share to raise

$$\Delta A = \Delta N P_S \qquad [33]$$

which can be written also as

$$\Delta A = \Delta N M E_S \qquad [34]$$

which means that

$$\Delta N E_S = \Delta A/M \qquad [35]$$

The resulting delta E_S from this approach has a positive part, from employment of the added assets, of $(R_A/N)\ \Delta A$, and a negative part, from dilution of the common stock (since the overall earnings must now be spread over more shares) of $\Delta N\ (E_S/N)$. (This neglects second order effects.) The net ΔE_S is then

$$\Delta E_S = \Delta A R_A/N - \Delta N E_S/N \qquad [36]$$

which, from Equation 35, is

$$\Delta E_S = \Delta A R_A/N - \Delta A/NM$$
$$= \Delta A(R_A - 1/M)/N \qquad [37]$$

Comparing Equation 32 with Equation 37 tells that borrowing is better than selling equity if

$$i < 1/M \qquad [38]$$

For instance, if $i = .05$, then M must exceed 20 before it is best to sell more common to raise the needed funds, if the impact on E_S is the sole criterion.

Market Versus Book Value for the Common; Average Cost of Capital

In the example just cited we suddenly observe that the price-earnings multiple of stock on the market might well be a factor in deciding whether to borrow or not. Since, in Equation 38, the reciprocal of the multiple M is pitted against the cost of debt capital, i, it is tempting to jump to the conclusion that $1/M$ is the cost of equity capital, C_Q, and when $1/M$ is less than i we should sell stock to minimize the overall cost of capital, otherwise we should borrow. We know the general relation between C_Q and M, for a steady dividend growth company, is

$$C_Q = R_V/M + g \qquad [39]$$

How do we distinguish between this cost of equity capital and the apparently quite reasonable but different one we can infer from Equation 38?

The answer is that Equation 38 is a special condition for raising capital to maximize E_S. "Cost of equity capital" describes what rate of return the purchaser of shares expects when he pays P_S for a share. According to Equation 39, when he buys a share in a steady growth company he expects both dividends and a growth of those dividends in line with the C_Q he has in mind. The multiple, M, that he is willing to accept in buying his share is then as Equation 39 states it. As managers of the corporation we must recognize that P_S and M go with a whole future scenario, not just any, one-time ΔE_S increase. If we fail to perform on that scenario, or so it appears, P_S will fall and so will M. The purchaser expects the rate C_Q, not $1/M$, even though the condition described by Equation 38 directs us to sell shares rather than borrow to maximize delta E_S.

However, we must now provide further discussion on the impact of market price on financing. As a first step, note that as we contemplate raising funds by sale of common shares we are concerned solely with the market price, P_S, of the common and not with the balance sheet's stated or book value of a share, Q_S, which is the shareholders' investment plus retained earnings, the sum divided by the number of shares. These two quantities, P_S and Q_S, will not be the same except by coincidence.

Q_S represents an integrated past history of years or decades of fund raising. It is the funds realized by selling equity shares and by generating earnings that are retained and reinvested. P_S, on the other hand, represents the market's present impression of the future performance of the company. The market, we imagine, uses a discount rate of C_Q to derive the present value, P_S, from the estimated future dividends of the company. When the corporation sells a single additional share of common at price P_S, the new shareholder expects a return on his investment at the going rate, C_Q. If the corporation does not appear to expect to satisfy this rate of return requirement, but rather to be below or above it, the market price of the share will adjust accordingly, going down or up. But the same applies to every present holder of every share of common stock, no matter when that share first happened to be issued and what the values of C_Q and P_S might have been at the time. The corporation either satisfies all of today's shareholders, who now seek C_Q as a return against today's market price, regardless of when they purchased their shares, or the market price of the common will shift as trades of shares take place.

Accordingly, the corporation must expect to pay future dividends, that is, a cost for the use of its entire equity capital related not to Q, the book value of the shareholders' equity on the balance sheet, but instead to market value, that is, to NP_S where N is the total number of shares outstanding. The *average weighted* cost of capital for a corporation using a debt of D and common stock of market value NP_S is then

$$C_A = \frac{iD + C_Q NP_S}{D + NP_S} \qquad [40]$$

which can be rewritten as

$$C_A = \frac{iD + C_Q NQ_S P_S/Q_S}{D + NQ_S P_S/Q_S} = \frac{iD + C_Q QP_S/Q_S}{D + QP_S/Q_S}$$

or

$$C_A = \frac{iR_{DA} + C_Q(1 - R_{DA})P_S/Q_S}{R_{DA} + (1 - R_{DA})P_S/Q_S} \qquad [41]$$

When the market value, P_S, and book value, Q_S, happen to be equal, then

$$C_A = (iD + C_Q Q)/(D + Q)$$
$$= (iD + C_Q Q)/A$$
$$= iR_{DA} + C_Q Q/A$$

and finally,

$$C_A = iR_{DA} + C_Q(1 - R_{DA}) \qquad [42]$$

A typical set of figures for a large technological corporation* might be $i = .04$, $C_Q = .13$, $R_{DA} = .25$, and $P_S = Q_S$. Substituting these values in Equation 42 yields

$$C_A = .04 \times .25 + .13 \times (1 - .25) = .01 + .0975$$
$$= .1075$$

In this example the preponderant cost of capital is the equity capital portion. This suggests that if this corporation needs funds it should borrow rather than sell shares. This would be true for any company as long as i is lower than C_Q. Of course, among other things we have

* See Appendix B.

not been told what the R_A and R_V of this corporation are. Abandoning the typically strong company for the moment we can imagine a quite different one for which the R_A happens to be very low, so much so that the dividend (also low) and interest costs are barely being covered as it is, leaving little for reinvestment in growth. Such a company cannot borrow more very readily. Clearly, arranging an R_{DA} for a corporation to minimize the cost of capital and doing this out of context, that is, ignoring other aspects of the condition of the company, would be unwise.

Often, Equation 42 is used as an approximation to Equation 41. This is the same as saying that P_S/Q_S is close to unity on the average for that company, and its management does not want to react too much to market price fluctuations as it estimates its cost of capital. In practice, over the decade preceding the publishing of this book, the ratio of P_S/Q_S has been between .75 and 1.5 for most large technological corporations, often substantially different from unity. Thus, the calculated cost of equity capital usually should best be based on market price. Many companies use an average, smoothed out over the past year or more, so the short-term market fluctuations will not enter.

Equation 41 tells us that the value of P_S/Q_S influences the weighted average of the cost of capital, C_A. For a given R_{DA}, that is, a given balance between debt and book value of the total assets, the value of C_A will rise as the market value of the shares exceeds the book value. This is because the cost of debt counts less in determining C_A as the effect of the equity cost term in Equation 41 rises with increasing P_S/Q_S. Partially, at least, this results from the fact that even though C_A is defined (and properly) to reflect market, not book, value of the equity shares, R_{DA} is defined using book value. It is only fair and realistic to remind ourselves that a company with high P_S/Q_S (which most often implies high R_{EQ}/C_Q) can borrow more heavily (use a higher R_{DA}) than one with a low P_S/Q_S (which implies a low R_{EQ}/C_Q).

A high P_S/Q_S company, in other words, need not suffer from a higher C_A; it need only increase its leverage somewhat to lower its C_A as its P_S/Q_S ratio rises. Furthermore, as Equation 41 shows, no matter how large P_S/Q_S may become (even if the market goes wild with optimism regarding the stock's potential) C_A can never rise above C_Q.

Equally, no matter how low P_S/Q_S may sink (in disillusionment over the future of the company) C_A will not go below the value of i. Since P_S/Q_S for any company may vary a good deal over a few years, C_A may also vary. However, the value of the whole concept of cost of capital goes in great part to comparing that value against company performance in generating a return. That comparison usually requires years for good evaluation. Thus, we should also average C_Q over time.

Almost uniformly corporations use book values of debt and equity to check whether they are in a satisfactory range of borrowings and leverage. So do banks and bond holders. However, account would certainly be taken by a lender of large differences, if they exist, between P_S and Q_S in rating the R_{DA} and the debt carrying capacity of a company. Take for instance the following extreme example. A company raises $10 million by selling common shares and invests the $10 million in a patent it plans to exploit. All of a sudden a competitor announces an even newer invention which he claims, but does not prove, is superior. The market price of the shares collapses to one-tenth its previous value. However, the company does not change its balance sheet. It argues it has no business taking a $9 million write-off in its stated assets (the patent), and a corresponding write-down of the book value of stockholders' equity merely on the claim of a competitor. Suppose now that the company wants to sell long-term debt in the form of debentures, or at least to arrange short-term loans from a commercial bank to exploit the invention. What will the potential lenders look at as the equity base for the loan, for judging whether the company will possess a reasonable debt-to-equity ratio? Will they use the $10 million Q value on the books, or the $1 million new market value, the NP_S figure? Probably the latter.

The market price may differ from book value for many reasons at any moment, some justified and others not so deserving. In this text we shall sometimes be making our points around the assumption that NP_S is close to Q—but not always. A bit more analysis might help to clarify the importance of recognizing the distinction.

Consider first a corporation of the steady nongrowth type with no debt, that is, D = 0, g = 0, and $R_V = 1$ ($E_S = V_S$). The market price per share, given a C_Q and a purchaser who has the correct impression of the company as we have described it, is, as we know,

$$P_S = V_S/C_Q = E_S/C_Q \qquad [43]$$

Also, the earnings per share is given by

$$E_S = R_A Q_S = R_{EQ} Q_S \qquad [44]$$

with R_A and R_{EQ} being equal and Q_S equal to A_S because there is no debt. Thus

$$P_S/Q_S = R_A/C_Q = R_{EQ}/C_Q \qquad [45]$$

This says that if the company's earnings performance is described by $R_{EQ} = C_Q$, then the appropriate value for the market price of a share, P_S, for this model of a no=growth corporation would be the book value of a share, Q_S. If R_A exceeds C_Q then the market will presumably notice this, and share-holders seeking only C_Q will bid the stock up in the ratio shown, that is, if they believe this model describes the company well.

Still holding to this model, we can readily confirm for one example the advantage of $P_S/Q_S > 1$, the expected consequence of $R_{EQ} > C_Q$. Suppose the company for the year ahead sees a performance

$$E_S = R_A Q_S \qquad [46]$$

It believes that if it quickly injected more equity, namely $\Delta Q = \Delta N P_S$, by selling ΔN shares at the market price, and if it could maintain its R_A, it could build volume and realize instead

$$E_S' = R_A Q_S' \qquad [47]$$

where

$$Q_S' = (Q + \Delta N P_S)/(N + \Delta N)$$
$$= \frac{Q}{N} \frac{1 + \Delta N P_S/Q}{1 + \Delta N/N}$$
$$= Q_S \frac{1 + P_S \Delta N/Q_S N}{1 + \Delta N/N} \qquad [48]$$

from which, since $R_A (= R_{EQ})$ remains constant,

$$\frac{E_S'}{E_S} = \frac{1 + (P_S/Q_S)\Delta N/N}{1 + \Delta N/N} \qquad [49]$$

If $P_S/Q_S > 1$, then the earnings per share will rise through sale of more common stock. If $P_S/Q_S < 1$, then the earnings per share will fall as more shares are sold.

Still retaining $g = 0$ and $R_V = 1$, let us now assume some debt leverage. Again from Equation 43,

$$P_S = V_S/C_Q = E_S/C_Q \qquad [43]$$

However, now

$$E_S = (R_A - iR_{DA})A_S \qquad [50]$$

where

$$A_S = Q_S/(1 - R_{DA})$$

from which

$$E_S = \frac{R_A - iR_{DA}}{1 - R_{DA}} Q_S \qquad [51]$$

Comparing Equations 46 and 51 yields

$$\frac{P_S}{Q_S} = \frac{R_A - iR_{DA}}{(1 - R_{DA})C_Q}$$

or

$$\frac{P_S}{Q_S} = \frac{R_A}{C_Q} \frac{1 - R_{DA}i/R_A}{1 - R_{DA}} \qquad [52]$$

Comparing Equations 52 and 45 we see that if $R_A > i$ the leveraged, steady and nongrowth company will do better on market price related to book value than the unleveraged one. This is not surprising because, for a given R_A, the debt leverage causes R_{EQ} to be higher (higher as compared with C_Q) and this leads to the P_S/Q_S rise. Typically, for well run technological corporations the R_A/i ratio will be two to one or higher. Specifically, for an example of $i = .04$, $C_Q = .13$, $R_A = .12$, and $R_{DA} = .30$.

$$\frac{P_S}{Q_S} = \frac{R_A(1 - .30 \times .04/.12)}{C_Q(1 - .3)}$$

$$= \frac{R_A(1 - .10)}{C_Q(1 - .3)} = \frac{.9R_A}{.7C_Q} = 1.3R_A/C_Q$$

which says that given the right combination of operating parameters, the market price may exceed book value even if R_A is *less* than the cost of equity capital. However, as we shall shortly demonstrate, R_A must exceed C_A, the average cost of capital, if in this model $P_S/Q_S > 1$.

It will be instructive to look at this model in a different way, with the emphasis on the relation between R_{EQ} and C_Q, rather than R_A and C_Q as was just done. Off-hand it might seem we should have done that at the outset since R_{EQ} is the return on, and C_Q the cost of, equity capital. We could have taken Equation 43 and the definition of R_{EQ}, namely,

$$R_{EQ} = E_S/Q_S$$

and the price-yield equation of a steady, nongrowth company, Equation 43, to derive immediately

$$P_S/Q_S = R_{EQ}/C_Q \qquad [53]$$

which is identical to Equation 52, since

$$R_{EQ} = \frac{R_A - iR_{DA}}{1 - R_{DA}}$$

However, this hides that using debt leverage to provide the assets the business requires raises R_{EQ} over what it would have been with R_{DA} zero (if $R_A > i$, as indicated by Equation 28.) It is R_A that measures the ability of the company to generate earnings on the assets employed, regardless of how those assets were financed. Accordingly, it is generally more meaningful to derive the relationship of P_S to Q_S in terms of R_A and the degree of leverage, as measured by R_{DA}. This Equation 52 does for us.

It is worth noting that if $R_{EQ} = C_Q$, even in this example in which leverage is used, P_S will equal Q_S (Equation 53). In view of this, from Equation 42,

$$C_A = iR_{DA} + R_{EQ}(1 - R_{DA})$$

which is identical to R_A as obtained by transposing Equation 27. This says that, much as we might expect, if the return on total assets employed, R_A, equals the average weighted cost of all capital, C_A, then the return on equity, R_{EQ}, will equal the cost of equity capital, C_Q, and vice versa. But is this true more generally? Let us examine a more general case that the model of a steady growth company affords us.

Let us consider a steady growth company with $R_V < 1$, $g > 0$, $R_{DA} > 0$, and $g < C_Q$. Then, of course

$$C_Q = V_S/P_S + g \qquad [54]$$

But

$$V_S = R_V E_S = R_V R_{EQ} Q_S$$

Substituting for V_S in Equation 54 we obtain

$$C_Q - g = \frac{R_V R_{EQ} Q_S}{P_S} \qquad [55]$$

which can be written

$$\frac{P_S}{Q_S} = \frac{R_V R_{EQ}}{C_Q - g} \qquad [56]$$

or

$$\frac{P_S}{Q_S} = \frac{R_V(R_A - iR_{DA})}{(C_Q - g)(1 - R_{DA})} \qquad [57]$$

We should note that if $R_{EQ} = C_Q$, $P_S/Q_S = 1$, and $C_A = R_A$. To confirm this, we observe

$$g = (1 - R_V)R_{EQ}$$
$$= (1 - R_V)C_Q \qquad [58]$$

This means

$$C_Q - g = C_Q - C_Q + R_V C_Q = R_V C_Q$$

and in Equation 56 we have

$$P_S/Q_S = \frac{R_V R_{EQ}}{R_V C_{EQ}} = R_{EQ}/C_Q = 1.$$

Also, from Equation 57

$$1 = \frac{R_V(R_A - iR_{DA})}{R_V C_Q(1 - R_{DA})} = \frac{R_A - iR_{DA}}{C_Q(1 - R_{DA})}$$

from which

$$R_A - iR_{DA} = C_Q(1 - R_{DA})$$

or

$$R_A = iR_{DA} + C_Q(1 - R_{DA}) \qquad [59]$$

and, finally, from Equation 42, this says

$$R_A = C_A$$

Furthermore, if $R_{EQ} = C_Q$ then, substituting Equation 58 in Equation 15, we obtain

$$C_Q = R_V/M + g = R_V/M + (1 - R_V)C_Q$$

or

$$C_Q = 1/M \qquad [60]$$

precisely the relation between C_Q and M that we obtain if $g = 0$. (We remind ourselves that this is for a steady growth company, and, moreover, one for which R_{EQ} happens to equal C_Q, and not for companies generally.)

Let us try some typical figures in Equation 56. First, in the familiar

$$g = \frac{1 - R_V}{1 - R_{DA}}(R_A - iR_{DA})$$

substitute: $R_A = .1$, $i = .05$, $R_{DA} = .2$, $R_V = .5$, and $C_Q = .12$. Then

$$g = .5(.1 - .01)/.8 = .045/.8 = .056$$

Substituting in Equations 56 and 41 we find that

$$P_S/Q_S = .88 < 1$$
$$C_A = .1045$$

However, if $R_A = .15$, $i = .05$, $R_{DA} = .2$, $R_V = .3$, and $C_Q = .15$, then

$$g = .7(.15 - .01)/.8 = .7 \times .14/.8 = .122$$

and

$$P_S/Q_S = 1.87 > 1$$
$$C_A = .1382$$

Thus, in general the market price of the shares may be expected to differ from the book value of the shares in either direction. This is true even for a model steady growth company. In actual stock market life, additional causes of differences will exist. The various stock purchasers and sellers will vary somewhat as to the C_Q's they will seek. Their perceptions regarding the future performance of any company will not be the same, and a steady growth company will only occasionally be so perceived. We have established here, however, that even with a fixed C_Q and a clearly defined future performance scenario the logically correct market price of equity shares will in general be different from the book value of the equity. (See Appendix B.)

Consequences of the Market Misjudgment of Stock Values

Suppose the high probability forecast of a corporation's management—they believe the odds are very high that the future will unfold close to their prediction—leads them to believe that the common stock should be $45 per share. Instead it is $22.50. They perform a careful estimate of the present value of the steadily growing flow of dividends, using as a discount rate the C_Q that their study of relative rates for return on investments (against the spectrum of risks) suggests is appropriate for their company, and they confront this troublesome two to one factor in their result. This they interpret as meaning that if they sell shares to raise funds, they will overpay on cost of equity

capital. Their reasoning is analytically as follows:
  The equation

$$C_Q = R_V/M + g \qquad\qquad [61]$$

expresses the correct relationship. The market presumably uses the same C_Q, by definition of it, and has available, from published data about the company, the same R_V. Since the market nevertheless chooses a lower M' rather than the correct M, it must perceive a lower g' rather than the correct g, where

$$C_Q = R_V/M' + g' \qquad\qquad [62]$$

Now, management feels it knows almost for sure that g, and not the lower g', will result. Thus the purchaser of a share at a multiple M' will in time actually realize a rate of return, C_Q', given by

$$C_Q' = R_V/M' + g \qquad\qquad [63]$$

From Equations 62 and 63 we obtain

$$C_Q' - C_Q = R_V/M' - R_V/M$$

or

$$C_Q' = C_Q + R_V(M - M')/MM' \qquad\qquad [64]$$

  Let us take an example: $R_V = .3$, $M = 10$, $M' = 5$. Then

$$C_Q' = C_Q + .3 \times .1 = C_Q + .03$$

If the cost of capital should be .12, it will cost the company .15 instead, a substantial difference. (Due to the nonlinearity of compound discounting, a small change in C_Q, the discount rate, can mean a large change in payout.) It may be worth it for the company to improve its communications to prospective shareholders (although SEC regulations preclude promising future results. It would be dangerous to do so anyway, because of the consequences of being wrong and being sued with justified success for the plaintiff). If management is right, the future will unfold as it predicts. This probably will be observed by the market gradually, and, if so, the stock will rise and the present owners, or the new ones to whom they might sell, will reap the benefit.

The management should probably try to refrain from selling shares if it believes its stock is too low. It might well consider buying back some shares and realizing the added return itself, if it has excess cash. It might even contemplate borrowing, if its R_{DA} is low, to obtain the cash for the purchase.

What if the situation is the other way around? What if M' is much larger than M in Equation 64? Then the corporation can get equity capital at a bargain price. It has not been uncommon for technological corporations, particularly new ones, to be greatly overrated by the market for a substantial period. Most often the management does not know that M is too high, the optimism for the future applying to those running the operation as well as those who overzealously choose to finance it. Suppose a corporation deserves an M of 5 in Equation 64 and the market rates it at $M' = 10$, with an $R_V = .2$. Then

$$C_Q' = C_Q - .2 \times .1 = C_Q - .02$$

If the cost of capital should be .12, it will be .10 instead.

The difference between the market's incorrectly conceived future of a company and its actual promise could be much greater than illustrated by these examples. The true situation could involve no growth or even a decline or collapse of dividends, and yet the market could gauge the company as having high growth potential—or vice versa. In view of this we conclude the chapter by raising a question about the ethics of a corporation's selling more equity, if it is convinced that the stock is highly overpriced.

Clearly, management should seek not to have this happen. It is bad enough to sell shares at too high a price because of unfortunate but existent management optimism, a sincere misjudgement of the future shared with the stock purchaser. But if management has evidence that the stock is too highly priced, it has an ethical obligation and a legal requirement to make the facts known. The only limit to the fullest of disclosure is to avoid trying to be too exact. The management cannot predict the future accurately, so it cannot describe precisely the degree to which the market price has risen too high, and it is not legally required to try.

Problems

2-1. A typical shareholder who has just purchased common stock in a company widely regarded as in a growth mode and whose stock multiple is $M = 20$ and dividend payout ratio is $R_V = .2$ expects to be able to sell his shares one year later and obtain enough of a higher price that his return for the year, including capital gains and dividends received, will add up to 14 percent of his purchase price. Assuming that the multiple of the common stock remains the same from year to year, what percentage increase in earnings per share in a year must the company achieve so that this shareholder will get the results he expects?

2-2. A corporation with no debt sells enough common shares to increase the book value of its equity by 10 percent and uses the added assets to increase its earnings by 10 percent for the first year after the sale. How much did the earnings per share change? Express the answer in terms of the ratio of market price to book value of the common shares at the time of sale.

2-3. A company produces a product for which the market has had a need expected to continue for many more years. Unfortunately, the net earnings are only twice the interest charges (both after taxes) on the substantial bank loans the corporation is carrying, and the loan agreements contain a clause requiring the termination of dividends whenever earnings in relationship to interest charges fall to this level. What is R_A for this company if $R_{DA} = .6$ and $i = .05$?

2-4. For a steady growth company, $i = .04$, $R_V = .25$, $R_{DA} = .3$, $C_Q = .13 = R_{EQ}$. What are C_A, the average weighted cost of capital, g, and R_A for this company?

2-5. A company with $R_A = 3i$ is considering shifting from $R_{DA} = .25$ to $R_{DA} = .5$ to increase the return on equity, R_{EQ}. What percentage change in R_{EQ} will result from this doubling of R_{DA}?

2-6. What is the weighted cost of capital, C_A, for a company whose market value of the common shares is equal to their book value if $i = .05$, $C_Q = .15$, and $R_{DA} = .4$? At these values of i and C_Q, how high a leverage, as measured by R_{DA}, would the company have to use before the cost of its total equity and total debt would be equal and what would be the value of C_A?

2-7. If $R_V = .3$, $R_{EQ} = .20$, and $C_Q = .15$ for a steady growth company, what would you expect should be the ratio of market to book value for the common stock? If $i = .04$ and $R_{DA} = .3$, what are the values of g,

M, and R_A for this company? Comment on the possible inappropriateness of the steady growth model for this company.

2-8. A company is perceived by the market as a steady growth company in the C_Q = .13 category. The multiple is 9 and R_V = .3. What growth rate does the market expect for this company? If the growth rate actually turns out to be half of this, by what percentage will the purchaser of a share over-pay?

2-9. A steady nongrowth company pays out all annual earnings as dividends and has an R_A = .09 with i = .05. With a rate set by the market on cost of the new equity capital of C_Q = .15, the company sells enough shares of common to reduce R_{DA} from .6 to .5. Calculate the ratio of the new equity funds raised by the sale to the total assets (which total remains unaltered, since all of the new funds are used to pay off debt). Calculate the ratio of new total annual earnings to previous total annual earnings. What would you expect might be the ratio of market value to book value for the common shares sold? By what ratio will the annual earnings per share change after the sale?

2-10. A company is in a growth field, although it is in third place against competitors in the same product line. The two leading competitors are doing better in return on assets employed. This company has an R_A = .10. It pays dividends on its common of 30 percent of earnings and finds it is not generating enough capital out of earnings and after dividends to finance the expansion required to hold its share of the market against the two top competitors. Its debt is already regarded as too high by the financial investment firms who have been asked to consider an offering of debentures. Therefore, the management is considering issuing more common shares, or perhaps preferred shares or convertible preferred, or lowering the dividend in order to retain more funds for reinvestment. What quantitative analyses should be made as an aid in deciding which alternative is the best?

2-11. A company in a field with substantial growth has shown a steady pattern of return on assets employed of R_A = .12, has a dividend policy of R_V = .3, and maintains an R_{DA} = .25, with i = .05. Its common stock is selling on the market at a price to earnings ratio of M = 8. A new management cuts personnel expenses, thus quickly increasing return on assets employed to R_A = .15. Assuming the new management maintains the dividend and debt ratios as before and invests all earnings after dividends in further growth, calculate the originally expected growth rate and the growth rate to be expected after the new management's action. Compare the dividends before and after. If the stock price multiple rises to 16 based on the market's higher evalua- tion of the new, higher returns and anticipated growth, estimate the rise of the common stock price by comparing the after with the before price. Calculate an approximate cost of equity capital, C_Q, before and after, and speculate about the reasonableness of your answer.

2-12. Several years ago a company issued convertible preferred stock paying a dividend of four dollars a share and convertible to two shares of common at the request of the preferred shareholder. At that time the common dividend was fifty cents per share. About a year ago the common dividend, which has risen steadily, passed two dollars per share and is now $2.25. Most convertible preferred shareholders con- verted during the past year. Some preferred shares have never been submitted for conversion. The preferred shares have been selling on the stock market somewhat above the market price of two common shares. Speculate about why some holders of preferred shares have not converted.

2-13. A purchaser plans on a $C_Q = .15$ as he buys convertible preferred stock with the following estimate of the future dividend stream. He will receive the $5.00 preferred dividend at the end of each of four years. At the beginning of the fifth year, confirming that the common dividend just paid has also reached $5.00 (as he expects) he will then exercise his privilege to convert to common, share for share. He will then expect a $5.50 dividend at the year end (fifth) and continue a growth rate of 10 percent in this dividend from then on. How much should he pay for a share of convertible preferred? If the company does not meet his expectations and he holds the preferred indefinitely re- ceiving his $5.00 annual dividend regalarly, and if that "non-convert- ible" preferred should deserve a C_Q of only .10, how much if any will he have overpaid in buying a share of convertible preferred?

2-14. Derive an expression for a steady growth company showing, for constant R_V and g, how M might be expected to vary with variations in C_Q. Give approximate values of the percent variation in M for a one percent change in C_Q for each of these parameter ranges: (1) C_Q approx = .13, g approx = .065, R_V = .3; (2) C_Q approx = .12, g approx = .010, R_V = .9.

2-15. Repeat the example of the three-phase model presented in the chapter (Equation 21) with the following parameters: $C_Q = .13$, $g_1 = .20$, $g_2 = .08$, $n_1 = 4$, $n_2 = 6$.

2-16. In the chapter example of conversion of a new corporation's preferred stock shares to common, debt ($R_{DA} = .3$) was added to finance faster growth and a g of .084 was realized. Redo the analysis to determine what R_{DA} would need to be used to provide $g = .09$. What now would be the present values on day one of a share of common and a share of preferred?

2-17. In the chapter example of a new corporation issuing $10 common stock and $15 preferred, it was found that at $C_Q = .15$, the initial purchasers of preferred had overpaid somewhat. At what C_Q would the day one present value be essentially the $15 purchase price. [Extrapolation between two trial and error C_Q's will suffice.]

2-18. From the annual report of a technological corporation, assuming $P_S = Q_S$ and $C_Q = .13$, estimate the value of i, R_{DA}, and C_A. Redo your estimate assuming $P_S = 1.5\,Q_S$.

2-19. The management of a corporation believes that at the market's present C_Q of 15 percent and with present $2 dividend and the expected future steady growth of the dividends the appropriate market price for the common should be $30 per share. The actual market price is $50. What rate of return will the stock owners who buy at $50 actually realize rather than C_Q, assuming the management is right in its estimates of the future?

2-20. A steady growth company has $g = .075$ and $R_{EQ} = .15$. If $C_Q = .15$, what might be expected to be the stock market multiple, M, of the common shares and how would you expect the market price and book value of a share to compare? What would be a probable R_V for this company?

2-21. It was shown in this chapter that for a steady growth company $M = 1/C_Q$ if either the growth is zero and all earnings are paid out as dividends or $R_{EQ} = C_Q$. Derive expressions for the deviation of M from $1/C_Q$ in the two regions: (1) g is very small and R_V is close to unity; (2) R_{EQ} is close to C_Q.

2-22. Two companies each having $R_{DA} = .3$ and $i = .05$ are in a $C_Q = .14$ category. What is the weighted average cost of capital for Company

No. 1 if its $P_S/Q_S = 1$? For Company No. 2 if its $P_S/Q_S = 1.5$? To bring the latter figure down to the former, how much would the R_{DA} for Company No. 2 have to be increased?

2-23. Show that for a steady growth company

$$C_A = i \frac{1 + uy}{1 + y}$$

where

$$u = C_Q/i$$

and

$$y = \frac{P_S(1 - R_{DA})}{Q_S R_{DA}}$$

Also show that if $P_S/Q_S = 1$, then C_A in this equation becomes R_A, and if $P_S/Q_S > 1$ then C_A will be larger than when $P_S/Q_S = 1$.

2-24. Show that for the steady growth company whose P_S/Q_S ratio was described by Equation 57, this ratio can also be written as

$$\frac{P_S}{Q_S} = \frac{R_V}{R_V - 1 + C_Q/R_{EQ}}$$

2-25. Rederive the formula for cost of capital (Equation 41), if part of the equity is in the form of nonconvertible preferred shares.

2-26. A company with no growth pays out all its earnings in dividends. Its debt is just equal to its equity and

$$R_A = C_Q = 2i$$

(1) What is its average cost of capital? (Express it as a ratio of i.) (2) If this is a steady condition, what would you expect would be the ratio of the market value of a common share to its book value?

3

INVESTMENT ANALYSIS

The Need for Investment Evaluations and Comparisons

We assume in this chapter that the corporation has capital at its command which it invests seeking the best return. A healthy firm will produce a continual flow of investment proposals well in excess of the corporation's capability to fund them. A company in bad shape will have, either despite its condition or because of it, a list of imperative investment requirements beyond its overall capacity. In all instances, the management is presented with difficult choices and resource allocation problems. It must have visibility of the actual and potential flow of funds, both from spending or earnings accumulation. It must also have means for objective comparative analysis to judge the alternative benefits to the corporation of distributing funds in different directions and thus be in a position to optimize the overall return on investment.

Examples of the many areas where investment decisions will have to be made in the normal course of operating a technological corporation include: research and development of new products; market development expenditures with the objective of improving market share; investments in fixed assets to enhance current operations, increase capacity, improve manufacturing technology, or make possible marketing in other geographical areas; acquisitions of assets of other companies to expand the product line; financing leasing arrangements to serve customers who are in a position to lease but not buy; setting up a new source of supply for components and materials that otherwise might be obtainable only unreliably from existing sources. These examples are in no way meant to be all inclusive. It is not usually

74

difficult for a technological corporation to list ways, even very attractive ones, in which it can spend money, what with technological advance continually offering chances for altering products and the techniques of manufacture. The evaluation system of the company must be such that it ensures an economic optimization process is at work and that a proper balance is maintained between sustaining the economic health of current operations and developing new business opportunities.

We do not mean to suggest that each investment a corporation makes is one it can choose to make depending on investment return considerations and the weighing of positive potential benefits against risks. Some corporate investments have to be made. For instance, in recent years investments to meet government pollution control and employee safety standards have used up a large fraction of the available cash flow of American corporations. In effect, such investments, in the narrowest economic sense, did not produce any return at all. This requires that the other, truly optional investments, must have a hurdle rate of return above the cost of capital sufficient to cover the ever present noneconomical and forced investments.

Some investment decisions are not fatal if they turn out to be wrong. Others are quite irreversible and affect a company for a long time. For instance, decisions to allocate expenditures for major plants and facilities virtually commit a firm to a course of action, a given technology, a specific location, and often can determine the pattern of much of the company's annual operating expenditures for years ahead.

Future Benefit; Present Cost

Investments inherently represent a present sacrifice for future benefits. We put money down today to obtain a future stream of funds whose present value to us we must learn to assess to see if it is greater (even though it arrives later) than the funds we are required to invest now. What we will receive in the future always involves an element of risk. We can be very clear about the investment we make now. This means we are engaged in trading a certain present cost for an uncertain future benefit. Presumably we know the average cost of capital for our corporation today, and we also know that we much prefer that the return on the investment of that capital exceed this cost. In spite of the time delay in our receipt of the benefits, and, in fact, taking account of this delay, we must calculate a meaningful rate of return to compare against the cost of capital that makes possible this return. We shall now discuss ways of doing this.

Net Present Value

Undiscounted Payback

One of the most common ways to assess an investment is to ask how long it will be before the investor will get his money back. As shown in Table 3-A, an investor who puts in $100,000 the first year and $50,000 the second, and then expects to get back $75,000 each year thereafter (at least for a while) looks at the cumulative cash flow and sees that his original investment is all returned by the end of four years. A corporation using this approach for comparing investments would presumably rank an investment as better if its payback period is shorter.

As a method to evaluate investment, the payback concept in this simple form is highly inadequate. The method totally neglects the cost of capital, and yields no return on investment figure for the critical comparison with that capital cost. It does not consider cash flows after the investment has been recovered. In effect this method assigns a weight of 1.0 to all returns before recovery of the investment and 0 to all recoveries afterward. It ignores the important "the bigger the better principle:" all things being equal a bigger return is preferable to a smaller one. If all the corporation gets back for its investment after a few years is the money it put in and no more after that, then it will of course have generated nothing to compensate, or account for, the earning power of the capital that has been invested all of that time. It will have had a return of zero, which is certainly less than the cost of capital.

This method of evaluation, though widely used, is an aid only for a quick rejection of a bad investment. If the payback period is very long, that is, it it takes a long time for the investment to come back, with no gain, then we might be forgiven for concluding that we are unlikely ever to see a return that exceeds the cost of capital.

Table 3–A   Undiscounted Payback

Year	1	2	3	4	5
Cash flow—annual	−100	−50	75	75	75
Cash flow—cumulative	−100	−150	−75	0	75
		Undiscounted payback = 4 years			

Table 3–B Discounted Payback

Year	1	2	3	4	5
Cash flow—annual	−100	−50	75	75	75
Discount factor at 12%	.893	.797	.712	.636	.567
Cash flow—discounted	−89	−40	53	48	43
Cash flow—cumulative discounted	−89	−129	−76	−28	15

Discounted payback approximately 5 years

Discounted Payback

In Table 3-B we take the same scenario of cash-in and cash-out as was listed in Table 3-A, but this time we recognize that gauging the present value of a later cash input or cash outflow requires that an appropriate discount factor be applied to those later events. If we take account of the assumed cost of captial of 12 percent, then it takes one more year before the corporation gets its investment back. This takes care of one fundamental defect in the use of undiscounted paybacks. Now when we speak of payback, we mean with a return of 12 percent. We obtain more than we put in and the difference represents a rate of return at the discount rate we used. Any funds we obtain in the years after the payback constitute the evidence we seek that the investment is successfully yielding more than the cost of the capital invested. Is this method of evaluating investments then wholly satisfactory?

It is still an inadequate way to contrast various investments, because it does not allow for comparing the relative values of delivery of returns on quite different time scenarios. A shorter payback period does not make an investment necessarily superior. Given the same size of investment, say, $1 million, it is admittedly more valuable to the firm to have that million back, properly discounted for the cost of capital, in three years rather than six. However, the three-year return may be the *total* return, although a scenario that brings the investment back in the later six years may go on for another ten years to provide substantial additional returns. The method provides no comparative rating of these two cases. It would be better to use a means of evaluation that compares investment opportunities by including their full histories of events versus time. Except as a sort of early, partial guide, we should not be interested in a method of judging investments that merely measures the length of time to get 100 percent of the investment back, even if the method also tells us that the cost of capital has been exceeded.

Present Value at Specified Discount Rates

To add to clarity with regard to the concept of present value of a series of cash flows, consider the example listed in Table 3-C. Here we borrow $1 million to be repaid three years from now with interest at a six percent rate compounded. We invest the $1 million in a project that will yield $500,000 at the end of each of the three years. As Table 3-C illustrates, at the end of Year 1, we owe the initial amount of $1 million plus the $60,000 interest. At the end of Year 2 we owe that augmented total, plus additional interest. Finally, at the end of three years, we must pay the total shown of $1,191,020. Meanwhile we have received a total of $1,500,000 and our profit is $1,500,000 − $1,191,020 = $308,980. But this ignores the fact that the $500,000 received each year could be earning interest for us in the interim.

It is much better to look at the whole problem on a present value basis. Thus, as Table 3-D shows, each of the $500,000 positive cash flows received at the end of each of the three years has a decreased present value at the beginning of the first year because of the 6 percent discount. Calculating the net present value as the difference between the $1 million investment and the $1,336,510 return, we have the result of $336,510.

It will be useful to check this result by imagining that we borrow, at the beginning of Year 1, not the $1 million, but rather exactly the present value the returns represent, namely $1,336,510. Then we further imagine, Table 3-E, that we partially repay this with the $500,000 income received at the end of each year. Thus, as the table shows, at the end of the first year we add to the initial amount

Table 3–C (amounts in dollars)

Year	Initial amount	Interest	Amount to be repayed
1	1,000,000	60,000	1,060,000
2	1,060,000	63,600	1,123,600
3	1,123,600	67,420	1,191,020

Table 3–D   (amounts in dollars)

Year	Return	P_V @ 6% discount
1	500,000	471,700
2	500,000	445,000
3	500,000	419,810
		1,336,510

Net P_V = \$1,336,510 − \$1,000,000 = \$336,510

borrowed the interest on that amount, and see that we owe \$1,416,700. We repay this in part with the \$500,000 income, leaving, to start the second year, a new beginning-of-year amount of \$916,700. At the end of the second year we owe that amount, plus interest of \$55,000 for a total of \$971,700. Again we apply the \$500,000 just received to reduce the debt. Finally, at the end of the third year, when we receive the last payment of \$500,000 and use it to pay off the remaining loan, we are exactly even.

The idea of net present value, the integrated sum of all discounted cash flowing in and out, leads to a number of possible ways of setting up evaluation comparisons for investments. For competitive scenarios of cash flow, we can use the same discount rate for all and figure a net present value, P_V, for each candidate investment. Given the same number of dollars invested initially, a higher, positive net present value would cause the investment that created it to be preferred. Given two different sizes of investments, I, say \$1 million and \$2, million we might divide the calculated net P_V for each investment by the initial investment, I, to calculate a relative profitability ratio, P_V/I, for each.

The net present value approach is still not perfect, of course, because two projects with the same amount of investment at risk might turn

Table 3–E   (amounts in dollars)

Year	First of the year amount	Interest	Year end amount to be repaid
1	1,336,510	80,190	1,416,00
2	916,700	55,000	971,700
3	471,770	28,300	500,000

out to have the same P_V but with the returns delivered on very different time schedules. Everything else being equal, we would prefer earlier payoffs. How dependent is the net present value upon the time phasing of the cash flows? This depends on the discount rate. That is, the ranking between two projects is not independent of the discount rate chosen for the analysis. To illustrate this, assume that two candidates for investment yield the same net present value and that each has the same initial investment put up entirely at the beginning of a period. Each produces a series of steady cash flow benefits. They differ in the amount and duration of those cash flows. If P_V is the net present value of all the cash flow in both directions, I the initial investment, R_I the discount rate, F_1 the annual cash flow taken out of the project (constant for all years, 1 thru n) and n_1 the number of years the flow takes place, then

$$P_V = -I + F_1 \sum_{n=1}^{n=n_1} 1/(1 + R_1)^n \qquad [1]$$

or

$$P_V = -I + F_1 x(1 - x^{n_1})/(1 - x) \qquad [2]$$

for the first investment candidate, where

$$x = 1/(1 + R_I)$$

(We have made use of Equation 9 of Chapter Two.)
The second investment alternative produces the same P_V with the same R_I but with a different flow history. It is described by

$$P_V = -I + F_2 x(1 - x^{n_2})/(1 - x) \qquad [3]$$

Comparing Equations 3 and 2 we see that

$$F_1(1 - x^{n_1}) = F_2(1 - x^{n_2}) \qquad [4]$$

which, remembering that $x < 1$, says that if $n_2 > n_1$, then

$$x^{n_2} < x^{n_1}$$

and

$$1 - x^{n_2} > 1 - x^{n_1}$$

so

$$F_1 > F_2 \qquad\qquad [5]$$

Suppose now that we compare these two investment scenarios using a different, say, a larger, discount rate, R_l. Then x would become smaller, and the two P_V's for the two investments would no longer be equal. Which P_V would be greater, the one with the longer period, n_2, or the other? The answer lies in which of the two critical contesting terms, $(1 - x^{n_1})$ or $(1 - x^{n_2})$, changes most and in which direction. If x diminishes, each of these two terms rises. Again, if $n_2 > n_1, x^{n_1}$ is a larger, more significant quantity than x^{n_2} and a change in it due to x changing has a bigger effect than a change in x^{n_2} in the two critical terms. Specifically, if x diminishes, x^{n_1} falls, $1 - x^{n_1}$ rises and P_{V1} will be higher than P_{V2}. A rise in discount rate will tend to favor the investment alternative that brings in the returned cash flow earlier.

If we had used a lower discount rate, the investment whose returns spread out later would have yielded a higher net present value. For any investment scenario in which the input is made early and the outflow of cash is delayed, the net present value will fall as we apply higher discount rates, of course. However, in comparing two investment alternatives on a net present value basis the answer we get as to the superiority of one over another may depend on the discount rate we choose to use.

It will be instructive to digress here for a moment and repeat that a shareholder who pays P_S for a common share in a steady growth company with initial dividend V_S who expects a stream of dividends growing at rate g (the model we have already used) could evaluate the investment by the net present value route. The cash put in would be P_S and the cash returned would be the series of dividends. If he discounts those dividends to calculate present value at discount rate C_Q he would find the net present value is zero if

$$C_Q = V_S/P_S + g$$

This statement should not surprise the reader at this point if he understands how this equation was derived in Chapter Two.

Before continuing our discussion of techniques to be used for investment evaluation and comparison, let us discuss the question of the most useful discount rate for present value calculations.

Choice of the Hurdle Discount Rate

Cost of Capital as a Hurdle Rate

In comparing and evaluating investments by estimating over the history of the investment the net present value of cash inputs and outflows, it is important we use the most sensible discount rate. One possibility, of course, is simply to use C_A, the average cost of capital for the corporation. If the net present value of an incremental investment, with all of the cash flow discounted at that cost of capital, turns out positive, then the corporation might be expected to favor the investment. If it turns out negative, the corporation might choose to forego the investment, unless some separate issues are involved, like a compelling need to develop and add a product because of competition's effect on the company's general product line activities. Alternative projects for use of limited funds could be rated simply by examining their net present values, each as a ratio of the initial investment. All investment calculations would use the same discount rate, the average cost of capital. This choice of discount rate to judge investments is made by many managements.

One shortcoming of the use of cost of capital as the hurdle rate is easily rectified by adding a safety factor increment to the average cost of capital. Some of the investments will do better than estimated, but chances are a lot more of them (the proposers of the projects tending to be optimistic and competing with each other to capture the corporation's backing for their activities) will turn out poorer. So the hurdle rate for comparing investment opportunities ought to be placed at something above the cost of capital to provide margin for error.

Influence of Debt-Equity Ratio

Usually a corporation is not at precisely the debt-equity ratio its management regards as optimum, but rather is working toward it. For instance, the corporation may have excess cash which it could use to pay off some of the debt and end up with a lower debt-to-equity ratio. But suppose the debt-to-equity ratio is already too low, that is, the corporation is not using enough leverage. Then it can be argued by management that it should allow a lower hurdle rate of return temporarily and get that extra cash invested. The hurdle rate for new investments to exceed becomes, for a while, merely the present earnings capability after tax of that extra cash. This will be close to, but might be lower than, i, the interest rate on debt after taxes and almost certainly will be lower than the cost of equity capital, C_Q, and even the average cost of capital, C_A. It is, therefore, a low hurdle rate for investment decisions. Yet for the special circumstances described, the corporation would show a higher return if it added such low return investments in preference to the even lower income from purchase of C.D.s, commercial paper or government bonds with its excess cash.

It is fairly rare for a technological corporation, even a mature one, to possess excess cash and no debt. Such a condition is limited to a few corporations with remarkably outstanding positions in highly profitable technological fields and domination of their markets. These corporations may have so high a rate of return on assets employed that the resulting positive cash flow is more than they can use, at least temporarily. Of course, they do not usually choose to solve this problem by looking for new products that can merely beat, as to return, the interest income their excess cash brings in with short-term safe investments. It is natural that they would seek instead product expansion potentials comparable with what they have become accustomed to. Since those very high return product areas are not easy to find, the fortunate corporations meanwhile build up funds. Usually a technological corporation with cash it cannot employ well to expand its existing product line finally will find some other company to acquire with the cash or, after a reasonable period of searching, a totally new and promising product area for investment.

A company with little debt and no surplus funds may decide it should borrow money and invest in building its present product line, using more leverage to enhance the return on the shareholders' equity. Under such circumstances, when its existing debt-to-equity ratio is considered far too low, it may argue that the hurdle rate for new investments should simply be the cost of the borrowed capital, i, the after-tax interest rate on the loans. The reasoning would be that as long as it earns more than this interest rate, which might be around 5 percent after tax, the company should profit by doing that borrowing and extending its product line. The average cost of capital for the corporation will go down by the process as a better balance of debt and equity is approached.

However, the company's overall average return on assets employed will also go down, if the company invests in projects with a return merely equal to i. Growth potential is related to maintaining a good level of return on assets employed. Thus, even granted a low debt-to-equity ratio, the company may be regarded as one with an eventual low growth potential, if it settles for low return projects. It may be judged as deserving a lower multiple on the stock market and its stock price per share for the common may drop. Still, a condition of inadequate debt leverage can be expected to push management toward consideration of lower hurdle rates than it might otherwise use.

It is all a matter of alternatives. If the company does not have enough ideas for new products that will be outstanding performers, it has to consider putting its available funds into product areas that are less promising. Of course it could also pay bigger dividends, giving more of the money being generated back to the shareholders. This essentially would be telling the shareholders they would do better to take their money and invest it elsewhere. For a technological corporation to lack project proposals that promise profitable growth is almost fatal to the management's image of competence.

Hurdle Rate to Provide Growth

Let us consider an approach to selection of the discount rate for evaluating investments for technological corporations that possess an abundance of growth opportunities. We assume a company with many innovative product ideas and numerous available areas for justified investment in new plants and facilities. Such a corporation might ask what return on investment is necessary to maintain the attainable growth by reinvestment of earnings after taxes and dividends. The answer could be the proper hurdle rate for investment analysis. Projects that do well enough to provide enough return for plowback to keep the growth going, without externally added financing, would be serious contenders for investment. Projects that appear unable to do this in the best scenarios drawn up for them would be rejected.

Let us recall that

$$g = \frac{1 - R_V}{1 - R_{DA}} (R_A - iR_{DA}) \qquad [6]$$

and assume that for the period ahead, in which the candidates for incremental investments are to be evaluated and compared, all of these operating parameters remain constant. Thus, additional equity (retained earnings) put back into the business to finance growth will be accompanied by a proportionate share of additional debt so that R_{DA} will remain constant. Also recall that

$$E = (R_A - iR_{DA})A = R_{EQ}Q \qquad [7]$$

and

$$R_{EQ} = \frac{R_A - iR_{DA}}{1 - R_{DA}}$$

which can be transformed to

$$R_A = R_{EQ}(1 - R_{DA}) + iR_{DA} \qquad [8]$$

Finally, also recall

$$R_{EQ} = g/(1 - R_V) \qquad [9]$$

Before we go to some examples, it is well to pause to emphasize that Equations 6–9 relate to the annual (or at least periodic) performance of a corporation. E is the earnings in a given period and R_{EQ} is the ratio of E to Q for that period while g is the period-to-period growth rate. In contrast to these periodic figures, we have been discussing in this chapter the matter of the return on an incremental investment. The cash flows relating to a specific investment may require many years before the history of the investment is fully written and an evaluation possible. The annual performance of a corporation is merely a year's exerpt of how the corporation is faring. That year's reported performance is a sum made up of pieces taken out of a large number of incremental investment scenarios. The relationship between annual or periodic results and the final results of individual investments that contribute to these periodic results is thus complex. In the next chapter we shall give this more attention. However, we should expect that if R_{EQ} is greater than C_Q year after year quite steadily and (an alternate way of putting it) if R_A is greater over a long time than C_A, the average cost of capital, then the corporation should prosper.

However, usually a reported R_{EQ} for a period will not exactly equal C_Q, and (however these two quantities may relate at any given time for a company) even if R_{EQ} exceeds C_Q regularly in the annual reports, this does not tell us what the growth rate of the company is. If a desired growth rate, g, is set by market demand for the corporation's products, and a dividend ratio R_V is also specified, then the R_{EQ} the company must meet so as to grow at rate g by reinvestment of earnings is determined by Equation 9.

To illustrate, let us take some figures for a large, successful technological corporation during a period when $i = .04$ and $C_Q = .13$;

namely: $R_{DA} = .3$, $R_V = .35$, and $g = .09$. Then from Equation 9, the company requires

$$R_{EQ} = .09/(1 - .35) = .1385$$

and, from Equation 8, it equally requires

$$R_A = .1385(1 - .3) + .04 \times .3$$
$$= .11$$

Over an extended period, if the corporate management succeeds in making internal incremental investments for which the rate of return equals or exceeds .11, the desired $g = .09$ will be maintained by plow back of earnings.

We note that R_{EQ} exceeds C_Q, the cost of equity capital, in this example. Recall that for the model of a steady growth corporation

$$C_Q = V_S/P_S + g$$

or

$$C_Q - g = R_V E_S/P_S \qquad [10]$$

Since

$$E_S = R_{EQ}Q_S \qquad [11]$$

then

$$\frac{P_S}{Q_S} = R_{EQ}\frac{R_V}{C_Q - g} \qquad [12]$$

Substituting the specifics of our example, which means we assume the company fits the steady growth model, yields

$$\frac{P_S}{Q_S} = .1385\frac{.35}{.13 - .09}$$
$$= 1.21$$

which says that the market, in adjusting the market price of the stock to yield to a stock purchaser the return of $C_Q = .13$, will push that price above the book value. Just as $R_{EQ} > C_Q$ in this example, we can readily confirm that $R_A > C_A$. From Equation 41 of Chapter 2

$$C_A = \frac{iR_{DA} + C_Q(1 - R_{DA})P_S/Q_S}{R_{DA} + (1 - R_{DA})P_S/Q_S}$$

which, with the specified quantities for this example yields

$$C_A = .1065$$

Returning to the discussion of proper R_I choices to evaluate internal investments, a proper hurdle rate for some companies is merely the par that they find they can adhere to in practice. If the company typically enjoys an R_A of 15 percent and has many competing projects for its limited investment funds, with most appearing to be able to yield returns this much or higher, then it matters little to the company in choosing R_I that its cost of capital, C_A, is, say, 10 percent on the average. The company has been and expects to go on enjoying that 5 percent differential. So it uses 15 percent as the hurdle rate in making present value analyses of contenders for incremental investments.

In choosing a hurdle rate for return on investment, a company must be very careful to take account of its diversification. Employing a single, fixed hurdle rate for all operating units of a diversified company, and even for the various product lines of a company not highly diversified, is generally not sensible. Assuming for the moment that all hurdle rates used by a company are above the cost of capital, it still would be simplistic to average the returns for the various divisions of the company and then announce that average as a hurdle rate for all divisions with new investments considered only if they appear to yield returns above that figure. It is forgivable to contemplate a future situation in which all units of a company always perform above the company's average, but not while sober. Some units may make substantial contributions to the overall operation—financial condition, image with the customer, morale of employees, maintenance of adequate size and stability—even though the returns are below the company average. Such units may deserve further investment, for instance to retain market share or broaden the product line defensively.

Internal Rate of Return; Discounted Cash Flow

We are now ready to go one more step and recommend a generally useful tool for evaluating, rating and comparing candidates for investment. In this method, a scenario of cash flows in and out for the proposed project is again set up and the net present value is calculated. However, the discount rate used is that which will make the net present value zero. We shall speak of it as the internal rate of return. An attractive project, for example, may be one for which the net present value calculates to zero if the discount rate used is 25 percent, while an unattractive one has an internal rate of return of only five percent, that is, five percent is the discount rate that will cause the present value of cash out to equal the present value of cash in. The analysis is independent of any predetermined discount rate. The general decision rule is that all investments with an internal rate of return greater than the firm's hurdle rate are acceptable. In the presence of a need for capital rationing, investment proposals are ranked in descending order of internal rate of return.

Until recently, this technique has not been as attractive as it might have been, because the calculations tend to be a bit complex. An exact solution for the R_I that causes P_V to equal zero involves solving a high degree polynomial equation in R_I. It is now easy and quick by a few trial and error steps and some extrapolation to get a sufficiently accurate answer with the aid of readily available, cheap hand-held calculators. Some calculators will give the internal rate of return directly.

We can best illustrate the concept of internal rate of return by examples. Suppose $10,000 is invested at the beginning of the first year and cash return is received at the end of each of four years as follows: $5000, $4000, $3000, $2000 (Table 3-F). Noting that the original investment comes back in just over two years we make a quick first guess that an R_I = 40 percent, is the internal rate of return yielding a net P_V of zero. However, as Table 3-F shows, R_I = 40 percent is way too high. We next try R_I = 20 percent and find it is only slightly high. R_I = 16 percent is a bit too low. Easy extrapolation results in the conclusion that R_I = 17.8 percent will yield a net P_V of zero.

A final example will further illustrate the internal rate of return concept, the calculating of that R_I yielding a net P_V of zero, and will compare it with the use of comparative net present value at a given hurdle rate to evaluate and select investments. We imagine and compare two projects. Initially $100,000 is invested in each. The cash flow returns are shown in Table 3-G. In Project A, $200,000 is returned in four years for a net cash flow (undiscounted) of $100,000. Project B has a somewhat delayed but eventually larger return flow (undiscounted) of $150,000.

When discounted for the firm's hurdle rate of 16 percent, Project B

Table 3–F

	Year	Cash flow	Discount factor	Present value
$R_I = .40$:				
	0	−$10,000	1.0	−$10,000
	1	5,000	.714	3,570
	2	4,000	.510	2,040
	3	3,000	.364	1,092
	4	2,000	.260	520
			Net P_V =	−$ 2,778
$R_I = .20$:				
	0	−$10,000	1.0	−$10,000
	1	5,000	.833	4,165
	2	4,000	.694	2,776
	3	3,000	.579	1,737
	4	2,000	.482	964
			Net P_V =	−$ 358
$R_I = .16$:				
	0	−$10,000	1.0	−$10,000
	1	5,000	.862	4,310
	2	4,000	.743	2,972
	3	3,000	.641	1,923
	4	2,000	.552	1,104
			Net P_V =	$ 309

again exceeds Project A. On this basis alone, if we had to choose one project, we would choose B.

However, when we calculate the internal rate of return, the R_I that brings the net P_V to zero, we find that Project A now wins out over Project B. The reason is not difficult to comprehend. It is because the higher returns of Project B occur later in time and the discounting process penalizes them more as to present value. But this is the way we prefer it. Particularly in a technological corporation do we encounter investment opportunities in which the eventual desired cash returns are delayed by many years. This delay adds greatly to the risks that something will change, that the market and the technology will develop differently from what is expected or hoped for.

Table 3–G

Year	Project A		Project B	
	Cash flow ($1000)	Cash flow discounted 16%	Cash flow ($1000)	Cash flow discounted 16%
0	−100	−100	−100	−100
1	50	43.10	0	0
2	50	37.16	50	37.16
3	50	32.03	80	51.28
4	50	27.61	120	66.24
Net cash Flow	100		150	
Net P_V at 16%		39.91		54.69
R_I for zero net P_V		34.9%		33.3%

Risk Assessment

Investment analyses, evaluations, and selections are meaningless without a description of the estimated future cash flows. But the future is not predictable, and so whatever scenario is set down has only a chance of turning out as planned. Given two investment opportunities competing for the use of limited capital, it is not enough to determine which has the higher internal rate of return. What if we believe that Project A, though exhibiting a somewhat lower return in its future forecast, has almost a certainty of hitting forecast, while Project B, despite a higher return, is loaded with risks? For B we are able to list many quite conceivable events that could happen to interfere with the pattern of cash flows we picture for it. Which, then, do we choose, A or B?

Obviously, in one way or another, the management must list risks, their nature, the spectrum of probabilities of their occurrence, and the negative consequences of the events, if they should occur, to the cash flow projections. In choosing hurdle rates for investment candidates, higher rates will be used for the riskier ones.

If the internal rate of return method is used to rate investment opportunities, it is likely that this will bias decisions toward the less risky candidates. Although this is not always so, this may occur because of the following combination of factors. A favored investment is one with a high internal rate of return. This often results when the positive cash flows occur early, since with a higher discount rate, the earlier returns will contribute more to the net present value of an investment. Again, the longer the time period before positive cash flow takes place, the greater the risk that unforeseen events will interfere with the scenario being forecast. To be safer, in other words, is often the same as seeking projects with high and early positive cash flows.

For a balanced, optimum program of investment, a technological corporation needs to be able to take some long-time risks. Some very advantageous, high technology products will require 10 or more years to attain profitability. We need to remember that, if judged by the internal rate of return analysis, long-range projects will automatically seem riskier and will have to provide very high positive cash flows eventually because of their lateness.

A technological corporation's management that seeks to limit its incremental investments to nonrisk ones lives in a dream world. Fortunately, experienced, sophisticated management will usually be able to categorize investment candidates into usefully chosen groups as low, medium or high risk. Sometimes it is even practical to sum up specific data and the judgments of available experts into quantitative probability figures.

To cite an example, a corporate management may decide to use C_A, the average cost of capital, as its average hurdle rate and have confidence that, say, its \$100 million of incremental investment this year will add up to a sensible, integrated plan with R_I exceeding its C_A of .10, because the investments are distributed, it believes, about as follows: \$50 million in projects with a 90 percent chance of yielding R_I = .10 or higher; \$25 million in investments believed to have a 60 percent chance of yielding R_I = .15 or higher; and the other \$25 million in projects deemed to have a 50 percent probability of delivering an R_I of .20 or higher. Considering its choices and objectives, the combination appears to management to be near optimum.* The higher probability of success projects carry the high risk ones, and, since there is substantial chance of the high risk ones becoming successful, the overall program allows the corporation room both to expand and experiment.

How does a corporation derive risk probability numbers? Usually

---

* A more thorough statement of this example would require, of course, that we define the probabilities for the projects' successes more rigorously and lay a theoretical basis for the concept of probability optimization. This is beyond this book's scope. This brief mention, however, presents the general idea.

this is approached by breaking each project down into key elements and assessing (sometimes only guessing from best experience) the odds as to the pieces. As example:

1. A competitor may launch an unusually aggressive program, cutting prices, adding more marketing staff and forcing lower profits than in the forecast. Will he really do this? Probably not, because he is known to have severe restrictions precluding such action. But perhaps there is one chance in ten and this is worth including.

2. The start-up of a new plant may run into labor supply problems. Admittedly the data are inadequate. A high and a low range of labor availability might be estimated with the best evaluation being of an equal chance for each.

3. A project hinges on the validity of a competitor's patent now in court litigation. What are the odds of losing the suit and sustaining a severe damage to the investment scenario if royalty costs have to be added? The attorneys and the most knowledgeable executives involved might be pressed to provide the probability estimates to include in the analysis.

4. A foreign subsidiary's forecast for return on an added investment depends greatly on that country's future inflation and currency exchange rates vis-a-vis the United States. The most highly regarded economic and political experts available might be asked for data and opinions as a basis for making the cash flow estimates. Their inability to forecast on the nose should be recognized. The spread of misses in past such economic-political forecasts and the consequences of being badly off should be studied.

5. Since the company has had to make many forecasts, the record shows a batting average for accuracy. Have the forecasts usually been better than the actuals by 10 or 20 percent quite regularly, the result of combining errors, some bad or inadequate data, and optimism about the competitors or the market demand? If so, inject a factor of .8 to .9 then as a probability discount to allow for this pattern of failure to meet past forecasts.

6. What does the record show about new technology projects? Has a technical project usually turned out to be tougher than anticipated, longer, costlier, with much more development needed to overcome unforeseen problems after the project starts? A compensating factor should be included to cover the probability that this will all happen again.

If perfect and complete social, political, economic, technological, marketing and human performance data were available to all technological corporations then the competition battle would merely hinge on a contest of skills in using these data. But, except in an exceedingly skimpy fashion, they are available to no corporation. Business operates with risk and uncertainty. Competitive skill goes to the searching out, selecting and utilizing of the best, most pertinent facts and judgements available, inadequate as they may be. Corporations (especially technological corporations that deal in the uncertainty of routes and speeds of science and technology advance) are rewarded if they are creative and wise risk takers. Accordingly, although we have introduced risk as a factor in evaluating incremental investments in this chapter, risk will be with us, at least indirectly, as an issue in all the remaining chapters of this book.

Problems

3–1. A company with no debt is considering choices of dividend policy and hurdle rates for investment returns. It is very conscious also of the importance to the company of maintaining growth by an investment of earnings. Plot growth of earnings against annual return on assets employed (assuming constant growth and other parameters will be maintained for years) for three different values of R_V: .1, .2, and .3.

3–2. Plot g against R_A, for R_V = .1, .2, and .3 assuming R_{DA} = .2 and i = .05. Repeat for R_{DA} = .4.

3–3. A company's management finds it has a weighted average cost of capital, C_A, of about 10 percent, which it expects will be continued over the next several years. It believes it can extend its product line with additional products, all with an estimated internal rate of return substantially exceeding this C_A. The management decides to restrict its expansion to those new product endeavors it anticipates will provide a high enough average R_A to maintain a growth rate of 12 percent by reinvestment of earnings after dividends without additional financing. Calculate what this hurdle rate for R_A must be to yield this result. Assume the interest rate after taxes is i = .05, and that an R_{DA} = .25 and R_V = .30 will be maintained.

3–4. Since the company in problem 3–3 seems to have made a decision to abandon some profitable product lines to attain a specific growth rate through earnings plowback, it is not surprising that some in management feel this decision is wrong. They believe that as long as additional product ideas are available to add to the company's sales and earnings, and as long as the internal rate of return to produce and market these products is greater than the cost of capital, it is good for the shareholders for the management to build the company sales and earnings higher. Discuss some of the main arguments on both sides. What do you think is the right conclusion and why?

3–5. A company sets a hurdle rate, $R_I = R_A$, when it analyses investments by the internal rate of return method. Using the return on assets, R_A, that is derived from the formula

$$g = \frac{1 - R_V}{1 - R_{DA}} (R_A - iR_{DA})$$

Compare the sensitivity of this hurdle rate, R_A, to changes in (a) the dividend payout ratio, R_V; (b) the growth rate, g, that the company wishes to adhere to, and (c) the debt to total assets ratio, R_{DA}. Assume that for this company these quantities are: $R_V = .30$, $R_{DA} = .25$, and $g = .10$ and that what is sought is the sensitivity to changes in these quantities in the region of these figures.

3–6. If R_A is greater than C_A for a corporation, then it would not be surprising that R_A, rather than C_A would be used as the hurdle rate for internal rate of return assessments of investments. However, suppose a corporation has been operating steadily with $R_A < C_A$. What might then cause it to be satisfied to use R_A, rather than C_A, as its hurdle rate? What would you expect the market price of the common relative to book value to be?

3–7. A corporation with no debt has $R_A = .14$ despite having one-tenth of its assets in surplus cash bringing in only a return of 5 percent after taxes. If the cash is invested in projects that are expected to produce an average return of 10 percent, how much would R_A be improved? If the market price of common stock equals book value, would it be better to buy back stock with the excess cash instead?

3–8. Assume an investment, I, is made with a constant return received annually of B for N_2 years, the number of years for undiscounted payback being N_1 years where, of course, $N_1 = I/B$. Show that for a very long pay back period, N_1, the internal rate of return, R_I, may be approximated by $1/N_1$. Also show that more generally, without approximation,

$$R_I = (1 - x^{N_2})/N_1$$

where

$$x = 1/(1 + R_I)$$

If $N_1 = 5$ and $N_2 = 10$ what is R_I by the approximate and the precise formulas (the latter by trial and error).

3–9. In this chapter it was shown that if an investment of $10,000 is made and this results in returns in the following years of $5000, $4000, $3000, and $2000 respectively, the internal rate of return is approximately $R_I = 17.8$ percent. Prove this figure to be correct in another way: Assume that using the first cash in-flow of $5000, interest of 17.8 percent is paid on the preceding year's balance ($10,000), and the remainder is used to pay back the investor, thus reducing the balance owed for the year that follows. If this is done each successive year, show that at the end of the four years the balance owed the investor will have been reduced to zero (or a negligible residue resulting from round-off).

3–10. A new company is financed by selling a block of common stock for P dollars. The net earnings reported for the first year are R_AP. No dividends are paid, no debt is used, R_A remains constant, and earnings are all reinvested to finance a steady growth of annual earnings at rate g for N years. At the end of the Nth year the earnings of that year are all paid out as the first dividend. After that the annual earnings remain constant at the Nth year level and the same dividend is paid yearly indefinitely. If the price P represents the true present value on the company's inauguration day of the future stream of dividends described, discounted at a rate C_Q, prove that $R_A = C_Q$.

3–11. In problem 3–10, suppose the indefinitely long duration second period following the first N years is characterized by a steady growth rate g_2 (where $g_2 < C_Q$) and a constant R_V just such as to provide a maximum of dividends, while still allowing ample retained earnings to finance the growth. Also assume the first dividend, again at the end of the Nth year, is not the entire Nth year's earnings but only a fraction R_V thereof. Show that again $R_A = C_Q$ regardless of the related values of g_2 and R_V.

3–12. A company has had a steady set of operating parameters (R_A, R_{DA}, R_V, g, and i) for 10 years during which g was .10. At the start its common stock sold for $18 per share, its then book value, it earned $3 per share and paid a dividend of $1.20. $R_{DA} = .4$ and $i = .05$. (a) Calculate the cost of equity capital, C_Q, and the weighted average cost of capital, C_A, at the beginning of this period. Show that $R_A = C_A$ and $R_{EQ} = C_Q$ at that time. (b) Draw up a table for the years 1 through 10, showing per share values for: earnings (starting with $3 for the first year); dividends (starting with $1.20 at the end of the first year); year end retained earnings; each year's beginning cumulative shareholders' equity (starting with $18 at the beginning of the first year). (c) Show that if the dividend stream is added to the cumulative shareholders' equity at the end of 10 years and the total is discounted to compute a present value at the start of the 10 years, this P_V will equal the $18 initial investment to yield a net P_V of zero at an internal rate of return equal to the C_Q calculated in (a) above.

3–13. A technological corporation uses internal rate of return, R_I, analysis to rate investments. As a rough guide line for initial sorting, it looks with favor on a short-term project (0 to 5 years to completion), if R_I exceeds the company's C_A of 10 percent, a medium-term project (5 to 10 years), if R_I exceeds 15 percent, and a long-term investment (10 plus years) if R_I exceeds 20 percent. What do you think is the rationale behind these choices of hurdle rates?

4

MEASUREMENT OF FINANCIAL PERFORMANCE

The Distinction Between Performance for a Period and Internal Return on Investment

In the previous chapter it was emphasized that the running of a corporation includes the making of a large number of incremental investment decisions. When management makes selections from many candidate investment opportunities, it should forecast the financial consequences of each investment. Specifically, it was proposed that the cash flows be estimated, the present values compared, and the internal rate of return, the discount rate that would bring the net present value to zero, also should be calculated. Guidance and control for the investment process should involve a hurdle rate, usually substantially above the average cost of capital, for the internal rate of return. The lower limit for acceptance of internal rates of return for investments would depend upon many characteristics of the company's situation, particularly about its market opportunities and its financial condition. High risk projects generally deserve the assigning of a higher hurdle rate than the safer and surer projects.

Now, if in substantial part, good financial management of a corporation suggests this kind of careful analytical evaluation of incremental investments, then surely the corporation will want to arrange an accounting system that will make visible the actual histories of the various investments as they unfold. The management of the various projects in which investments were made would need to know how these programs are progressing. Steps then could be taken to enhance the attainment of the planned success or perhaps even to exceed it, if

97

possible. Also future forecasts and investment decisions will be superior in quality as a result of benefiting from experience.

However, we must note again that in any substantial technological corporation, the investment decisions are numerous. All are not going to be followed in detail by all levels of management. Those management strata concerned with the details of the original forecasting and the implementation of a project being forecast will want to monitor what happens to that particular project. The overall effect of investment decisions and the follow through after decision are much more likely to be judged by higher management on a periodic basis, perhaps monthly, annually or quarterly. Moreover, when the reported results of all of the divisions of a large corporation are put together in single reports for the corporation as a whole, periodic reports alone are made, not records on individual investment decisions. Admittedly, sometimes the corporation may make what it regards as a momentous decision about an individual project and, under such circumstances, the top corporate management will be extremely interested in seeing figures that tell how that specific large project is developing. Such project figures are not likely to go outside the corporation.

Government regulations about corporate disclosures, the eligibility rules for sale of the shares on the stock market, the requirements of public accounting firms who examine and certify to the financial reports of corporations, the expectancy of shareholders, and the general need of a corporation to tell its story to its constituencies, are all met by quarterly reports of modest detail and annual reports of substantial detail. These reports describe the financial state of the corporation at the beginning and the end of the period and the revenues, expenses, taxes and earnings for that specific period.

In this chapter we shall give attention to the matter of periodic performance figures for a corporation. We shall include those items that are usually reported in the quarterly and annual reports of corporations and will discuss these periodic figures and their value to management in measuring how the corporation is faring. Also we will note how such figures are interpreted by the outside world to judge the corporation, not, of course, for the purpose of management, but rather to decide whether to hold, sell or buy shares of the corporation, to consider its value for merger, or to judge its management's capabilities.

We know by now, of course, that when we describe what has happened in a corporation during a specific time period, say one year, the report is really a sum and integration of the large number of events that relate to all of those investment decisions. The annual results are a summary of what has happened during that one-year period to separate activities which as individual investment scenarios may require quite a number of additional years to play out. To begin to develop some relationship between the judging of financial performance by periodic measures against following each investment decision over the period required for that decision, let us take specific examples of projects that we can assess both for annual performance and overall internal return on investment.

An Investment's Annual Results

Let us start with an exceedingly simple case. A corporation invests P in a project from which the cash flow return to the corporation is a constant value, $R_A P$, for each of N years. The project's contribution to the company's annual reported after tax earnings is also $R_A P$. (The annual depreciation expense, an amount, T, is reinvested in the project each year to keep the facility in an as-new condition necessary to maintain the earnings. Thus the gross cash flow, $R_A P + T$, reduces to $R_A P$ as a net flow.) The assets on the books assigned to the project remain equal to P, the added assets each year for replacement just equaling the depreciation write-off. The reported annual rate of return on assets employed is equal to R_A, of course. At the end of N years, the project is liquidated and the assets, of book value P, are then returned to the corporation.

Management, in analyzing this project, calculates an internal rate of return, R_I, by setting to zero the P_V of all cash flow in and out of the project. Thus

$$O = -P + \sum_{n=1}^{n=N} R_A P x^n + P x^N \qquad [1]$$

where

$$x = 1/(1 + R_I) \qquad [2]$$

or

$$R_I = (1 - x)/x \qquad [3]$$

From Equation 1

$$1 = R_A \sum_{n=1}^{n=N} x^n + x^N$$

$$1 = R_A x(1 - X^N)/(1 - x) + x^N$$

and

$$R_A = (1 - x)/x = R_I \qquad [4]$$

For this project, the reported annual rate of return on assets employed is equal to the internal rate of return on investment on the project. If the corporation has many projects and all have the same basic pattern and the same R_I, then the corporate R_A will equal R_I. However, this project happened to have a rather special unfolding of cash flow against time. This case illustrates that the relation between internal rate of return on multi-year investments and the annual reported R_A of an activity pursuing those investments need not necessarily be hidden and difficult to extract, although most often that is so.

Suppose a corporation sets up a new division by making an investment, I, and the division is profitable from the beginning, providing a positive cash flow back to the corporation starting at the end of the first year. If the division's performance fits the steady-growth model, has a constant R_A, a steady-growth rate and pays back a constant fraction of its growing earnings in cash to the corporation, then following the pattern of previous similar derivations (such as Equations 1 thru 4) will show that R_I will equal R_A. This relation will be true as well if the division does not go on growing forever but is liquidated at some point, provided the book value of the assets are fully recovered. (Problem 4–10, end of chapter).

However, more generally it is difficult indeed to relate R_A to the R_I's of the investments that constitute the activity whose progress is being reported annually, as the next example will demonstrate.

Assume that in a portion of a corporation's existing plant, a special facility, is created for assembly and checkout of complex equipment. The investment is $10 million, all in apparatus. With none of the inventory or work in process on the books of this new profit center, and all its expenses covered by billing the parent company (that pays promptly), no working capital is needed. This division will operate for ten years. The apparatus will then be junked, and the depreciation expense will be taken straight line at $1 million per year. The arrangement is expected to generate an incremental after-tax profit per year of $770,000. (The division charges the parent company for the task of assembling and testing the product it turns out the same price the company had been paying previously and finds this exceeds its costs, including depreciation, by the $770,000 figure.) Table 4–A shows the cash flow in thousands of dollars. When discounted by 12 percent, the company's hurdle rate, the net P_V is zero, and the project meets the company's basic investment return criterion.

Let us now look at this example in another way. We suppose this division, or subsidiary, to have its own separate annual accounting. Its initial balance sheet (at end of year zero) will show a book value on the assets side of $10 million, all in apparatus, and an equal balancing item of $10 million equity, which is the parent company's investment in this entity (Table 4–B). Also, the parent company is very interested in the cash being generated, and it shows this interest by leaving the "funds for investment" on the books of the subsidiary, where it is being produced, and then borrowing it for use elsewhere at 12 percent return. When this "interest" income is added to the $770,000, each year, a higher E than in Table 4–A results. Thus, the first year's cash flow is $770,000 plus $1,000,000 depreciation for a total of $1,770,000, labeled "funds for investment." At 12 percent, this nets an added income of $212,000, which brings E for the second year to $982,000, as shown in the table.

When the 10 years are over, the operation is abandoned and the

Table 4–A

End of Year	Earnings ($1000) (E)	Deprec. ($1000) (T)	Cash flow ($1000) (F)	Discounted 12%
0	—	—	−$10,000	−$10,000
1	770	1,000	1,770	1,580
2	770	1,000	1,770	1,411
3	770	1,000	1,770	1,260
4	770	1,000	1,770	1,125
5	770	1,000	1,770	1,004
6	770	1,000	1,770	897
7	770	1,000	1,770	801
8	770	1,000	1,770	715
9	770	1,000	1,770	636
10	770	1,000	1,770	570
			Net P_V = 0	

Table 4–B

End of year	Assets ($1000) Equip.	Funds for in- vest.	Total	Equity ($1000) Retain. earn.	Total	E ($1000)	R_{EQ} or R_A
0	10,000	0	10,000	0	10,000	0	—
1	9,000	1,770	10,770	770	10,770	770	.0715
2	8,000	3,752	11,752	1,752	11,752	982	.084
3	7,000	5,972	12,972	2,972	12,972	1,220	.094
4	6,000	8,458	14,458	4,458	14,458	1,486	.103
5	5,000	11,242	16,242	6,242	16,242	1,784	.11
6	4,000	14,360	18,360	8,360	18,360	2,118	.115
7	3,000	17,852	20,852	10,852	20,852	2,492	12.0
8	2,000	21,762	23,762	13,762	23,762	2,010	12.3
9	1,000	26,140	27,152	17,140	27,140	3,378	12.5
10	0	31,043	31,043	21,043	31,043	3,903	12.6

corporation takes the accumulated $31,043,000. It is easily verified that 10 will grow to 31.043 in 10 years at a compounded annual rate of 12 percnt.

We can cite other equivalent ways to construct the same investment. We could imagine, for instance, that this division is a separate corporation that sold $10 million of common stock, paid total dividends of $1,770,000 for each of ten years and then closed shop. The investors would have registered a C_Q of 12 percent. As still another way to do it, no dividends at all might have been paid by this separate corporation, the funds instead invested at 12 percent, Table 4–B. When the corporation is liquidated after 10 years, the assets would then be distributed to the shareholders. With the $31,043,000 in hand, the shareholders would again have realized the yield of 12 percent.

Let us focus now on the annual reported earnings, as shown in Table 4–B. This is a business entity that is showing increasing earnings, E, each year and an improved R_A (or R_{EQ} since with no debt = R_A = R_{EA} = R_{EQ}) each year as well. We have arbitrarily (again for simplicity) used year end assets in calculating R_A from E/A. If we had used average assets employed during the year (by averaging the two year-end numbers) the results for R_A would be somewhat lower, but the difference is not important for this discussion. The main point is that the annual values of R_A are difficult to use as a judge of the financial progress of this subsidiary. If we looked only at the R_A performance for a few years, we might argue that the figures are too low and the entity is a drag on the overall corporate performance.

To make even clearer the point that annual measures must be interpreted carefully, note that we could have chosen to extract the excess cash each year and put it back on the corporate books. Neither the assets nor the income on it would now appear in Table 4–B. The parent corporation, shown by its consolidated balance sheet and profit and loss statement, would exhibit the same total assets and total income, of course, but the subsidiary's annual performance would now look quite different. E would not now grow each year but would stay constant at the $770,000 figure. R_A would start at 7.7 percent for the first year and rise rapidly as A diminished through depreciation. (Now we would have to use for A each year some suitable year's average. Using year-end figures, A would be zero for the last year's R_A calculation and R_A would be calculated as infinite, which even the most optimistic manager would reject). The subsidiary, seen now as having constant earnings and an R_A rising to very high figures, might be considered an extremely valuable component of the corporation!

This example illustrates that the connection between the rate of return, R_I, on an incremental investment, which may take years to complete, and the annual ratios (such as R_A or R_{EQ}) is not a simple one, even for a single investment project. The annual performance figures for a corporation as a whole represent the integrated sum of the pieces for that year of numerous investment scenarios. This means it is difficult to rely on annual performance figures to see how various investment decisions are doing. For that, management will have to arrange detailed accounting over the life of the specific investment, comparing actual against forecasted events.

Judging an Operating Unit's Performance

The keystone measure for the annual financial performance of a segment of a corporation is the return on assets employed, R_A. Of course, many other measures are important for a thorough evaluation of the details of the business. Numerous aspects of the profit and loss results and the balance sheet of the operating unit are of interest to the management of that unit and to the management of the whole corporation. But R_A occupies a central position.

Why distinguish between a segment of the corporation ad the corporation as a whole? To begin with, although it is true Securities and Exchange Commision regulations (and the now broadly recognized need for effective communication of what is happening in a corporation) require that a corporation provide information on the various principal segments of its business, nevertheless, the judging of a segment of a business is largely for management's benefit. They need to know whether the segments are well directed, whether things are going in accordance with expectations, the trends are satisfactory, or problems are arising—all with the idea of triggering appropriate management action to improve the situation, even if it is satisfactory and especially if it is not. It is not the prime business of the manager of a segment how the overall corporate entity finances the assets allocated to him. The corporation presumably has many other operating units. Taken in combination there are optimum strategies, accounting practices, and operating and financing decisions that will dictate to the corporation what debt-to-equity ratio to use, whether to take steps to defer taxes or move cash from one place to another or shrink an activity or assign new and larger assets to the manager so his business may be expanded. Equity, that is, shareholders' investment, does not have the meaning for an operating division of the corporation that it has for the corporation as a whole. There is no stock market trading in shares of the division. The shareholders do not invest directly in the separate segments of the business. Thus, in judging the segment, it is the return on the assets employed, without the inclusion of interest charges, namely, R_A, that is most fundamental.

The return on assets employed, a ratio, can be used for valuable comparisons between a company's unit and one of a competitor, even if the sizes of the two units are very different. It is interesting, for example, for a company to compare the return on assets employed by one of its units making computers with the performance of IBM and to make it a habit to seek to understand in substantial detail why differences would be expected and what factors they stem from. Similarly, IBM would probably want to account for the difference between the R_A of a mini-computer manufacturer and that of its most comparable unit.

If the performance of a unit of some corporation is to be compared with a competitor which is a corporation reporting its results as a total corporate entity, then the matter of interest charges and cost of capital must be noted carefully. If the intention of corporate management is to emphasize to all division managers that they will not be competitive and will not be attaining adequate financial performance unless they cover the interest charges, then we must remember that interest is only part of the cost of capital. A redoing of the financial figures of each division to account for the cost of capital is not fully accomplished by assessing each division a piece of the corporation's total interest charge, say, in proportion to the assets being employed by that division. Some corporate managements prefer to modify the measure of an operating entity's performance by taxing each unit's return with a capital investment charge. Specifically, from the R_A is subtracted C_A, the average cost of capital to the firm. The difference is the residual or incremental return on capital above its cost. Thus these managements introduce a hurdle level for profitability as a basis for judging the performance of all units of the corporation.

For a large corporation, the depreciating assets are many in number, some relatively new and some in their last days. The denominator, in the calculation of R_A, will be the net book value of the assets, that is, the cost of acquisition of those assets less the cumulative depreciation. In computing incremental returns on an asset, it is possible to arrive at some misleadingly high figures in the last year or so as the book value of the depreciating asset collapses to zero. This same result can be obtained sometimes in judging the R_A of a division whose total assets may be largely an old facility that has been so depreciated that its book value is tiny, even though the facility is still active and valuable. That division may report a very high R_A, although it is actually being managed poorly. It might simply look good on paper because the real value of the assets being employed is much above the book value. Of course, it is possible to arrive at newly defined operating asset figures and direct the division to use those when reporting results to higher management so the reported results will have meaning for comparative purposes.

When we said earlier that many other measures need to be employed, we meant to include working capital ratio, ratio of current assets to current liabilities, makeup of the current assets as to inventory and cash, and ratio of receivables to sales. These and many other ratios will tell both the manager of a division of the corporation and the higher level corporate management how things are going. Growth rates and the cash flow of corporate segments are also of interest, to say the least.

The corporation is the sum of its parts and all performance measures of the segments are pertinent to the performance results for the corporation as a whole. But figures for overall corporate performance do not automatically afford the corporate management, and still less the managers of the separate elemets of the company, an adequate view of the pieces to make possible suitable actions. It is the segments that must be acted on to make changes, because it is in those operating entities that the assets are used to generate cash and earnings.

Commonly Used Measurement Ratios

In addition to the very important return on assets employed, the manager of an operating unit and others in the corporation concerned with judging and monitoring that unit's activities will be very interested in the capital turnover or $R_{SA} = S/A$, the ratio of sales to assets employed. The so-called sales margin is equally conspicuous as a ratio of great interest; it is $R_{ES} = E/S$, the ratio of earnings to sales. In seeking a high return on assets employed, it is often useful to think of it as consisting of a product of these two ratios:

$$R_{EA} = E/A = E/S \times S/A = R_{ES} \times R_{SA} \qquad [5]$$

Since we are now considering a segment of a company with the interest charges on corporate debt kept out of the judging of the segment's effectiveness in realizing a return on assets assigned to it, then R_A is the same as R_{EA}. So, in this instance

$$R_A = R_{ES} \times R_{SA} \qquad [6]$$

The way to improve R_A is to improve R_{ES} and/or R_{SA}. These two quantities lead more directly to the operating conditions that determine their values.

To get the turnover, R_{SA}, higher, the assets must be used more efficiently. The sales realizable from those assets must be increased. It will not do, to realize a high R_A, merely to increase the sales, if this requires employing proportionately more assets. The trick is to look carefully at the process of creating the product and selling it to see if these functions can be performed with less assets used, both fixed and variable assets. For instance, is the operation carrying more inventory than is necessary? Are there idle machines? Is the division diligent in collecting its receivables? Is the work under completion spending too long in the plant?

These questions will lead to other questions whose conscientious answer may improve the turnover. Perhaps a temporarily higher expense for more marketing effort will yield more sales for which the plant has ample capacity and will not need enhancement. Perhaps the product can be improved so there will be more sales and more production can be put through the same fixed assets. Maybe the techniques of assembly and test can be improved so that the investment in work in process can be lowered. Maybe unused assets can be sold off.

To judge whether or not the turnover indicates good or poor management it is useful for every business to compare the results with those of similar competitive companies whose published figures may be available. For technological corporations manufacturing hardware products the turnover usually will be found to be between two and four times. This much leeway exists because there are so many different kinds of specialized products. If the comparisons are meaningfully made, the turnover figures of corporations, when all are in the same specialized field, are most often within a 25–30 percent deviation range from each other. If your company has a lower turnover, by two to one, than the others, you had better learn why.

Some products are best produced with a great deal of automation and thus will involve relatively higher investment in plant and facilities. If such higher investment is justified, and a lower turnover can be tolerated, there will be more than an equivalent decrease in the manufacturing costs and the sales margin, R_{ES}, should be higher.

To increase the sales margin, R_{ES}, one has to either decrease the cost of producing the product and marketing it or raise the price and have that accepted by the customer. The price will be determined by competitive considerations, the quality of the product, the confidence in both the product and the company that sells it (that is the acceptance by the market), and generally the product's economic effectiveness, meaning the real economic value of the product to the customer. To get the price up the company must seek a superior position regarding some or all of these factors, compared with competitors. If the company feels it has a basically inferior position with its product quality, marketing effort, company image, and the cost effectiveness of its product, then it also should consider getting out of the business.

The answer to higher R_{ES} often is to get costs down. One important factor in lowering costs is to enjoy a high volume, which means to be successful in sales. Sometimes the price should be lowered because this will cause so great an increase in volume that it will enable costs to come down proportionately more than the price was lowered and hence increase the sales margin. We shall discuss these points more in the chapters relating to marketing and manufacturing. For the moment it will be enough to get used to the idea that return on assets employed can best be attacked, controlled, and made to rise by thinking of it as being the product of two other ratios, the turnover and the sales margin.

Some of the total expenses of a corporation manufacturing and selling a product can usually be very closely tied to the volume of sales and hence vary with the sales volume. Presumably, if no sales were being booked at all, the corporation could take some steps to cut expenses that would have been associated directly with the production of products sold. It would not need to buy materials and components and could lay off most of the labor. The company would still be left with the expenses that are less directly associated with the sales volume, the fixed expenses. For instance, the plant would still be there and depreciating. Presumably the corporation president would still have to be compensated, insurance bills would still have to be paid, and the research lab working on products of the future could not be cut out entirely. The reports for the Securities and Exchange Commission would still have to be filed, as would those to the shareholders. In an extreme recession or a major calamity to the sales position of the corporation or one of its product lines, the so-called fixed expenses would be reduced somewhat as well. In that kind of emergency everything possible would be cut to the bone. But reducible fixed expenses in such a disastrous situation should not be thought of as the variable expenses that go up and down with sales.

Using C_v for the variable expenses that rise and fall with sales volumes and C_f as the fixed expenses that do not, then for a given amount of sales we will have a breakeven when $E = 0$, or

$$S = C_v + C_f$$

If the sales revenue, S, exceeds the sum of both C_v and C_f then we will have something left over that will constitute the earnings; that is

$$E = S - C_v - C_f \qquad [7]$$

It is very useful for management to know what kind of a margin of safety there is, that is, how far away from breakeven and a loss position the activity appears to be. One ratio that measures this is

$$E/(E + C_f) \qquad [8]$$

This ratio is defined as the margin of safety. What is desired is that this ratio be as close to unity as possible, meaning that the fixed expenses compared with the earnings should be low. In some respects it is easier to see that this ratio is meaningful, if we substitute the equivalent quantity, $S - C_v$, for $E + C_f$ from Equation 7 and express the margin of safety alternatively as

$$E/(S - C_v) \qquad [9]$$

The expression in the denominator, the difference between sales and variable expenses caused by those sales, is a rather significant quantity. It is called the contribution margin. Clearly, this margin had better be above zero or there is little point in having sales at all. That is to say, if the variable costs, C_v, associated with a given amount of sales revenue, S, is greater than S, then no contribution is made at all by the sales. They eat up more than they bring in, and we realize no residue of funds to help cover the fixed expenses. If the contribution is not positive, enough so, in fact, to exceed the fixed expenses, then nothing will be left over for earnings. The contribution margin is almost the first thing that an operating manager looks at. Is he, through his sales, generating a large contribution margin or a small one? If the contribution margin is at least equal to the fixed expenses, then the operating manager knows he has a breakeven. The contribution margin ratio, defined as the contribution margin divided by sales,

$$(S - C_v)/S \qquad\qquad [10]$$

is a measure of the relative size of the contribution portion of sales revenue to that revenue.

The lower the fixed expenses as a percent of sales and the higher the contribution margin, the greater will be the earnings. If both the variable expenses and the fixed expenses are small compared with the sales, then the earnings will be high. The margin of safety, $E/(S - C_v)$, then will be high and the contribution margin ratio, $(S - C_v)/S$, will also be high.

But what is high? This usually means a comparison with par for that kind of product in that kind of business. A supermarket, we are told, operates with a very small contribution margin. The variable costs directly associated with the product, say a can of peas, is close to the wholesale cost to the retailer of that can. Presumably he sells it with a very small sales margin, and needs an enormous sales volume to overcome the fixed costs of operating the supermarket with something left over for earnings. In typical technical products the earnings after taxes will range from 5–15 percent of the sales dollar, that is, the after-tax R_{ES} will be from 5–15 percent. Technical products are diverse, but the fixed and variable costs, on the average, over many, many different kinds of products, are comparable in magnitude. The normal margin of safety is between 10–20 percent (with E meaning after tax earnings). If this margin falls to 5 percent the company should probably sense trouble ahead. If it is over, say, 25–30 percent, then the company is doing remarkably well. (Again, care must be taken to make valid comparisons with successful competitors selling similar products.)

The contribution margin ratio, $(S - C_v)/S$, for technological corporations can vary widely and still be satisfactory, depending on the specific product line. Some products, like a complex satellite system, may be sold in quantities of only one per year. Others, like minicomputers and, still more, hand held calculators, may be produced in large quantities. The part of the sales dollar that variable costs use up varies greatly, depending on the specific activity. This ratio may range from 25–75 percent and be satisfactory because of the diversification of technological products. But a corporation in the business of producing a few satellites a year, each one custom built and costing in the tens of millions of dollars, should strive to develop a situation in which the total costs of design, creation, testing and launching of the satellites sold is mostly variable expenses directly associated with the sale, and not fixed expenses. It would be bad if a division of the corporation doing this work had to keep in readiness a full complement of all the specialized personnel needed to turn out a satellite, whether they made a sale or not. When the contribution margin shrinks well below the fixed expense, which it easily then could do, the division would be in a loss position. When it has a good year, one in which it succeeds in selling an exceptionally large number of spacecraft, the margin of safety then had better be high, so the earnings in the good year will be more than enough to make up for the losses in bad years. During a peak sales year the contribution margin ratio should be closer to 75 percent than 25 percent.

Now that we have discussed several ratios that help in focusing management actions to track down and act on weaknesses, or conversely, help to illuminate strengths, it will be useful to show a final breakdown of the return on assets ratio. Recalling all previous definitions, we can write

$$R_A = E/A = S/A \times E/(S - C_v) \times (S - C_v)/S = S/A \times E/S \quad [11]$$

or

[Return on Assets Employed]
$$= \text{[Turnover]} \times \text{[Margin of safety]}$$
$$\times \text{[Contribution Margin Ratio]}$$
$$= \text{[Turnover]} \times \text{[Sales Margin]} \qquad [12]$$

Example: Performance of a Division

Let us turn now to the example of a company's Division A whose five year $P \& L$ is shown in Table 4–C. Table 4–D shows the end of the year balance sheets. The total assets, consisting of working capital and the fixed items of plant and equipment, are balanced by the corporate investment. No debt is shown, although the corporation uses debt as well as equity for financing, because the corporate debt is not meaningful to the balance sheet of the division.

In Table 4–E, the ratios useful for analyzing the activity are shown. Finally Table 4–F displays the five year cash flow. As to the latter, we note that earnings plus depreciation generate some positive cash flow. However, the division has apparently required more cash investment for the first three years. The parent corporation, to provide funds to balance out the negative net cash flow, has had to leave the generated cash flow in the division as well as make incremental investments. The corporate investment is the sum of the cumulative retained earnings and these cumulative incremental investments. Thus, as the reader can readily confirm, the corporate investment figure for the 5th year of Table 4–D, namely, $3,870,000, is the sum of the retained earnings, plus the cumulative net cash flow requirement. That is, the sum of the figures for earnings ($50,000, $205,000, $362,500, $575,000, and $762,500) and of net cash flow requirements (−$1,375,000, −$665,000, −$592,500, −$280,000, and −$437,500) equals $3,870,000. In the fourth and fifth years the division generates more than the investment required and the net cash flow turns positive. In Table 4–F we have also derived the cumulative discounted cash flow at 12 percent discount rate and can observe that at the end of five years the net P_V is a minus $1,754,000.

Now what can we say from these figures about the health of this

Table 4–C   P & L for Division A

Year	1	2	3	4	5
		(thousands of dollars)			
Sales	1000	2000	3000	4000	5000
Variable costs	550	1100	1500	2000	2500
Contribution margin	450	900	1500	2000	2500
Fixed costs	350	490	775	850	975
Pre-tax earnings	100	410	725	1150	1525
After-tax earnings	50	205	362.5	575	762.5

Table 4–D   Balance Sheet for Division A

Year	(thousands of dollars)				
	1	2	3	4	5
Current Assets					
Cash	50	75	100	125	150
Receivables	500	1000	1500	1750	2000
Inventory	650	975	1300	1500	1700
Total	1200	2050	2900	3375	3850
Current Liabilities					
Accounts payable	225	425	600	750	950
Working Capital	975	1625	2300	2625	2900
Plant & Equipment	500	800	1200	1300	1500
less cum. depreciation	50	130	250	380	530
Net plant & equipment	450	670	950	920	970
Total Assets	1425	2295	3250	3545	3870
Corp. Investment	1425	2295	3250	3545	3870

division? The sales have built up rapidly and the R_A is beginning to be very satisfactory, in the last two of the five years above the 12 percent hurdle rate of the company. We know, however, that R_A (for one or two years, at least) does not tell us much about success in investment decisions. A conspicuous characteristic that seems wrong about these results is the low turnover, R_{SA}. Typically, in a technological corporation (other than a utility) the turnover rate would be two or three times larger. Even at the fifth year, the turnover is only fair.

Table 4–E   Operating Ratios

Year	1	2	3	4	5
$E/A = R_{EA}$	50/1425	205/2295	362.5/3250	575/3545	762.5/3870
	.035	.089	.112	.162	.197
$E/S = R_{EA}$	50/100	205/200	362.5/3000	575/4000	762.5/5000
	.05	.1025	.121	.144	.1525
$S/A = R_{SA}$	1000/1425	2000/2295	3000/3250	4000/3545	5000/3870
	.70	.87	.92	1.13	1.29
$E/(S - C_V)$	50/450	205/900	362.5/1500	575/2000	762.5/2500
	.111	.228	.240	.288	.305
$(S - C_V)/S$	450/1000	900/2000	1500/3000	2000/4000	2500/5000
	.45	.45	.50	.50	.50

Table 4–F   Cash Flow

Earnings + Depreciation – Increases in WC & Fixed Assets
(thousands of dollars)

Year	1	2	3	4	5
Earnings	50	205	362.5	575	762.5
Depreciation	50	80	120	130	150
Cash inflow	100	285	482.5	705	912.5
Increased WC	975	650	675	325	275
Increased fixed assets	500	300	400	100	200
Cash outflow	1475	950	1075	425	475
Net cash flow	–1375	–665	–592.5	280	437.5
Discount factor @ 12%	.893	.797	.712	.636	.567
Discounted cash flow	–1228	–530	–422	178	248
Cumulative discounted cash flow	–1228	–1758	–2180	–2002	–1754

The facility may be too large for the volume of business. It was perhaps designed much too generously for the size of business planned, or the marketing activity has not been properly set up to bring in the sales of which the facility is capable, or else the judgment of the management in putting the division together was simply wrong about the sales potential of that product line.

At any rate, the operation so far may be a disappointment to its sponsors. It has not yet attained the hurdle rate of 12 percent for return on investment. This latter point is clear from the net P_V at 12 percent. It is highly negative ($1,754,000) at the end of five years. On the other hand, if the sales can keep rising while the assets remain close to constant and, if the earnings rise with sales, then the division can become a superlative contributor. We appear to be examining the division at a crossroad in its performance history.

The contributions margin should improve as the product line beds down, the learning experience in manufacturing begins to have some weight, a higher sales volume permits cost reduction, and the fixed expenses become a smaller fraction of the total. If all of these potential plusses can become actuals, the net present value will be brought to zero and the whole operation (over a total period presumably substantially longer than five years) will turn out to meet the 12 percent hurdle rate and perhaps exceed it. But at the moment it is not a proven good investment for corporate management. It is at best only part way to success and there is a good chance that the scenario the management had in mind was for somewhat better results. Most, though not all, investments in technological corporations are not based on a ten-year period, but rather one closer to five, to provide the completion of a start-up phase. At that point it is either hoped the net present value at the hurdle rate has been brought to zero or the evidence is very strong it will reach that value in a time shorter than another five years.

Finally, let us overlook for a moment the matter of the internal rate of return to the parent corporation in implementing and investing in this division. Instead, let us look only at the last year or two. The annual figures, particularly R_A and R_{ES}, are excellent for a technological corporation. If these figures hold and the sales are either steady or grow over the next several years, then the division will almost certainly generate a positive cash flow sufficient to meet the corporation's criteria. Let us examine this possibility further.

With debt not involved we can symbolize the assets assigned to the division equally as Q or A and use R_{EA}, R_A, and R_{EQ} interchangeably. If the parent company is looked on as the investor seeking R_I (the hurdle rate for the company), then the present value of the division to the company, P, is given by applying the standard formula for a steady growth company, namely,

$$C_Q = V/P + g \qquad [13]$$

with appropriate substitutions of nomenclature. Using R_I for C_Q and F as the cash flow back to the parent corporation growing steadily at rate g (in analogy to dividends) we obtain

$$R_I = F/P + g \qquad [14]$$

Let us now speculate on the sixth and following years, and do so reasonably optimistically. First assume the earnings stay at the fifth year level for years ahead and that the annual depreciation expense just exactly covers the funds that have to be allocated and reinvested each year to maintain the equipment and facilities in a like-new condition. Also assume no further additions need to be made to the working capital or fixed assets. Then, from Table 4–F, the cash flow to the parent company will be the earnings, $762,500. With $g = 0$ in Equation 14,

$$R_I = 762,500/P \qquad [15]$$

and with $R_I = .12$,

$$P = 762,500/.12 = \$6,354,000 \qquad [16]$$

which is much in excess of the total investment of the corporation in the division of $3,870,000 (Table 4–D). This does not say anything about the past, the fact that in the past five years the corporation did not receive adequate return on its investment in the division. We have only shown by this calculation that with the (optimistic) assumptions about the future of the division we chose, it has a present value to the corporation greater than the book value of the corporation's present investment in it.

Next, we suppose that a growth rate of $g = .08$ is justified by the market for the products of the division. Using the standard formula

$$g = (1 - R_V)R_{EQ} \qquad [17]$$

we now interpret R_V as the fraction of earnings paid out in cash from the division back to the corporation, for which we substitute the more appropriate symbol, R_F, where $F = R_F E$. The generated cash not paid back to the parent is invested to provide the growth. Using $g = .08$ and $R_{EQ} = .197$ (from Table 4–E) we have

$$.08 = (1 - R_F).197$$

from which

$$R_F = 1 - .08/.197 = .594 \qquad [18]$$

In Equation 14,

$$R_I = (.594 \times \$762,500)/P + g \qquad [19]$$

or

$$.12 - .08 = \$452,860/P$$

or

$$P = \$452,860/.04 = \$11,321,000 \qquad [20]$$

which exceeds even more the present (fifth year) corporate investment of \$3,870,000.

This example emphasizes several points important in analyzing the results of a segment of a corporation by looking at annuals for a period of time. That segment (or profit center for a particular product line, division, subsidiary, or whatever) usually has a number of activities contributing to the financial results for the period being reported. Some may be start-ups, while other activities may involve mature products manufactured and sold on a steady pattern that has not changed for years. The annual results tell us something about the overall profitability of the segment being reported and suggest to the analyst, as he scrutinizes the ratios, areas of strength and weakness. However, we learn little in any detail about the success, or lack of it, of the entity in meeting corporate hurdles regarding internal rates of return on individual incremental investments. As to these, the annual results may give us only an unclear average or trend, some clues, perhaps. Those who operate the segment need to be knowledgeable about the details and ready to add interpretations. More especially they need to know what is going on, and has been happening or may happen, over many years.

Judging the Overall Performance of the Corporation

To measure the financial performance of the corporation as a whole for a period, management will use all of the reported results over that time frame of each operating unit making up the corporation. The sum total of the activities is obtained by adding up these separate unit figures and then tossing in some additional items stemming from corporate management's activities. Some important functions, and the expenses caused by them, are carried on by the corporate staff and the top corporate management or are handled by outside specialists for a fee. Moreover, some tax, interest, currency revaluations, and other financial items affecting the P & L and balance sheet are held at corporate level and must be added on top of the operating divisions' assembled and integrated numbers.

Corporate management typically will attempt to assign expenses, wherever practical, even those (like income taxes) paid and controlled at corporate level, to the operating divisions with appropriate formulas for allocation. Thus, an average tax rate, that for the corporation as a whole, may be assigned to each operating unit so that after tax results may be reported by the units. Similarly, interest and other charges are often allocated to result in a net earnings report so the individual earnings contributions to the corporation's bottom line earnings can be better judged and compared.

For the corporation as a total entity, the reports for a period, say a year or a quarter of a year, will include sales revenues, costs of sales, net earnings before and after taxes, interest paid, capital expenditures and depreciation for the period, cash flow, dividends paid, new investments in the business, any additional equity stock issued or bought back to be retired or put into the treasury, and the earnings per share. Included in the balance sheet will be the working capital and its several components, the fixed assets, intangibles, short-term loans and long-term debt, deferred taxes, and equity or shareholders' investment, including the cumulative retained earnings.

With the figures mentioned above for the total corporation in the foreground, the internal rates of return on individual projects that obtained their initial launching that year or in any prior year go far to the background. Thus the period return gives us no information about whether those investments individually are or are not giving a satisfactory internal rate of return. Presumably if the company does well on an annual basis, year after year, then it must be making sound investments more often than not. However, the period being described to us by these figures only gives us a cut of one piece of the whole time span of each of the huge number of investment decisions that cumulatively have added up during this period to these particular results. Of course we examine periodic figures and compare them to the year before, or the quarter before. Through comparisons of year-to-year or quarter-to-quarter results we can get some feel about whether this particular year seems to constitute a sharp deviation or an anomaly, or is instead a further confirmation of an expected trend that is good or bad, promising or discouraging.

Comparing R_A with C_A

As to profit and loss, for the corporation as a whole there is again a paramount interest in R_A, the return on assets employed. As with the operating divisions of the corporation, where R_A is so important, R_A tells us much about how well the corporation as a whole is internally making use of its assets. If the company has a high debt-to-equity ratio, but not so high that the interest costs are unusually large, we will not be surprised to see good earnings, if R_A is substantially larger than i. At the same time, we will expect to see a high return on equity, R_{EQ}, since the company is highly leveraged. Generally speaking, with a high R_A, the company is managing its assets well, that is utilizing its assets effectively to create a basis for earnings. If the debt-to-equity ratio appears to us to be too low or too high, that is another question, one that says that the company may not be financed properly. However it has been financed to acquire those assets, it is using them to advantage.

A critical judgement regarding the quality of the reported R_A of a company is, of course, a comparison of R_A with C_A. If R_A exceeds C_A over a substantial period, it would be expected that the market price of the common stock will exceed its book value, that is, $P_S/Q_S > 1$. (Recall the discussion of Chapter 2 of the steady growth model.) If R_A is reported often below C_A, then we would expect the stock to perform poorly on the market. Such a situation is not favorable for any corporation. If the market price of the stock is far below the book value and if the latter is balanced by corporate assets that are not over stated, then some might suggest that the management ought to be fired and/or the company liquidated, its net worth then dispersed to the shareholders, presumably with gain. In principle, a company can go on for years quite stably and even grow modestly with R_A below C_A but there are serious handicaps all the while, particularly for a technological corporation that must grow to hold market share and protect its future position.

In the relation between growth rate and the main operating characteristics of the corporation, namely,

$$g = (1 - R_V)(R_A - iR_{DA})/(1 - R_{DA}) \qquad [21]$$

the ability to finance growth from within is clearly heavily dependent on R_A. Admittedly, a new corporation with exciting prospects may not yet be in a profit position. It may have either a small or negative R_A. Such a corporation may, nevertheless, be able to sell common shares to raise capital, and even with a very small R_A may be able to leverage more than is desirable in the long term and forego dividends to finance a high g. However, speaking of an established technological corporation with a need to operate in what will be considered a sound range for R_V and R_{DA}, too low an R_A will directly and severely limit g. It will also likely be accompanied by low P_S/Q_S for common shares and a low multiple, M, thus making external financing also difficult.

Suppose, for example, that such a low R_A company wishes to raise more capital through sale of common shares, keeping R_V and R_{DA} constant. Let us say it adds 25 percent to its outstanding shares, selling them at a price P_S where $P_S/Q_S < 1$. For that company assuming the same disappointing R_A is applied to the augmented assets, let us ask what happens to earnings per share as a result of this stock sale. This is covered by Equation 49 of Chapter 2, namely,

$$E_S' = E_S \frac{1 + (P_S/Q_S)\Delta N/N}{1 + \Delta N/N} \qquad [22]$$

Since $P_S/Q_S < 1$, then the earnings per share will fall, if more shares are issued. Observing or sensing this, the market will probably cause the market price of the shares to fall further, if more shares are offered. In effect the market will be saying to the company, "With your inability to get a return at least equal to the cost of capital, the more capital you acquire, the further we need to devalue the expected usefulness of any assets made available to you."

Conversely, a company with the image of continuing to get a higher return than the cost of capital should expect the market to set a higher price on its shares than book value. When that company raises more capital by selling shares and on that added capital continues realizing a higher return than the cost of the capital, the earnings per share should increase. The company will be able to pay a higher dividend, if it chooses or put a larger fraction of its earnings into further investment (again, we assume) with the expectancy it will earn more than the cost of capital on that additional investment. Under such circumstances its market price and multiple will rise.

At the extremes there is, of course, a practical limit. The high return company will not be credible if it tries to raise too much capital. The poor return company will not be able to sell too many shares because the market price will collapse even as the sale is attempted because of the foreseen, imminent dilution for shareholders.

Just as R_A should be compared with the average cost of capital, C_A, so R_{EQ}, the return on equity, should be compared with C_Q, the cost of equity capital. R_{EQ} is important in judging a corporation's performance because to the shareholder, the owner, it is the return of his equity that counts with him, or so it would seem. That equity is generally leveraged to increase R_{EQ}. Given R_A as the real measure of successful use of assets and a well-chosen debt-equity ratio, R_{EQ} merely follows. If the shareholder has confidence the corporation has not over borrowed, he may not care about the details. Then the return on his equity, R_{EQ}, is mainly what may interest him and a quick comparison of reported R_{EQ} against his estimated C_Q tells him something important. (See typical figures in Appendix B)

Competitive Comparison of Margins

Particular interest attaches to the turnover rate, S/A, and the margin on sales, E/S. Here the corporation will be judged against its plans, its previous year's results, but even more particularly, by the results of the corporation when compared with leading competitors. If the turnover appears too small, then management should wonder why it needs so much in assets employed or how it might attain higher sales with the same assets. The corporation, even if it is small and not highly diversified, is almost certain to have more than one product. With each product will be associated some inventory, receivables, and fixed assets. Tracking down the utilization of assets, examining the potential of getting more sales with the same assets, figuring how to cut inventories, or collect faster on receivables—these acts will carry management right back to the operating divisions. The results for the corporation as a whole, particularly compared with competitors, will add guidance, however, to the question of what should be expected from the operating divisions.

The same general remarks can be made about the sales margin. If on the whole it seems to be low, management will look first at overall costs. Perhaps the corporate expenses are too high. It is necessary again to go back to the operating divisions to examine the costs to see where they can be cut, to try to increase the profit margin. It is equally important to see what can be done about the pricing. Perhaps, as is most often the case, it will be decided that the turnover and the sales margin are related one to the other, particularly if the results are unsatisfactory. For example, it may be that the way to cut costs is to have a bigger volume; perhaps this means to invest in improving the product. It may even be sensible to reduce the price a bit to obtain more sales. But we are repeating what we already have said about analyzing the operating divisions' numbers rather than discussing improving results by drawing conclusions about the performance measures of the corporation as a whole. Corporate sales margin gives us only an average, a consolidated number. It is required that we trace that number, when unsatisfactory, to those operations where low sales margins are dragging down the average of the whole, if we are to make the results for the whole better.

Earnings Per Share

Probably no single figure reported periodically for a corporation attracts more interest, both by management and outsiders, including especially shareholders, than the reported earnings per share. This is natural and proper—up to a point. However, quite often the reported earnings per share figure receives far too much weight and attention by management, present and potential future shareholders, security analysts and the business media. The importance of earnings per share as a measure of performance is obvious. It says a great deal about the profitability of the company during the period and relates to the potential for dividends and for plowback of earnings to ensure future dividends, growth of the operation, and protection of the product lines by capital backup to support their continued production and marketing.

The shortcomings of earnings per share as an overall measure of the corporation's situation are many, starting with the fact that a reported E_S represents earnings generation only for that one particular period. Granted, anyone examining the corporation, seeking to understand whether it is successful, will have available past periods' earnings per share figures and will consider the latest one in the context of what has gone before. But earnings per share alone is too small a part of the story to give us a clear indication of degree of success or failure. As a minimum the net cash flow per share should be scrutinized. In fact, it would appear to go more directly to dividend and growth potential.

For example, a company might have what appear to be reasonably high per share earnings that have increased from year to year, without yet having paid a dividend and without any real indication that it ever will. The earnings per share may be rising, the operation growing, but the earnings not sufficient to maintain the growth without additional equity capital or debt capital added each year. Now it is one thing to keep bringing in more investment, if the corporation is headed for a period when it will pay dividends or it presents a credible case that the retention and reinvestment of all available cash is the best way to reach the ultimate high value of the shares the investor hopes for. In principle, this could go on forever, with the company simply plowing back and entering new fields continually. Though this approach keeps diverting the stream of earnings away from payback to the investor, enough investors nevertheless might stay happy, convinced that the market price of a share will be larger next year, and believing they can always cash in their shares or hold them and obtain a high gain, one at least the equivalent of a generous stream of dividends.

Earnings per share is a particularly inadequate indicator of corporate health, if it is not looked at on a long-term basis. For instance, it is quite common for a new management to come in and immediately increase earnings per share, looking good against the lackluster performance exhibited under the previous management. Research and development and advertising expenses can be cut quickly, for example, even though this might hurt the future of the company on a long-term basis. Start-up costs necessary to prepare for wider geographical marketing or modernizing the facilities can be deferred for a while, particularly if the company enjoys a strong market position at the moment. The new management will appear to have made a turnaround with these cost reductions. The earnings per share increase may be accompanied by a rise in the multiple and a stock price surge. The new takeover management may even have acted on the basis of large stock options or a strong position in the existing stock. Their determined intention might have been to get the market price of the stock to rise, then cash in and divorce themselves from the company before the later collapse.

A high earnings per share figure does not mean a high net cash flow. For example, if a severe requirement exists to increase working capital (perhaps to hold market share by expanding if the competition is doing so, or to redo a technologically obsolescent plan), then the truly available cash flow per share might be small even with an increasing earnings per share figure. The growth rate possible through internal growth alone may be too limited. It must be remembered that in the formula

$$M = R_V/(C_Q - g) \qquad [23]$$

for a steady growth company, M does not necessarily remain constant with the happy result that a higher E_S automatically means a higher market price, P_S, for the stock through the relation

$$P_S = ME_S \qquad [24]$$

Instead, for given C_Q, g, and R_V, M is the dependent variable in Equation 23. If g or R_V is diminishing, then M will be lowered accordingly. A company can show higher E_S for some years and find its stock price not rising or even going down.

The earnings per share often may be increased by the corporation's borrowing more funds, increasing its R_{DA}, and using those funds to buy back some of its own shares so that the total earnings will be spread over a fewer number. The corporation's business fundamentally will not have changed. To increase the debt may have been a good idea if its debt originally was too low, that is, if the corporation was insufficiently leveraged. It was a bad idea if its debt was already high. We do not learn whether it was a good or bad move from the earnings per share figures alone.

To illustrate the manipulation of E_S by varying N and R_{DA}, consider a company with given assets requirement, A, and given ability to derive a return on them, R_A. The company borrows ΔD to buy back and retire ΔN shares where

$$\Delta D = \Delta N P_S \qquad [25]$$

Before the purchase

$$E_S = (R_A - iR_{DA})A/N \qquad [26]$$

After the purchase

$$
\begin{aligned}
R_{DA}' &= (D + \Delta D)/A = R_{DA} + \Delta D/A \\
&= R_{DA} + (\Delta NP_S)/A = R_{DA} + (\Delta NP_S Q)/NQ_S A \\
&= R_{DA} + (\Delta N/N)(P_S/Q_S)(1 - R_{DA})
\end{aligned}
\qquad [27]
$$

while

$$
E_S' = \frac{(R_A - iR_{DA}')A}{(1 - \Delta N/N)N}
\qquad [28]
$$

From Equations 26 and 28,

$$
\frac{E_S'}{E_S} = \frac{R_A - iR_{DA}'}{R_A - iR_{DA}} \frac{1}{1 - \Delta N/N}
\qquad [29]
$$

For example, suppose $R_{DA} = .2$, $R_A = .16$, $i = .05$, and $\Delta N = .2\,N$. Then if the market at that moment sets $P_S/Q_S = 2$

$$
R_{DA}' = .2 + (.8 \times .2 \times 2) = .52
$$

$$
\frac{E_S'}{E_S} = \frac{.16 - .05 \times .52}{.16 - .05 \times .2} \frac{1}{.8} = 1.12
$$

Again, if $R_{DA} = .4$, $R_A = .09$, $i = .05$, $\Delta N = .2\,N$, and $P_S/Q_S = .5$

$$
R_{DA}' = .4 + .6 \times .2 \times .5 = .46
$$

$$
\frac{E_S'}{E_S} = \frac{.09 - .05 \times .46}{.09 - .05 \times .40} \frac{1}{.8} = 1.2
$$

In both instances, the earnings per share were made to rise. The biggest boost (giving to some uninformed observers the impression that the company was making earnings progress) was for the company with the lowest R_A performance and a poor market to book ratio for the stock.

As we shall learn in Chapter 10, a company that enjoys a high stock multiple can merge with a company of low multiple and pay for the acquisition by issuing more shares and then trading those shares at market value for the shares of the low multiple company. If the high multiple company in a merger that this share-trading brings about is the surviving corporation, then its earnings per share will be increased by the merger. Yet the combination will not necessarily be able to do more for its shareholders than the original company. This will be explained fully in Chapter 10. We only wish to note here that a change upward in E_S through merger action could be misleading.

A company could have a record of high and increasing earnings per share, an R_{EQ} greater than the average for that category of corporation, and still be in serious financial trouble. It might have, for example, so high a debt that it has difficulty convincing anyone to loan it more money. This condition could cause it to have a low multiple. It cannot go to the market to sell more shares because, as judged by the low multiple, considerable doubt might exist about whether it can keep up its earnings per share growth or even its present earnings per share level. These doubts could be strengthened because of the possibility of the company's losing market share to a stronger competitor, unless it gets strong capital infusion to enable it to have an even higher growth rate (capital we have just said it will have a difficult time acquiring in an unfortunate "chicken and egg, which came first" pattern).

While reported earnings per share for each quarter and year are important numbers to management and to the outside, the figures are only part of what needs to be examined and studied in great detail to understand whether a corporation is or is not being successfully managed.

The Balance Sheet

In Chapter 1 we briefly discussed that the goals and objectives of management would include having a good balance sheet and we gave at least a beginning explanation of what good means. Let us now elaborate on this.

The working capital and the items that make it up, the fixed assets and intangibles on one side of the sheet, the debt and equity on the other, need to be examined for year-to-year changes and for their reasonableness for the nature and size of operation. Competitive comparisons are important. Again, for a large and diversified corporation, corporate management will have to go back to the operating divisions' balance sheets to track down anything that appears unsatisfactory. The management will look at the makeup of the current assets and current liabilities and the ratio of one to the other for comfort and acceptability. For each kind of business or product line, history will teach what are acceptable receivables as a ratio of, say, a year's sales. The same will be true of inventory, both for raw materials and for work in process. The banks will be particularly interested in the ratio of current assets to current liabilities. These current assets are the front line for conversion to cash in an emergency, and the current liabilities can do the company in if they have to be paid and there is a cash bind. Thus the current assets should liberally exceed the current liabilities.

The ratio of working capital to fixed assets and of both to annual sales will be important. Again, however, the particular kind of effort involved, be it petrochemical refining or computer manufacturing, will tell the management what kind of ratios are typical. If the corporation as a whole seems to be out of line, then it is necessary to see where these assets are and how they are being used.

Obviously there can be no strict rule that tells either the management or the outside judges what is the right debt to equity ratio for a particular corporation. On the other hand there are some rough guides that can be cited. The debt is too high if the periodic earnings at present, in previous years, and more particularly in the years ahead are inadequately greater than the interest charges. One has to assume a recession might be just ahead or that an important breakthrough by a competitor will occur that will destroy the pricing situation and sales potential. Inflation could accompany recession, with working capital requirements and interest rates rising as earnings fall. (This will be discussed more fully in Chapter 11.) Under all these circumstances, with the debt still to be paid, the company could be in serious difficulty, if it has either too high a debt to equity ratio or inadequate coverage by net total earnings of the interest charges. Here the dividend ratio figures importantly, the interest and the dividends considered more or less fixed. If the earnings, even with the anticipated downturn, cannot cover the dividends and the interest charges together, and this with a very wide margin, this may mean the company is undercapitalized. It then might need to sell more shares to improve its equity position and pay off some of the debt.

If the company has a strong balance sheet with a high margin of coverage of the fixed obligations, is pioneering in new and excitingly promising fields, has an excellent position against its competitors, then it becomes important to hold that position by being sure there is enough capital available for expansion. Looking at the debt-to-equity ratio on the balance sheet at any time of the year does not automatically tell the reader whether it is too high, too low, or just right. Granted the special circumstances of the need for capital, however, the management or an outside analyst would expect to see that serious comparisons are made of sale of more equity or arranging of additional borrowings as alternatives for raising the required additional capital to put on top of the retained earnings in order to provide for the required growth.

To judge whether the debt to equity ratio is proper requires knowing the market and product position of the company, the potential for growth and higher earnings and dividends stemming from additional investment, the relative cost of capital from additional debt or additional sale of equity stock, and the available coverage for all emergencies.

Growth and Market Position

In examining a corporation's condition by looking at periodic figures a very important parameter is growth, particularly for a technological corporation. High technology is characterized by change and expansion. A successful corporation with high technology products should find its products altered as the technology advances and its volume growing as its ideas, application engineering experience, and acquaintance with market potentials cause it to produce more technological innovations as vehicles for growth. If the corporation is not going up year to year in sales and earnings, then this needs to be explained. Of course, again emphasizing that the report for a period covers no more than that period, there may well be good reasons for temporary downturns and even deliberate cutting back as a tactical move toward a strategic goal of growth.

Especially to be watched are growth patterns of a company as it reports its periodic results is the matter of the market position in its product endeavors against competitors. This is so important that it and related matters will be expanded upon in Chapters 9 and 10. For the moment it is sufficient to say that in judging the overall corporate performance from periodic reports the judgment can hardly be said to be complete unless growth patterns are studied for sales, earnings and the important operating ratios of turnover, return on assets employed, and sales margin.

Problems

4-1. A division of a company has employed constant assets of book value $2 million for 10 years. It has reported $300,000 earnings after taxes each year, and the cash flow to the parent company has been the same. (The annual depreciation expenses having been exactly equal to the annual reinvested earnings.) Suddenly a technological breakthrough by a competitor requires considering liquidating the division. If the division is looked upon as an investment of $2 million made 10 years ago, what is the internal rate of return assuming liquidation with only half of the book value of assets recoverable as cash?

4–2. In the chapter example described by Table 4–A and 4–B a 12 percent internal rate of return, R_I, was used. Select an incremental after tax earnings figure enough greater than the $770,000 figure used in the example to attain an $R_I = .15$.

4–3. One million dollars is invested in new test equipment which is expected to operate for 10 years and then be discarded with no salvage value. During those 10 years cash is realized from cost savings in production as a result of using the new test equipment to the extent of $250,000 per year. Assume straight line depreciation at $100,000 per year for the 10 years. Draw a curve with net present value of this investment as the ordinate and the discount rate as the abscissa.

4–4. Study the annual and 10-K reports of two technological corporations of your choice and compare them for: sales margin, turnover, R_A, R_{EQ}, R_{DA}, and working capital ratio. From these comparisons, can you draw any confident conclusions about the relative performance and financial conditions of the two companies? What qualitative factors not disclosed by these figures might alter or dominate your conclusions?

4–5. A product line's performance history over the 10 years of its activity is characterized as follows: initial start up R & D costs, $250,000 per year (after taxes) for the first two years; $1 million investment in fixed assets and working capital at the start of the second year; in the third year and continuing through the 10th, the product line generated $250,000 cash (after taxes and reinvestment to maintain depreciation equipment, with added working capital investment negligible); assets and product line sold for $200,000 at end of tenth year (with a resulting loss of $800,000). If the company has been using a hurdle rate on investment of 15 percent, should the company have gotten into this product line? What was the R_A reported annually for this product during the eight years of earnings and the total undiscounted positive cash flow?

4-6. Derive an expression to show the effect on earnings per share, if more common shares are sold and the proceeds used to retire debt. Assume that for the pertinent period ahead A, R_A, and i remain unaltered by the sale.

4-7. A corporation's management is annoyed because the market price of their common shares is only 60 percent of book. They think it deserves to be much higher, since they expect in the immediate year ahead to have R_A = .15 with R_{DA} = .25 and i = .05. Keeping A constant, they borrow enough capital to buy back and retire 20 percent of the outstanding shares (without causing the market price to change). What should happen to E_S? A little later, as the new E_S is observed by the market, with the price multiple also increasing by 10 percent (as naive buyers intent only on E_S, misinterpret its rise to mean the company is more promising), what should happen to the stock price?

4-8. A company pays no dividend, plowing all earnings back to finance growth. It enjoys P_S/Q_S = 1.8 at the moment. For the year ahead it expects R_A = .16 with R_{DA} = .4 and i = .05, which will yield E_S = $1.00. It quickly sells 15 percent more shares and succeeds in doing this without the market price altering, announcing that it is doing so to finance even higher growth. It expects to so expand volume, and obtain volume benefits, that R_A will increase to .18. It also borrows more, keeping R_{DA} constant. How much will the stock sale increase assets employed? What will happen to earnings per share for the year ahead? What will happen to market price of the stock and its ratio to book value if, after the market observes the trend, it raises the multiple by 15 percent?

4-9. Japanese companies typically operate with debt leverages that would be considered far too high in the United States. If they earn enough to pay the interest and finance growth, they are likely to satisfy the banks. As an example, consider a Japanese company with R_{DA} = .85, R_V = .1, and g = .10. What is R_A for this company? If R_{EQ} = C_Q, what is C_Q and what is the weighted cost of capital if i = .05? To maintain these parameters on a long term basis, should the hurdle rate for internal rate of return on investments, R_I, be .05, R_A, or C_A? Explain.

4-10. A corporation creates a division to handle a new product line which is profitable from the beginning and provides a cash flow back to the corporation. Suppose the initial, and only, investment in this division by the corporation is I. For N years the division has constant R_A and pays back a constant ratio of earnings in cash flow, while with the rest of available cash financing a constant growth of earnings, g. If, after the Nth year, the division is sold at the then book value show that the internal rate of return to the corporation was $R_I = R_A$.

5

ORGANIZATION AND CONTROL

The Infinity of Organizational Schemes

Not only is there more than one way to skin a cat, but there are more than ten ways to organize a group intent on skinning a cat. A corporation must be organized. It cannot be chaotic in assigning roles and in arranging for materials, money, work assignments and information to flow among the numerous people inside and outside of the company whose participation is vital. There must be rules, procedures, and clarity about the functions of organizational units and the missions and expected interactions of people. Employees, both management and general, need to know a proper share of what is going on to exercise their responsibilities and perform their tasks. Authority must be delegated, and means must be available to assign credit and place blame. Otherwise the corporation will not be able to handle its problems and match its resources to commitments and opportunities.

Granted all of this, how fully organized must a corporation be? It is possible to over-organize. It would be wrong to set rules and procedures covering every eventuality and to insist on the most rigid adherence to such complete regulations. It is a practical impossibility to describe totally everyone's role and to separate the functions of various entities within the corporation with such accurate, nonconflicting prescriptions of their activities as would avoid gray areas, conflicts, a degree of confusion and error, and, people being people, incomplete coordination and cooperation.

An infinite number of methods to organize to get the work of the corporation done effectively can be conceived. Many theories about how to organize best can be helpful, but no one theory or any collection of them will really cover everything. One reason is that people are in the act. Humans are not only complex, but also far from totally predictable. The actions and reactions that are predictable suggest people will present problems if we try to insist their behavior should fit any theory exactly. Beyond this, it is also true that the individuals available to the corporation, be they the top management or the assemblers on the production line, are not perfect. If a truism of organization exists that is beyond question, it is that vast differences in people should be assumed. Each individual in the corporation is a bundle of competence and incompetence, cooperation and lack of it, zeal and disinterest. The problem in part is to organize to enhance the positives and minimize the negatives.

For instance, it is preferable that the head of marketing possess the highest of comprehension concerning every other function of the company, such as engineering, manufacturing or financing. However, the corporation may have no choice but to settle for someone who is only partially knowledgeable and appreciative of these other aspects, and this may not be too bad if he is a crackerjack at managing the marketing effort. This may mean, however, that the way the corporation is organized and run requires a plan for making up for the shortcomings of the marketing manager. Other talents within general management will have to be tapped to provide the necessary breadth of competence and coordination.

No one is ideal for his job. Good organization requires an assembly and assortment of assigned responsibilities, means of coordination and communication, and methods of monitoring, review and control that make the best use of the best people available for the jobs. If the limitations of key people are sufficiently severe the corporation will suffer, of course. Good organization, as well as good management, means to put adequate weight on arranging for and improving the competence and other positive characteristics of the people of the corporation.

Of course, technological corporations have some special organizational problems. The complexity and diversification of the products, relationship with the customer (which may involve a great deal of cooperative application engineering), technological obsolescence factor (which involves adaptation to change)—these and many other special characteristics of technological corporations put high stress on the continual need for critical examination of the patterns of assignment of responsibility and authority and of communication and control. It is one thing to organize a corporation for steady success if the product is mature, the market is rather highly predictable, and emphasis is on one or two main company functions, such as manufacturing (getting the cost down and holding it there) and marketing (selling the customer who already has used the product for years and knows for sure what it will do for him). It is another to organize a unit that has not previously existed and define for it a product even as it is being sold and used for the first time by new customers. This is a not uncommon situation for a substantial fraction of the product activities of a technological corporation.

Putting incompetent people into critical posts or putting effective people into unsuitable jobs is almost as certain to cause failure of the corporation as its being in the wrong business. This is particularly so in a technological corporation. The technological effort and the non-technological tasks are so different, and the basic talents involved in the different activities are so difficult to blend that great care must be taken in assignments. Good management requires that each important appointment be analyzed carefully and then the appointment decision reviewed regularly. When assignments do not work out, the blame is not to be placed on the appointee who usually is asked to take the position and is not presumed to comprehend fully how he might be most useful to the company. It is the management above that makes the decision, and it is the management that should be rated on its appointment decision effectiveness. Usually personnel reviews are of the personnel rather than of the management that put the personnel in place. Both kinds of reviews are essential to the management of personnel and the attainment of a good organization.

High technology is a dynamic field with the products and techniques for manufacturing them changing rapidly. One technological development leads to another, and systems of doing things are affected by advances in the components of the system or new systems concepts that bypass the whole approach. Over a period of time, a technological corporation will have to alter products, manufacturing facilities, marketing strategies and application engineering, and shift emphasis to some extent back and forth from components to systems. All this means that the technological corporation's organization must be very flexible. Flexibility goes not only to formal organization, but also to the utilization of personnel, adaptability of facilities and equipment, and a general receptiveness by the management to change and skill in exploiting it.

In long-term planning of strategy to advance, continue with or drop an existing product line or to start a new one, some attention must be given continuously to the possibility of having to abandon the plan. A new program may deserve being abandoned part way along, or an expansion program deferred. A plan to sell off a line of activity no longer considered desirable may not be workable as actual conditions develop. By organizing to be adept at handling changes of plans as they are called for, the chances of suffering from over-rigidity and a tendency to adhere to and try to complete what has become a bad plan are diminished.

The number of possible and practical organizational schemes is infinite, but this does not mean the organization can be arbitrary and random. Certain basic requirements apply to all good organizations. But after all of the available organizational principles are considered and made use of, plenty of options will remain. In view of the complexity of corporate endeavors it is just as well to admit we do not have adequate principles to guide us in organizing a company and we shall have to employ common sense, hunch, and trial and error. In what follows in this chapter, all these factors will be noted.

The Essential Functions

A technological corporation requires certain identifiable and separate functions although they may be grouped in varying ways for effective executive supervision and for harmonious working relationships with each other. Included among these functions are research and development, engineering, manufacturing, marketing, distribution, customer service, financing, accounting, financial performance analysis, legal, patents, and relations with the public, labor, shareholders, community and government. Overall there must be strategy and planning and integrated monitoring, evaluation, control and leadership. As we shall make increasingly clear in this text, a typical, strong technological corporation will be diversified both as to product lines and geography. Some organizing of the corporation by product lines, by nature of the market and by geographical location is inevitable. Although it might appear communications is simply inherent in the task of overall integration, a proper flow of information is critical to make the corporation work, serve up needed data for carrying on operations and provide the understanding and motivation for the people involved. Those within the corporation need good communications to perform their tasks, and those on the outside require it to appreciate the corporation and deal with it in a complementary manner.

Each function we have outlined above can be broken into distinguishable subfunctions, which to some extent often become separable units. For example, manufacturing will include a personnel group engaged in doing the hiring for manufacturing, a purchasing department, a tool design group, quality control, security, facility maintenance, and many others. The company's legal function may be partly decentralized so that some legal activities (like contracts with customers and suppliers, affirmative action, and labor law) become parts of the various divisions where these legal actions occur. A corporation is also certain to require legal effort on behalf of the corporation as a whole, representing it and ensuring good legal practices for the corporation as distinct from the handling of legal problems that arise in the operations of the various decentralized divisional portions of the corporation.

In a similar way the accounting function will be partially distributed among operating groups, all of whom have to account for their purchases, sales, labor costs and the rest. At the same time, integrated accounting and auditing must be done on the activities of the whole corporation.

For each of the various levels of the corporation, the descriptions of the functions and of the functions within the functions again offer numerous organizational options. And always the organizational pattern is partially dependent upon the human factor in each of the organizational units. The idea is to make the best use of the people available and arrange the best means for communication and cooperation among them.

Organizing for Clarity of Responsibility

It would seem self-evident that every unit of an organization should have a clearly spelled out responsibility. To exercise that responsibility it needs to be given the proper degree of authority. If each essential function is covered by assigning it to a group of competent specialists, all such groups understand what the responsibility of each is, and each is given the authority to act within its domain of functions, then it would appear the organization is sound and the work of the corporation will go on smoothly and efficiently.

But real life experience precludes our being sanguine about this. After the first fundamental step of assigning functions, responsibility and authority is completed, many complications must be recognized and handled. Gray areas appear as we assign discrete functional responsibilities because much of the effort required for effective activity in a corporation involves great interaction and cooperation among the separate units.

As an example, the top management of a corporation may assign the responsibility to design the product to an engineering department, giving the leader of that group authority to hire and fire his staff and an adequate budget to cover all of his costs and enable him to do his design work in the time schedule and at the depth and quality desired. (It could equally well be a product division's manager, and not the corporate level, that assigns engineering responsibility in this way. In this instance, the product general manager has the responsibility to handle that product line. He has reporting to him an engineering group, and he decentralizes the design responsibility to his engineering group's manager.) But hold on. The manufacturing group also has a leader, and he is assigned responsibility for manufacture. He is expected to control his operation totally and to meet management's requirement that he manufacture the product within certain costs, time schedules and other criteria. But what if he finds the engineering design he is handed cannot be manufactured within the constraints to which he is committed? Does he have the authority to reject the design and demand one different and superior from his standpoint? He can hardly be truly responsible for manufacturing and not have a say in seeing that the product is designed so it can be manufactured.

Clearly, the organization must have means for bringing together the engineering and manufacturing responsibilities and authorities. Joint effort must take place with an appropriate level of decision-making organizationally above both engineering and manufacturing. At that higher level of authority some of the responsibility for both engineering and manufacturing obviously continues to reside and so it cannot have been decentralized completely to either engineering or manufacturing.

About marketing, we can make this same point as to delegation of authority and definition of responsibility, especially in relation both to engineering and manufacturing. Experienced leaders of engineering, manufacturing and marketing will recognize the necessity for intelligent and timely interactive effort to be so compelling that it must constitute a limit to the degree to which responsibility and authority can be articulated and assigned to each of them. Obviously, this same pattern of interrelationships exists to a degree among all of the separate functions into which the organization is at least initially divided.

Staff and Line

A highly valuable concept in the organizational problem of responsibility and authority allocations is the use of line and staff relationships. In line relationships the reporting channels along which authority and responsibility flow are relatively easily charted. Thus the product line manager might have such a direct line relationship to his engineering department's manager. The engineering manager knows that his (only approximately clear) responsibilities and authorities can and will be amended, extended and perhaps curtailed by the product manager to whom he reports. Also, (see Chart 5–A) the various other executives reporting to that same product manager can expect leadership from the product manager as he coordinates the interrelationship of their functions.

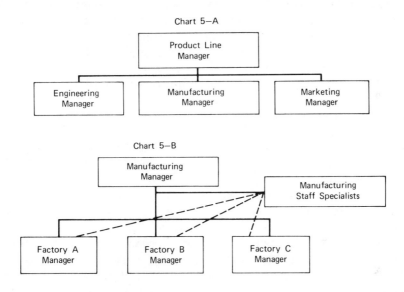

Chart 5–A

Product Line Manager

Engineering Manager

Manufacturing Manager

Marketing Manager

Chart 5–B

Manufacturing Manager

Manufacturing Staff Specialists

Factory A Manager

Factory B Manager

Factory C Manager

In order to discharge his line obligations effectively a manager will most often find it advisable to have some human extensions of his own knowledge and awareness. He will hire a special staff for this, and through use of this staff will exert better control of the interacting activities that report to him in a line fashion (see Chart 5–B). For instance, let us say the head of manufacturing of a product line activity has three separate facilities. They may be engaged in making virtually the same products, or they may be making different components of the same with one of them perhaps being an overall assembly plant. Or possibly within the same product line responsibilities of the manufacturing head, there are some distinctly separate individual products. At each of the plants expertise will be available for handling personnel matters (labor relations, employee training, seniority and compensation practices, etc.). The manufacturing head will want to ensure a high quality of such task performances at each of his three facilities.

He will want to avoid the duplicative hiring of hard to acquire experts at each location and to get the advantages of a degree of uniformity in practice so he can shift talent back and forth between facilities. For many such reasons, the line manager will find it desirable to have associated with him as his own staff specialist a senior employee who is expert in these employee, labor and related problems.

Now, the manufacturing manager can hardly hold each plant's manager responsible for what goes on in that plant, including the employee and labor relations problems, if he gives that responsibility also to his senior staff assistant. At the same time, if that staff assistant is competent and has the respect of the manufacturing manager and each plant manager, then those plant managers will see that their personnel executives are cooperative and communicate well with the manufacturing manager's staff assistant for that special function.

Throughout a complex organization we always see a combination of line and staff relationships. If the functions are properly chosen and the right people are in the jobs, then all of the line executives will find advantageous the interspersing of staff aids to themselves and to the higher executives in the organization to whom they report. The quality of effort will be better throughout. If a specialist working as a staff assistant to a line executive believes some things ought to be done or changed in the line activities reporting to that executive, then generally the staff specialist is unable to direct action on his own authority. Instead he usually advises all concerned what he thinks should be done and to some extent he sells the idea that his proposals are sound. If the line manager to whom that staff specialist reports has himself bought the proposals, he will then presumably direct that they be implemented. Over a period of time, if a staff assistant's suggestions are never or rarely incorporated or his advice never heeded, then the chances are that either the position is ill conceived or the wrong person is in the job. This is not always the right conclusion, because sometimes a staff specialist may be very important as a critic and heckler, constantly goading, urging and ensuring visibility in all the line operations about the quality of activities in his field— this even though his specific recommendations are only occasionally incorporated in their entirety.

In line to staff relations the characteristics of the individual holding the staff position become extremely important. Ambiguity cannot be totally removed in assignment of responsibility between line and staff executives, and, strange as it may sound, this ambiguity is part of the necessary process of effective management. A busy manager with several line operations reporting to him needs to have his brain power extended by others who, although they do not have a direct line authority to issue directives, can be counted on to look at things from the standpoint of the manager's overall responsibilities, opportunities and problems. The authority that a staff member may in actuality possess will vary greatly from one situation to another. It will depend on the manager to whom he reports, on his personal relationships to all of the lower level line managers who report to the same top level, on the function itself, but most especially on the personality makeup and skill of the individuals involved. Sometimes staff executives monitor activities to help the line executive know what is going on. Equally often, staff executives make evaluations within their functional specialty to aid the line manager to whom they report in deciding whether the line operations are the way he wants them to be. Often staff executives emphasize particularly the long range planning, attempting to look ahead and to provide alternative strategies for everyone, while the line operators are busy with the day to day problems of the near term. In still other instances staff specialists may assist their line executives and other managers who report to that higher level in arriving at better general policies to guide the actions of all.

Staff responsibilities and authorities will thus vary greatly and the degree to which the line operators must recognize and be guided by the opinions of staff officers also varies. If a generalization is possible, it is that a staff executive does not have direct control over operations. That control generally goes through the line, but that control line is influenced by the staff, usually strongly and properly so.

Organizing for Good Communications

Granting that a practical degree of clarity about responsibilities and authority exist, and that the managers in charge of each line or staff function are reasonably competent and compatible with each other, then further organizational development can come from looking at the organizational problem as one of communications. The right people have to know the right things at the right times. Even if everyone knows the responsibilities and authorities assigned to him, it is only a good beginning. Much more is needed. Carrying on the work of the corporation requires a great deal of information flow. The executives must be aware of what is going on in their areas and they must transmit certain substantial parts of that knowledge to the level of executives to whom they report, to those who report to them, to certain of the other line executives whose functions tie in closely with their own, and to various staff employees. Everyone cannot know everything and should not try. A part of the problem is selecting what information needs to flow to whom, how often, and in what form.

Making these choices requires an understanding of what people are expected to do with the information they are given. Thus to design the communications aspects of organizational structure requires detailed comprehension of how the corporation actually operates. The information to be transmitted and updated goes from general policy, strategy and goals to specific reports of what has happened and detailed proposals for actions, such as making capital investments, hiring personnel, settling labor union disputes and agreeing to contracts with customers. The information stream important to a technological corporation also includes analyses of decision alternatives, investments, system tradeoffs, and optimizations that can range from simple to highly sophisticated.

The essential information must be identified and responsibilities assigned for obtaining and communicating it. Obligations must be spelled out for considering the information, presenting it for decisions and, finally, exercising, delegating or requesting authority to act based on the information. If all of these matters are laid out with clarity, if the communication flow is adequate, understood by all, and works, then it probably means the organization is right. If people do not possess, obtain or transmit essential information, then the organization will not function. Thus, to attempt to organize for effective communications handling is not only a way to set up a sound organization; it is also an excellent means to judge, by periodic review of the communications pattern, whether the organization continues to be sound.

Communication will vary from written to oral. Certain regular reports will be expected by all those concerned; other reports will be special to assist in handling problems as they come up. Meetings will sometimes be scheduled periodically and at other times called especially to consider surfacing problems or opportunities or to act on evidence of a need for further coordination. Through memos, reports, telephone calls and meetings, the executives concerned and their staffs will either make the organization work or see, in their inability to get timely actions and decisions, that something is wrong with the organization. The fault could lie in the improper assignment of individuals to functions, choice of the wrong functional divisions, or the way in which all are set up to relate to one another. It also could be in failure to meet the vital communications requirements in the designation of functions, authorities, and responsibilities.

Analytical Aids to Management

At each of its various levels, management is occupied continually with decisions, study of alternatives, relationships and tradeoffs among the many key factors, optimization, probability spectra—to name only a partial list of analytical and integration tasks. Information pertinent to all these is critical and a company must organize itself to acquire and utilize the information. Alas, much necessary information is grossly incomplete. This results in much estimation and guesswork and the employment of broad ranges instead of specific values for some important parameters that cannot be tied down better. Many important factors cannot be satisfactorily quantified or even described so they can be dealt with logically in the elementary sense of this adverb. Data and judgments about all of the basic factors will arise within and without the company. The efficient selecting, correlating and evaluating of this available information is an enormous analytical task for management.

With the availability of the computer, it is now possible for a corporation to gather and process a vast amount of data and present it to management for contemplation as a preliminary to decision making. In fact, management at all levels of the organization now easily can be inundated with information. In designing an appropriate information system for running a technological corporation, management must focus on limiting the information to what is highly pertinent, adequately accurate and practically meaningful to the management process, either to get decisions made or, afterwards, to evaluate management by comparing actual results with anticipated results. The power of the computer and the zeal of those skilled in its use should not cause management to be swamped with information and analyses based on incomplete and inaccurate data. To use complex models that emphasize those aspects for which quantitive data are available and ignore those aspects for which it is not, can confuse or worse, mislead. For a controlled operation with balanced and calculated risks, the right depth of analysis and data processing needs to be set up for each area of management. Model building and algorithm development are helpful, if not overdone. The judgment of experienced managers is expected to set the right levels.

In recent years, with the advent of fast, large and economical computers, numerous analytical tools have been developed to aid in the process of information handling for management and assistance in decision making. Useful models can range in complexity from those that can be literally worked on the back of an envelope to those that require hours on the most powerful computers. Many of the highly mathematical methods require individuals with considerable skill along sophisticated, analytical lines and expertise in the formulation of individual problems so they can be programmed into computers. While management is rarely concerned with the actual carrying out of such detailed mathematical studies, and usually limits itself to broad system considerations, it is desirable that those in charge of decision making, no matter at how high a level, have an appreciation for the values and limitations of these tools. They should know when highly analytical studies are helpful and where they are of little value (and harmful if misinterpreted and misused). Thus, for example, some aspects of a decision may rest on information that is highly reliable and complete, while other equally important aspects may depend on fragmentary, insufficient data. Naturally, analytical methods are available to allow in an orderly way for the areas of doubt. The alternatives for consideration by management, if skillfully set up, acknowledge that assumptions were made in the absence of definitive data. Management must be adept at communicating with those who carry on the detailed studies to ensure the credibility of the assumptions, ranges and probabilities chosen.

Some highly theoretical techniques are based on the (reasonable) expectation that, if given a set of possible actions, management will select the best by the stated criteria. In actual practice, management may often be willing to live with methodologies that produce results that are good enough but not optimal. Management may not believe that the *best* answer is fully enough determinable and definable to make seeking it out a worthwhile and efficient enterprise, because management senses that too many factors are not known well enough to proceed on that basis. In decision analysis, it has been said that the best is the enemy of the good enough.

Typically, as decisions to be made by management move to higher levels in the organization, they encompass more indeterminate factors. Highly detailed data, probability spectra and decision-paths analyses move into the background, or will have been well established earlier. The remaining unsettled, often critical factors, those not lending themselves to such precise techniques, then begin to take over the attention of management. The specific experiences and judgments of the top managers themselves usually take precedence over the results of highly detailed, analytical formulations. Decisions are then based on the happenstances of their own personal hunches, similar situations these individuals may have had in the past and what they remember about success and failure of earlier strategies or comparable challenges.

If an operation has been relatively stable, it usually will begin to develop repetitive patterns in the way all the important parameters relate one to another. The sales and manufacturing volumes, pricing, scaling factors, timings and durations of various steps, breakdowns of costs, alternative decision paths available, flow of all elements of the system (material, finished parts, information, funds and manpower) may settle down in time into measurable and observable, steady behavior. Operations research on the activity especially can pay off then, and people trained to make this kind of analysis can be effective for improving the understanding of all of the relationships. For such mature operations it becomes possible to refine the overall system and improve decision-making. The best choice of actions can be selected against such criteria as cost or speed or minimum use of capital, labor or critical materials. In a highly technological corporation, the volume often is not high enough, and neither the length of time the product stays fixed nor its way of manufacture remains constant long enough, for these highly analytical approaches to yield the most effective results. Nevertheless, effective management of a technological corporation includes ensuring that in appropriate parts of the overall corporate operations, modern analytical techniques are being used to provide adequate analysis and research on the operation.

Usually, proper use of advanced analytical tools and computers can provide benefits in excess of the cost of their application. This textbook will not explore this matter further. It is only necessary to call attention to the fact that the management of a technological corporation could hardly claim to be modern, if it ignores, underuses or overuses the developing analytical methods that can aid a systems manager to relate the many components and parameters of the system to each other.

Communicating with All Constituencies

In the next section of this chapter we shall particularly consider the matter of organizing for adequate control of operations; but before leaving the communications aspect, it should be pointed out that, in addition to providing the basic communications flow required for executive control and decision-making, a corporation must be organized so that there will be an adequate flow of communication to the general employees and the outside world. When we discussed the various constituencies of management, we noted many external groups existing with a great variety about the kinds of information release legally required, virtually necessary, or at least desirable to ensure their understanding and cooperation. To some appropriate extent knowledge of goals and strategies, progress and plans, sometimes even problems, must be conveyed. The proper depth of information detail must be carefully chosen with a combination of common sense and creativity to maximize appreciation and motivation and avoid penalizing misunderstandings.

Forecasting and Operating Control

Forecasts–Short-Term and Strategic

The words control and out of control may be readily and correctly applied to conceptualize a reason to organize the affairs of the corporation carefully, or, in contrast, to describe the consequences of failure to do so. A sound way to arrange for control of the corporation is to have adequately detailed plans about what is intended versus time, that is, to have forecasts and schedules, then to report actuals, the results that have occurred, and to continually compare these actuals against the forecasts and plans. No one can foretell the future, but predictions and desires, continually updated and improved, are needed.

Typically, a well run corporation will have the twelve months ahead plotted on a monthly basis and the next two or three years on a quarterly basis. The forecasts need to be revised frequently, because of the dynamics of the world to which the corporation must adjust. The forecasts will show the main profit and loss items including sales, earnings, costs, and taxes and the chief balance sheet items, including fixed and variable assets. The cash flows, capital expenditures, and all of the ratios that we have discussed, including the returns on assets employed and sales margins, turnovers, and so forth, will be forecast. Always the actual results will be compared with the forecasts.

Forecasts usually start with sales projections and involve great uncertainties, whether in those sales estimates or in the numerous other scheduled items that must be assembled and analyzed for a complete forecast (capital, technical manpower, energy, materials requirements, etc.). All of the items scheduled involve assumptions, and some numbers are calculated based upon other assumed items. Thus, it usually is not sensible to have a single set of numbers or a single curve of expectancies for all the various parameters. Instead, forecasting is best done around a range of possibilities. Very often companies show maximum and mimimum expectancies with a probable somewhere between, or a best or worst and a likely, or an "optimistic" or "pessimistic," each company having its set of habitually used words to cover uncertainties.

Forecasting includes detailed attention to future capital requirements. Whether the capital needed by the corporation is largely generated from within or is a result of external financing, as the forecast stretches out in time it becomes extremely important for management to understand the general availability of capital to the industrial world and how it is affected by political, social and economic conditions of the world. The forecasts will show in detail what capital needs to be associated with the plans of each of the units of the company. But top management must go beyond this and have a familiarity with the entire capital investment picture of the company and the national economies in which the company operates in order to make its contribution to sensible, useful forecasting.

A growing factor now in forecasting is the matter of energy availability and its cost. At one time, most company forecasts could almost ignore the energy factor, because the cost of energy was generally small unless the company was in the energy generation business itself or an unusual user of energy. It could be assumed in that bygone period that the energy would be available as needed, which meant available at a satisfactory price. The situation is different now. Almost every corporation, especially a technological one, must be aware of the energy implications of the activities being forecast to be sure the combination of price and availability is consistent with the forecast.

Like energy, requirements for and the availability of critical materials must also be included in the forecast. If shortages appear to involve the corporation in substantial risk then alternatives, such as not going ahead with the scheduled program or developing substitute materials or living with the higher prices that may result, must all be considered and put into the forecast.

The forecasting of both needed and apparently available manpower is also important to a technological corporation. Almost at any given time in the last decade or two, but especially forseen for the decades ahead, it is probably sensible to anticipate increasing shortages of certain specialized technical personnel. Where there is an opportunity for profitable growth in a technological area, there will be strong competition in any scientist or engineer category in short supply.

Thus, no schedule is realistic unless it lists the requirements for technical manpower versus time, the likely turnover rate (recognizing that in a period of shortages, movement of scientists and engineers between corporations will be high) and the net number of scientists and engineers that must be recruited. The matter of obtaining the number and quality of specialists called for by the schedule of activities on the forecast must be considered in the same detail as the acquisition of capital called for by the forecast.

We must distinguish between forecasting for a near-term period as a means of having management control over operations on the one hand, and long-term or strategic planning to research and guide the selection of long-term goals and choose ways of meeting them on the other. The short-term forecast, to be effective for management control, must be taken seriously as a reasonably accurate indication of what the corporation wants and reasonably expects to accomplish in the immediate future. In creating strategic or longer range plans, it is important to avoid the decided negatives of confusing such plans with a cast-in-concrete financial forecast. Strategic planning should emphasize the options, assumptions, and major trends and use criteria for setting optimum courses of actions and making selections from the various alternatives. It is very important to avoid tying all levels of short-term performance rigidly to the implementation of a strategic plan. That plan may stretch out for many years during which time events may disclose unsoundness or bring about changes in options, risks and potential rewards.

Comparing Actuals with Forecasts

If the performance is very close to the forecast, this does not mean the operation is necessarily satisfactory. It may be highly unsatisfactory. Perhaps the management, at forecast time, simply faced an unhappy reality. It forecast a bad situation (although reluctantly, very likely). Then exactly that unsatisfactory set of forecasted happenings occurred, rather than an unanticipated, but preferred, satisfactory one. At other times a forecast may be exceeded with the actual results turning out far superior to the forecasted ones. This would not be universally interpreted by sophisticated managers as evidence that everything is going extremely well. It could mean instead that the forecast was overly pessimistic, that the forecasters were inaccurate and should be taken to task for their obvious failure to understand the business well. The superior results could indicate a new unforeseen opportunity, or that certain bad possibilities previously considered highly probable have instead evaporated. The question would then be raised about whether the forecast, even for the immediate months ahead, should be altered and the whole situation given careful review.

The forecast presumably lays a basis for the operation in that, if the future unfolds approximately as estimated and the corporation has prepared for that future, then it will not run into major embarrassments—such as insufficient cash, a sudden need to go out and raise equity capital or terminate some rather satisfactory activity, or the like. Experienced managers do not expect a complicated operation to go precisely according to forecast. Preparing for adequate financing, for instance, may include recognizing the possibility of an unforeseen near disaster. On the whole, however, the purpose of the forecasting, and of the later, continuing comparison with developing actuals, is to aid in the process of running an effective operation that will respond close to optimumly to the real-life opportunities and environment of the corporation.

The forecasting process itself is a foundation pillar for good organization. Creating a forecast clarifies and emphasizes responsibilities and authorities. Each unit of the organization, line or staff, is required by the process to anticipate needs and expenses. No intelligent discussion of the costs of performing a task and estimation of the people and facilities needed or changes to be made are possible unless the task is clear. Equally, if the forecasting exercise involves, as it must, presentations and proposals followed by approvals and alterations by the higher level executives, then the authority pattern of the company is emphasized and bedded down. The net result of the forecasting exercise is to give detailed signals to each operating unit concerned about what it has the authority and responsibility to do in the period ahead. If it wishes to deviate from forecast for any reason—a better idea or an unforeseen difficulty—then it may do so within discussed limits. Beyond this it must obtain additional approval. Before the operating unit comes to requests that approval, it must be prepared to show that the right analyses have been performed and proper coordinative exercises have been engaged in with other units that share the handling of the issue.

To judge the quality of internal management, few available techniques compare favorably with the straightforward one of simply comparing actual performance against the forecast or anticipated performance. Effectiveness of management for a past period can only be measured after the facts are in, that is, after the period is over. But the health of an operating division, the prospects of a product line, the success of an investment, can all be examined during the period, monthly, quarterly or annually. The prospects for ultimate success can be estimated from experience by experienced managers—this if they have the actual results to date to compare against the expectations.

Plans, forecasts, investment scenarios, and product line developments should all be laid out with adequate financial detail, but also with mileposts. On certain dates, a design should be complete, for example, on another the first sale or the first delivery of the product made. Manufacturing should be expected to complete a certain number of units by another date. Marketing should commence in a new area at a certain time. With these events on the forecast, the actual accomplishments should be compared with the anticipations. To be on schedule does not mean success is guaranteed and to miss schedule does not absolutely spell failure. But much can be learned to assess the vigor of the operation, the probability of future consequences, good and bad, and the quality of management.

Top-down and Bottom-up Forecasts

Good forecasting is done both from the top down and the bottom up. Top management should forecast the future as shaped by its broad extrapolations, its conceptions about the environment which the company will face, the expected growth in the market categories into which the company's products fall, the anticipated positions, strengths, and weaknesses of the company, its priorities and plans for investments and emphasis. Meanwhile, the organizational levels where details of individual products, projects, competitive pressure, and customer reaction are seen intimately should also prepare a bottom-up forecast.

Top-down forecasting is an absolute requirement in a technological corporation. Much of the forecasting about technological products results in long-time scenarios and involves assumptions about factors in addition to the corporation's own technology developments stretching out over many years. If a scenario takes substantial time for completion, then many things outside the corporation that could affect the project's success may change greatly. It is higher level management that must be looked to for the assessment of political, economic and social factors, general business extrapolations applying to competitors as well as the corporation and the long term goals and alternatives for the corporation. Some technological projects are so large in terms of funding and resource requirements that the project's risk assessment is important to the corporation as a whole. Indeed, top management must be concerned not only with the risk factors and the size of the investment but also with the arranging of external resources beyond what the corporation itself may be able to provide.

An integration of all the separate bottom-up forecasts represents one worthwhile picture of the company's projections. The top-down forecast is another. A careful comparison of the two will lead to a superior undertaking of the company's lines of business and to better plans, strategies, and operating forecasts. These than can be made the core of direction of the operation. The forecasting of the immediate period ahead, then, is both a means of control and a means to improve organizational precision and efficiency.

The same applies to longer range planning. Estimating the financial and other results for a year or two forward is bound to relate to the strategy for longer term growth or perhaps for the shrinking of some operations. Again, a useful forecast for a few years cannot be created unless it has been adequately discussed at the various levels of management involved and with the various parallel units of the organization that must join in bringing about the predicted and expected results. Investment decisions can be checked, or may even originate, through the forecasting process during which alternative strategies usually are compared. Questions will naturally surface on how much to decentralize authority, where it should be allocated, and for how substantial a period ahead. Control of investment of funds can be strengthened by injecting checkpoints into the schedule calling for timely reviews and additional approval before projects are allowed to continue, even if they appear to be going more or less according to plan.

The forecasting process, whether for short- or long-range activities of the corporation, shows up organizational weaknesses. A faulty forecasting effort may be recognized by higher management as evidence that the lower management attempting the forecasting is not in possession of adequate facts and alternatives regarding its activities. Equally, at times, an excellent forecasting job may show that unsatisfactory results are very likely to happen. This may start a series of actions intended to greatly alter the activity (or stop it), and this even includes the possibility of making organizational changes.

Profit Centers

Although all elements of a corporation have to participate in a forecasting and planning exercise if it is to be adequate, special roles must be played by the managers of profit center areas. A profit center is a unit of the corporation containing all the necessary functions that together produce costs and generate revenue. It usually is a segment of the corporation given responsibility for a product line or a geographical area. Even though profit center is often used to describe a decentralized activity whose delegated responsibility includes control over its profit performance by an assignment to manage both the revenue producing aspects and the expenses incidental to that revenue production, the name investment center is sometimes more appropriate. An investment center suggests that the assignment and delegation from top management to the unit's manager must seek an adequate return on investment. Although no single parameter is going to be used by top management to measure the performance of the so-called center, regardless of what adjective is put in front of center, either earnings by itself or sales standing alone surely is highly insufficient. The comparison of earnings with the assets assigned to the unit (that is, the return on assets employed) comes closest to providing a single satisfactory measure of the operating entity's performance.

The profit center's forecasts go a long way toward providing a complete picture of the financial results of the segment of the corporation being described. A large corporation may have hundreds of profit centers with such titles as divisions, subsidiaries, and groups. The head of a profit center is often called a general manager, because he will have several diverse and specialized managerial functions, such as engineering and marketing, reporting to him.

Adding up the forecasts or the actual results of all profit centers provides a large fraction of what the corporation needs to view its overall forecast or actual performance. As we discussed in the previous chapter, some costs of the corporation will be neither directly under the control of the profit centers nor directly generated within the activities controlled by the general managers of the profit centers. Such corporate costs include the corporate management's salaries, corporate advertising programs, the preparation of annual reports, numerous legal and financial integration tasks, public relations, industrial relations, and certain specialized services intended to serve all the profit centers to increase efficiency and ensure coordination. The corporation may assign some of its financing charges, the amortization of intangibles, adjustments of corporate financial results for foreign currency revaluations, and numerous other items as added cost burdens which the profit centers will be expected to include and absorb. They will often be allocated a pro-rata corporate charge without their being in control of those charges. This is sometimes a source of complaints by these general managers who see a sort of taxation without representation aspect to this practice. However, in a well led corporation, the corporate management will see that two conditions are met about corporate charges. First, it will have a competent, carefully chosen effort at corporate level, reserving for that level those functions that either cannot or should not be decentralized to the operating entities, the profit centers. Second, it will explain well to the profit center managers that these conditions indeed are in effect.

It is indicative of organizational strength if the profit centers are well conceived and properly monitored, evaluated, and assisted in their endeavors by corporate management (or whatever management layer has been set up to provide that leadership and coordination above individual profit centers). In some companies, group executives or executive vice presidents act to provide this type of aid and direction as an extension of the corporation's chief executive office.

Occasionally a profit center is created in which the various functions that go toward generating the profit or loss are only partially under the direct control of the profit center manager. For example, a single factory may sometimes be set up as a profit center. The factory manager is then in charge of the profit to be generated by that factory without having any responsibility and even any influence over the design of the product he manufactures or the sales and marketing of it. When this is done, presumably the management above has decided that it will obtain better control, visibility and assessment of the operation of that factory, if a price is assigned to the products, the output of the factory. The factory manager is responsible for keeping costs down to get a maximum difference between the price the factory is permitted to charge the marketing branch of the corporation and the cost of its creating that output. The difference is a factory profit.

The factory will pay for the costs of materials. It will carry inventories of raw materials on its books as well as purchased parts and work in process. It will pay for the maintenance of the plant and will account for its depreciation. Overall, the factory manager will seek a good return on the assets employed. It may appear that this is somewhat artificial, since the factory really is not selling the product to the outside world and the price charged by the factory to the marketing division is set not by the market or customer acceptance but rather by dictation from the higher levels of management. However, in some instances this is an effective way of assigning responsibility and ensuring control.

Profit center managers usually have considerable clarity about responsibility and adequate authority over the area of endeavor which they cover. But the authority cannot be absolute, as though that profit center were a completely separate corporation and the profit center manager the chief executive officer of it. Particularly in a technological corporation it is true that the best performance for any one profit center results in substantial part from actions elsewhere in the company. If profit center organization is overdone in a technological corporation, it tends to encourage the optimizing of the company's parts and, unfortunately, the optimization of the parts may not constitute an optimization of the whole. This will be clearer after we discuss the handling of large projects that are likely to require the cooperation of several profit centers.

Project Organization

It is common in a technological corporation that the effort often must be organized around specific projects. The project may be large or small, but usually the problem of organization arises when the project is large enough that it requires the assignment of a special management team to see the project through from beginning to end. Since the project is not the only work going on in the company, the main structure of the organization must remain. Yet, on top must be superimposed an integrating project management group. For what could be a period of several years, the project management is entrusted by the higher management level with special responsibilities and, most often, with special authorities to see that specific project through successfully.

If a research and development phase is to be followed by the design of products for production, this in turn followed by production and, finally, installation to serve the customer, then an overall project plan is necessary. Although this plan, and the forecasts of detailed activities to be accomplished at specific times, will very likely be subject to considerable alteration during the course of the project, it nevertheless constitutes a program of action to which everyone must adhere. This adherence will not happen without co-ordination, interpretation, monitoring, and general leadership.

The project management team, in dealing, say, with the corporate legal and accounting specialists, and with the line operations of engineering, manufacturing and marketing, must act partially as an extension of higher management. The project management must behave also a bit like a customer or sponsor who comes in to get various things done by units of the organization and negotiates with these entities for specific accomplishments during particular time periods for specific costs. Presumably, each engineering unit involved, and each manufacturing or marketing or other organizational entity will have other things to do besides catering to this one project team. They may not want to, or believe they cannot, assign to the effort on one project the first priority call on their facilities and manpower and even their own management attention. In this situation the project team is a bit like staff having to recognize a limit to its authority in directing line operations. The project management will look to higher management to referee and lead in negotiating and straightening out the inevitable, confused overlapping areas of priority, authority, and responsibility and the methods of communication, record keeping, information flow and rules for coordination deemed suitable for that project in the light of other corporate commitments, needs and goals.

Even within one unit of the company, say an engineering department, the manager of engineering may find it necessary to set up some project leaders (or substantial project teams if the complexity, priority and size of the project so justify) to see that there is an integrated approach to handling an individual project. The project work may require contributions from a number of specialized groups within engineering. The resulting organizational pattern is sometimes properly called a matrix organization. The project leaders and the functional specialty leaders possess intersecting responsibilities over the same segment of a job to be done. The functional groups, called upon by the project's management for specific tasks, cannot be directed fully on a detailed basis by the project team handling that team's one project. Again, there must be initial agreement, and continual renegotiation of the agreement, about the specifications of what is to be accomplished, over what time period, at what cost, with what kind of cooperative, integrated, harmonious effort with the other engineering project groups whose work must all be fitted in to make all the projects successful.

The word matrix suggests that a decision to be made, a specific action to be completed, a design to be firmed up or a selection from any alternatives to be settled involves two organizationally independent bosses (over a function, a product line, a field of endeavor, etc.). At the point of intersection, presumably, someone is hard at work on the task. He has two demanding clients as he looks both upward and sideways from his spot to the supervision on the boundaries of the matrix. He may actually be said to report to one or the other of these two supervisors, but he is in a position where he must satisfy both. The concept behind a matrix organization is particularly effective when key decisions involve balancing many interacting considerations, each of which can only be handled well by a specialist. Sometimes the balance is between marketing and engineering, but quite often it is between various aspects of marketing, manufacturing and engineering with each of these functional areas involving several important separate issues that must be caused to interrelate. But a matrix organization is not a committee in which there is no boss and where resolving of issues, the making of decisions, is vague and indefinite. There is always a boss above the structure who can lay out the clearest possible procedures for resolving matters and who stands ready to settle those that do not get resolved.

Sometimes a need exists for a project organization, because the commitment to a customer is made in terms of the project. To manage the program, monitor how it is doing, see how actual performance progress compares with the forecast for that project alone and, of course, strengthen the activity, if it appears not to be headed for a satisfactory conclusion, results must be presented to corporate management and the customer in terms of that project's accomplishment. This is in contrast with the integrated financial results reported by corporate entities covering many projects for a period. This matter of managing projects by looking at the progress of the project over a period of time, distinct from reporting the activities of the units of the corporation working on the project and many others during specific months or quarters or years, reminds us of our discussion of the distinctions between evaluating investments and analyzing reported financial results for a period. Indeed projects that justify project teams usually are multi-year investments. If the investment is a major one, some executive or a team of individuals should be assigned to watch and provide focused direction for the entire follow-through period.

For example, consider a very expensive foundry installation created to serve a number of manufacturing units of a company. Let us say the foundry is to be brought into being over a period of a few years, gradually attaining full capacity and utilization by the corporation. The facility is planned to start from scratch, employing new workers and training them. The corporation's manufacturing divisions will draw up appropriate schedules for the phasing in of that in-house foundry and compare them with purchasing cast components from the outside. After the startup period, during which the foundry will be in the hands of a special project team, the plan may be to disband that team and assign the foundry to one of the manufacturing divisions for continuing supervision and management. This would occur after the project has been successfully launched and thoroughly integrated into the operations of the company.

As another example, a new product may be decided on for engineering development, while at the same time an application engineering project is started within marketing to determine more precisely what the customer really needs. Meanwhile, knowing something of the pieces that have to be built, the manufacturing department may commence development of techniques for low-cost manufacture. A project team leader may be needed to furnish the coordination on that new product line among engineering, manufacturing and marketing. In this instance he is an extension of the level of general management that has line direction over engineering, manufacturing and marketing.

The project team concept and its incorporation into the organization is another example of the continual need for organizing to be most effective in getting the job done. This often requires recognition that very simple division of labors, with little confused interaction and no gray areas, although ideally to be sought, does not usually occur in the real world. A major problem of organization is to accept this limitation on simplicity and clarity and minimize it, but also learn to work with it.

A complex project usually involves many contributing groups, whose efforts must interact harmoniously, and a large number of individual steps to be taken in moving the project along. Most of the steps depend greatly on the timing and specific accomplishments of previous steps. Thus, it is inevitable that a good deal of time must be spent in planning and reporting. In a poorly organized project, failure can result even with an inordinate amount of time spent on details of scheduling. As a minimum, the effective management of a project requires deliberate listing of all of the important events with their relative timing and their mutual dependence. Since the number of such critical events in a large project lasting for many years is typically huge and the interactions and dependence of one event on another multitudinous, it is fortunate that computer techniques have been developed to assist in project management. A number of highly developed techniques for monitoring projects by following and analyzing the schedule of events and their interactions (a method named PERT is one such example) are available and should be incorporated in project control.

PERT (Program Evaluation and Review Technique) employs a logic diagram, or flow chart, to describe the program's progress. The diagram shows a series of blocks describing key events or milestones, the blocks connected by arrows or lines to show the relations among them and the flow of activity from one event to others. Some events are sequential. Others work in parallel. An adequate monitoring for program control purposes requires that this events diagram be drawn in very substantial detail. For example, an effort is made to identify required information needed to complete and reach each milestone. Decision alternatives about how to proceed are associated with and set down for each completed event, so that when the event occurs it is recalled that then new specific decisions must be made. Paths can be traced through the network, and the time required to accomplish work between the various blocks can be estimated. Times to reach the various milestones can be calculated by tracing the various parallel routes. Such detailed analysis of the events and their interrelationship permits more confident scheduling of milestones.

Most often, some important steps cannot be taken until other steps have been completed, hence there are critical paths through the entire forecast of events that determine optimum scheduling of activities and the earliest completion date of the project. If all has been properly understood and put into the computer, the project manager should know the effect of a given amount of slippage in any one event's date on the reaching of any other specific milestone. He should know when there is no use rushing one segment of the project, because another segment is the limiting activity. In the management of a complex project, it is necessary to minimize risk, at least unnecessary risk. One way this is done is to pay close attention to the schedule's decision points. At each of these points, options should be continually reviewed ahead of time. When a given point or milestone is reached, the situation should be carefully assessed before further resources are committed and before going along one or the other of the alternative paths for continued progress.

The Role of the Chief Executive Office

One of the most important problems of organization, particularly of a highly technological corporation, is the degree to which decision-making resides at the top of the organization, the chief executive office (CEO) level, and, in contrast, the extent to which responsibility and authority can and should be delegated. A balance of centralization-delegation must exist. This balance cannot be spelled out by formula and then made applicable to all organizations. Within one corporation it may change as the organization grows or changes, and it may even vary from one part of the organization to another. The chief executive office, that is, may exert greater control over some parts of the organization than others. The reasons may have to do with the relative strengths and weaknesses of executives, but more particularly are likely to be dependent upon the nature of the activities of each part of the organization and the degree to which those activities affect the corporation as a whole. These relationships and interdependencies may be expected to change with time also, and a soundly managed corporation will be continually re-examining the Cen-Del balance.

Cen-Del Balance is Essence of Good Management

A technological company cannot be managed well either by total centralizing of decision and control at corporate level or by the other extreme of total delegation to lower levels as though the various entities are independent companies. The essence of good management is a balance, the right hybrid, of these two different approaches. To understand better what the correct balance ought to be, consider some management issues at two distinctly different levels: (1) The detailed operating day-to-day management of a product line, and (2) the management aspects centralized in, and not delegated from, the CEO.

The product line manager must know his product, market, competition, product's application and potential, and costs. He must know the company's market share for that product and how its rise or fall will likely depend on pricing, innovative development, further capital investments to cut costs, or more marketing effort. He must know the makeup and dynamics of assets being employed, the profit and cash being generated and how these factors relate to market share growth. It would seem to some, perhaps, that the product line manager should operate much like the head of a small specialized company. Why not have the CEO provide guidelines for expected performance, a corresponding supporting budget, then merely audit to see that the product manager adheres to the guidelines and produces to forecast? His job, by this theory, is a decentralized one, because no one can do the detailed operating management for him.

But chances are the product line is not that isolatable. The product instead will be found to interrelate with many others in the company. It will share factory and marketing and engineering resources with other lines, for instance, or it will be part of a bag of products often sold together to the same customers. Furthermore, the criteria and the directives to the product line manager (about return on investment or growth or personnel practices, to mention only a few) fundamental to delegation, have to emerge from a chicken-and-egg analysis. What he should be asked to do by corporate management depends in part on what he can do, and how much of the corporation's resources should be put behind him, which depends in part on available competitive alternatives for allocation of corporate resources. What the product line manager thinks is a sensible plan for, say, market share penetration, R_A, or internal expansion constitutes essential input, admittedly. But his is a limited view. Comparisons and integration will greatly improve his directives as a basis for decentralized follow-through.

Essential Integration Required at CEO Level

At the other extreme, moving from product line management to the CEO, we see limits beyond which the CEO cannot delegate. One of these stems from the fact that the corporation is a single legal entity. The corporate level is the only point of focus for responsibilities to the shareholders and other constituents. It is the single channel of communication with the stock market, the only entity for the arranging of financing, and the only level at which debt-equity ratio level, dividend policy, and total capital budget can be decided. Only the corporate level can set overall corporate goals and decide how to allocate resources among the major areas of company activity that are directed by the principal executives reporting to the CEO.

Obviously, such control that must remain with the CEO cannot be handled well there without the benefit of inputs from operating and staff executives reporting into the CEO about performance, opportunities, problems, alternatives, and broadly based corporate ideas. The CEO does not perform its function in isolation. Granted this, after appropriate pondering and deciding by the CEO, why cannot the CEO reduce all of the deliberated and decided issues to numbers and qualitative descriptions, or at least ranges and guidelines, and then leave it to the executives below to operate in a fully decentralized way? The CEO, it could be argued, should be interested only in the overall results of their activities, not with detailed bits and pieces.

The answer is partly that this is exactly what the CEO should try to do. However, let us recognize that on almost every interesting and important issue, the interactive relationship between what has to be kept at CEO level and what can be delegated is difficult to describe in numbers or words so clearly that total delegation is meaningful. Sometimes stronger central action must precede delegation. Thus, the CEO cannot really assign a product manager a hunk of cash or shares of stock and tell him to use these for acquisitions of other companies. A wise decision to go ahead with an acquisition, and whether to do it by stock trade or cash, depends on the specific candidate for acquisition and the timing, and involves the whole company's position and alternatives, and not just the product areas it is intended to enhance. The

CEO cannot state the guidelines for a high degree of delegation until it deliberates with the executives below on the very facts which become the basis for delegation. By that time all of the interesting considerations are closely shared with the CEO and little is left for true decentralization. It is almost more true that the executives who head the decentralized operations have to act as members of the CEO for important issues than that the CEO can delegate action on those issues. Of course, similar practical limitations apply as well for delegation from any level of the organization to the next level below.

Another entirely different consideration sets a limit to decentralization from the CEO. Assume the company to be divided into two, four, six or eight main areas of endeavor, each operated by a general manager to whom the maximum control is delegated. What if, despite the best of planning, one of the general managers develops a serious cash flow problem? An advantage of being together in one legal entity whose financing requirements and sources are combined is that there will be a smoothing out of such misses. However, this smoothing may work only on the average and the long term. In the short term the deviations may unhappily all line up in the wrong direction. For safety in control the CEO has to be involved in some short-term direction of balance sheet matters.

Even with the maximum of delegation, no one manager below the CEO is the complete equivalent of the chief executive officer of an independent corporation. The integrating, managerial head of such an independent corporation can allocate the resources placed under his control. In contrast no one in charge of a piece of a corporation can expect to have total autonomous control over the resources under him. The cash a division manager generates, or the assets he frees, must be regarded as a part of total corporate resources which will be allocated from above in the shareholders' interest. The division or product line manager will participate very influentially in whether or how those resources—cash, people, factories—will be used by him, but the final decisions will rest with others who have a broader view and responsibility. No matter how complete are his guide rules for decentralized operations, the options available to him will be more restrained than if he were truly running a separate corporate entity facing the board and shareholders directly.

The Orderly Disorder of the Cen-Del Balance

Between the CEO's essential integration role and the operation of a highly decentralized product line lie numerous opportunities for ben-

160 MANAGEMENT OF TECHNOLOGICAL CORPORATIONS

efits in integration of related activities, comparisons of opportunities, efficient allocation of resources, and mutual aid and support to and between operations. The CEO cannot perform the integration, comparison, and resource allocation directly to the hundreds of product line endeavors. Moreover, the optimum number of levels below the CEO cannot be readily and uniformly specified. Thus the best Cen-Del balance between the CEO and the level of discrete product management is a grayish disorder, lacking black and white distinctions. The various executives operating decentralized units are partly in the integration business, partly operating a highly decentralized collective entity, partly interpreters to their employees of overall corporate goals and requirements, partly an extension of the CEO, partly a funnel for further detailed comparisons and allocations among the operations under their control, and partly delegators themselves. As we move down into the lower levels of organization, we can use similar words, though the integration function diminishes and the focus of concentration on specialized tasks increases.

Every operating management level of a corporation that does even a little integrating (say, of three or four highly related product lines) has to be aware of the importance to the corporation that it select products carefully, and allocate its assigned resources to seek the highest return on assets employed. It should expect its limited view to be augmented by further comparisons, allocations, and integration by the management level above that handles a broader array of such issues and alternatives. It is not alone a matter of product area selection and asset use optimization. Every unit, like the company as a whole, has management weaknesses, unforeseen opportunities it may not be prepared to handle, crises that will require for prompt handling a sudden infusion of knowledge and resources beyond what are available under that unit's control. The multi-level structure of a corporation should be ordered in the sense of clear responsibility to uplift and diffuse management competence. For this, great flexibility, or orderly disorder, in the idea of delegation is needed. No unit should be managed with such complete delegation to its manager that he can get into serious trouble, miss important opportunities, lapse into mediocre performance, or ignore key corporate goals and policies without this being noticed quickly and acted on by the integration process above and around him.

Problems

5–1. Choose an annual report of a technological corporation in which no organization chart is shown. Deduce a chart for the company from the clues you find in the report, and explain why you believe your chart is credible.

5–2. A technological corporation early had a functional organization with the heads of four departments reporting to the president: administration, engineering, manufacturing, and marketing. Later the organization was changed to a product line organization in which managers of three product line operating divisions reported to the president who also had an administrative staff to help him with coordination. Each of those product line divisions had engineering, manufacturing, and marketing departments whose managers reported to the division's general manager. Still later, the company returned to the original functional approach. What circumstances do you suppose might have developed that would have led to this change?

5–3. The following are the titles for some of the principal executives of a corporation:

President and Chief Operating Officer
Chief Counsel
Vice President, Manufacturing
Vice President and General Manager, Instrument Division
Vice President, International
Director of Marketing, Data Communications Division
Manager, Research and Engineering, Semiconductor Division
Director of Public Relations
Vice President, Manufacturing, Instrument Division
Chief Scientist
Chairman of the Board
Manager, Foreign Sales, Semiconductor Division
Director of Marketing Research

Draw an organization chart showing line and staff and reporting channels that you think would be consistent with the existence of these titles.

5–4. Consider two different technological corporations each at about a $100-million-a-year sales level. One is largely concerned with the development, manufacture, and sale of automatic, electrically driven control valves sold to chemical and petroleum processing companies. The other is involved in computer software and systems engineering related to computerization, with no manufacture of hardware but often with responsibilities for the delivery of complete systems including purchased computers, terminals, and ancillary equipment. Speculate about what major differences you might find in the organization of these two companies. If you did not know the products being manufactured but just had a list of the titles of the main players heading technical, marketing, accounting, legal, and other matters, how might you be able to tell which company is which?

5-5. A corporation has four divisions with related though substantially different product lines, each under a general manager. Each division has separate marketing, engineering, and manufacturing departments whose managers report to the division's general manager. Some of the corporate expenses are allocated to the divisions. These expenses include interest, currency translation losses and gains, general and administrative expenses incurred by the corporate management and corporate staff, and all taxes paid directly by the corporation to the government. How do you think the corporate expense allocation should be made to the divisions—in proportion to sales or assets employed or charged as actually incurred specifically on behalf of the divisions, or perhaps on some other basis?

5-6. A corporation has two major products both dependent on similar technologies. One product line is military weapon systems under contract to the Department of Defense. The other is commercial, consumer oriented applications of the same basic techniques. At present, the company is organized with a single engineering department. Two product line general managers place their R & D and product development with this engineering department but have separate marketing and manufacturing efforts under their direct control. The corporate management is being importuned by both of these product line managers to break up the engineering department into two separate groups catering specifically to their product line endeavors and reporting to them. They argue that the pooling of such diverse product line engineering in one organization is a handicap and that the engineering department manager is not adequately responsive to their requirements. The engineering department manager wants things as they are, claiming that breaking up the group into two parts would provide two relatively weak organizations or else a great deal of duplication that would add to cost and fail to obtain total utilization of all the expertise he is now able to arrange. What would you do if you were the chief executive officer? And why?

5-7. A leading producer of frozen foods and a major manufacturer of microwave ovens are merging. The new chief executive officer will be the oven company's former chairman. He arranged the merger with the idea that the customer for both is the same, that the large advertising budgets required can be cut, if the firms are combined, and the integrated image will increase customer acceptance of both lines. Moreover, he believes the frozen food line can be enhanced very profitably by creating and marketing foods ideally suited for preparation in the microwave oven. Also, he expects that the engineering of superior microwave ovens revolves in substantial part around matching the oven technology to the food being defrosted or cooked in the oven. He thus expects engineering synergism as well. Assuming that his hunches are at least partially correct, how would you organize the combined corporation?

5–8. A technological corporation with three product lines has four divisions. Three are domestic divisions under general managers who totally control the engineering, manufacturing and domestic marketing of the three separate product endeavors. The fourth is an international division whose general manager acquires products from the three domestic divisions for export and controls all overseas marketing, application engineering, customer service, contracts with distributors, and licensing to other companies in foreign countries. Also under him is a foreign-based assembly plant for some of the products whose components are produced by the domestic divisions. The three domestic general managers are dissatisfied with this arrangement. Can you suggest why? Would you alter the organization?

5–9. A small computer company has separate departments for marketing, manufacturing, and engineering. The last named has three design groups covering software, hardware components, and systems. It also has an R & D laboratory handling advanced explorations and special technical problems. In addition, three product teams cover the overall coordination with marketing, manufacturing, and engineering on the company's three main product endeavors, namely, an intelligent terminal for stock brokers, a general purpose minicomputer line, and a point of sale terminal for retailing. These teams' heads report to the company's president, as do the three main operating departments' managers. Describe the degree of, and limits on, the authority you think should be given the product teams' heads.

6

PRODUCT SELECTION

The Importance of a Product Selection Process

Some endeavors are ideally suited to a particular technological corporation. Many others are mismatches. In between these two categories will be found products from satisfactory to so-so. Corporations often are started around certain product conceptions that bring them initial success; then circumstances lead them into a range of endeavors where only a fraction make the best use of the corporation's resources, talents and position. It is basic to long-term success that a corporation cannot allow itself to be engaged in too many ill-chosen activities. Thus, a product selection process is a foundation pillar of good management.

This chapter will introduce a number of important concepts vital to sound product selection, but this matter is of such key importance that it deserves more attention and so will be brought up again in other chapters. For instance, discussion of some aspects of product selection for a technological corporation needs a prior consideration of many engineering, manufacturing, and marketing issues. We shall take up these issues in turn in the following three chapters. After that, further product selection fundamentals and details can be more efficiently and logically introduced. In this chapter we shall present rationale to make credible the value of imaginative, and yet careful, product selection.

We start our discussion with the technological input to product choices. In a technological corporation there is a tendency to go for product areas that are new, represent the very latest technology, or put newly discovered science to work. Technological breakthroughs can be a prime factor on occasion in providing sound corporate activity, but newness is not enough. Putting assets behind the broadening of the market for existing projects may be as important to a corportion as developing entirely innovative ones. A cost reduction program that enhances earnings, cuts prices, increases sales volume, improves the market position of the corporation and enables the product to be used in more applications may be equally satisfying.

The product selection process is not concerned alone with the choice of new areas of endeavor or even of where and when to expand the old, established activities. It is also important to analyze the products of a corporation on a continuing basis to see which ones should be gotten rid of. A successful product need not be held onto right up to the time of the eventual death of all its useful applications or its surrender to a successor product. When the product, inspiring and profitable as it may have been for the corporation in some former period, no longer meets corporate criteria, it perhaps needs to be dispensed with, the activity sold off to others or simply terminated, the assets assigned to it shifted to other efforts, and the closing losses, if any, taken calmly as presumably better in some circumstances than continuing the activity.

An old product may represent new penalties if continued. Some new developments may deserve to be halted in their infancy, if not aborted before birth. If it becomes apparent that it was a mistake to have started an endeavor, it may be far smarter to cut if off before it consumes even more available funds and management energy. Thus goes the continuing application of the product selection process to the entire product line.

A fundamental reason for attention to product selection from the very conception of a product idea is because costs escalate as that idea is developed to a mature product. Research and development explorations and market research, to maximize the match between the market potential on the outside and the company's potential for filling that market need with an appropriate technological solution, are expensive. A healthy R&D effort in a typical, strong technological corporation uses up a substantial amount of the earnings available for plowback. However, the next steps, product design and manufacturing startup, usually are several times more costly. A great deal of focus must be given to the details of design so that the product can be manufactured within reasonable costs. If it cannot be, the product selection is a poor one. The choice and development of materials and processes for manufacture and of methods of test and assembly tend to be fund-consuming procedures as well. Pilot line operations must usually be carried on before true production starts, and that activity is usually not cheap for high technology production. Then comes an even more expensive step, the commitment to plant and facilities for quantity production and distribution of the product.

If the product selection has not been carried out competently, then an overall loss much greater than the costs of the initial efforts will be incurred by the corporation. If the product choice was bad, perhaps some of the machinery and testing facilities and manufacturing space will turn out to be convertible to other things, but in the process a good deal of the capital investment will be lost. Preparing for success-ful sales means investing in the creating of a marketing organization and paying for a period of substantial effort by that organization before sales are brought in. Very often, in fact, it is necessary to build inventory, going ahead with manufacturing a quantity of products before any sales orders are attained to confirm without doubt that the market research and the product design efforts have been carried out correctly.

For every million dollars in research and development and market-ing research that yields a manufacturable and salable product, per-haps some ten million dollars will be placed at risk, a good part of that absorbed against earnings as startup cost, before the corporation makes substantial sales. Then some years will pass and some addi-tional startup expenses will be incurred, hurting annual earnings, before a solidly profitable phase is entered.

A product selection process for a corporation is a continuing effort applied to existing and potentially new products. It is a procedure for adding and subtracting products and comparing alternatives among them. The management of a corporation cannot allow the product selection process to be accidental or arbitrary. If the corporation does not do a good job of selecting out of a large list those activities that are right for it, the market place will do it for the corporation. Other companies will select the best products, leaving only the unsatisfactory ones for the unthinking management to ride with. The product selec-tion process should be deliberate and clear, even if it is only the review by and use of the hunch of the chief executive officer. Of course, if it is only that, then his hunches had better be good on a long-term basis.

Scenarios for Product Development

Typically the history of a new product development involves several distinct periods. In the first there is no income, only expenses, as the initial research and development, marketing research, design of specialized facilities and the working out of production techniques are accomplished. The net cash flow during this period is negative as is the annual contribution to earnings of the corporation. This is followed by a second period in which sales commence and some income is received. The earnings and/or the cash flow on an annual basis may become positive during this phase, but this is not usual during this second period for most technological products. The sales volume is too low and the cost yet too high at that low volume. Learning is still taking place in the factory and the design is being debugged. More working capital and equipment have to be provided as sales and manufacturing volume build, and the marketing, engineering and manufacturing startup costs will still be felt. Thus the par situation in this second period is that the net annual cash flow contributions to the corporation are still negative.

This is followed by a third period in which the product line is now profitable on an annual reporting basis, that is, the net contribution to annual corporate earnings is positive. However, the cash flow may not be. Indeed, if the product line is a success, a high market demand for it and the corresponding sales increase may require further expansion of facilities to meet the burgeoning sales volume. Given a high enough growth rate, the requirement for increased assets will exceed positive cash flow being generated from operations even with a satisfactory return on assets employed.

If all goes well, a fourth period is reached in which the cash flow is positive and so is the earnings contribution. The product is now mature. There may be continued growth during this period, but the cash being generated is more than sufficient to accommodate the growth in assets required to support the sales growth. This leaves excess cash to flow back into the corporation at last. With the main fixed assets partly written off (depreciated) but still able to provide amply for the production required, the R_A can become high and the product line makes an excellent contribution to reported annual earnings of the corporation.

Finally comes the decay period in which the product is nearing the end of its usefulness, no further enhancement of the product line is justified, and the sales fall off. This may happen gradually with satisfactory cash and earnings contributions from the activity all the way. The period will end with the product line abandoned and the remaining assets written off or transferred to other uses.

Any number of detailed scenarios can be constructed for the story of a proposed product. Each tale constitutes an estimate in which business wisdom and experience must be properly mixed with controlled imagination. Obviously the rating of a product development that manages to get through this kind of forecasting depends upon the numbers chosen for the key parameters in the analysis. Growth rates, length of time before the mature period sets in, sales volume to be reached for each stage, the return on assets to be expected during the various periods—the selection of all these quantities must be accompanied by substantial rationale for their choices. Thus, if a particular sales volume versus time is set down, there must be justification of at least two items. One is the market demand for the product within a price range that will represent profitable operation. The second is the market position of the corporation against competitors for the same or equivalent products. Also, of course, the assets to be employed must relate to the product details and the way it is to be manufactured. Sales margin and turnover need to be estimated and defended by listing and studying all elements of costs and pricing.

When all of these parameters (and the appropriate discount rate for figuring present values) have been selected, the question remains about how to terminate the scenario. How the product line is to be terminated, and what is to happen to the assets employed at that time is an important and interesting one. The scenario has to be provided with a credible, well thought out ending, or the product selection process is handicapped. Management is hardly going to be interested in a preconceived history for a product for one hundred years. Ten years is somewhat closer to the typical limits of interest of corporate managements as they examine the possibilities of one product candidate for investment against another. One reasonable assumption is that at the end of ten years the product line, whether it is continued or not, has a value to the company equal to the book value. Over the last decade the common stocks of corporations listed on the New York Stock Exchange have sold at prices not too far from book value, some above and some below. Almost all those corporations are planning to continue in existence. It is not too far fetched to assume the particular product line under consideration will go on and presumably be capable of generating such earnings and cash flow after the ten years that the present value of the positive cash flow to the corporation equals the book value at the discount rate being used. (See Appendix B)

Some product developments are planned around the belief that the product will be outmoded at the end of ten years. In other instances, a main goal for the product development is to create a profitable, going product line which in ten years will be seen to have the potential of substantial growth for another ten or twenty. Then the appropriate ten-year value of the line to the corporation may well exceed the book value. For a steady growth, g, indefinitely into the future, the formula for the value, $P_{V,10}$, of the continuing stream of cash flow at the ten-year point when the next year's cash flow is F_{10} and the discount rate is R_I is given by

$$R_I = F_{10}/P_{V,10} + g$$

or

$$P_{V,10} = F_{10}/(R_I - g) \qquad [1]$$

If the product line being analyzed is expected to go on growing profitably long after the ten years, it is also to be expected that the product line will change. Here it is useful to think momentarily of that product development as a separate corporation which in ten years has built up a market position in its product area and considerable know-how in the design and manufacture of such a product line. During the ten years new ideas will have come forth. The product will be improved and added to. New applications will turn up and the product line will be enhanced to encompass these.

Criteria for Choice of Suitable Product Lines

Existing product lines or candidates for added ones should be evaluated and continually based on the return on investment considerations discussed in previous chapters. The best estimate possible should be made of the financial consequences scenario of the product line for an adequate number of years. Initial investments and later ones for working capital and fixed assets should be plotted against time, and so should cash flows, earnings, sales growth, and all of the other important balance sheet and profit and loss items. Granted that this is a plotting of future activities and only an estimate, such a prediction will nevertheless be helpful in deciding whether the product line meets the criterion for return on investment that the company should set.

Another criterion for product selection, we remind ourselves, is that the risk be acceptable. If the risk is too high, it usually means that factors beyond ready prediction and control by the corporation may be very upsetting to the results. Then the criterion for the anticipated internal rate of return, if all goes well, should be set higher. In the next chapter we shall consider some examples of scenarios that are pertinent to the startup of new products based on internal R&D.

However, the two associated criteria of adequate return and reasonable risk apply as well to existing product lines. If it appears that a product line will fall below the appropriate hurdle rate for that company, meaning that it does not contribute as much as other opportunities for the use of like assets would appear to yield, and if the risk of even more severe negatives is too high, then consideration should be given to going out of that business. Since dropping a product line may involve some losses, the estimated losses should be compared with the difference between the return on assets employed in continuing this unsatisfactory product line compared with the return, if those assets were shifted to provide greater advantage in some other field. It could turn out that the potential loss in dropping the product is so great relative to the present return that it is better to keep on with the product line, even though it is below the average that the company could otherwise enjoy. There are risks that have to be assessed in getting out of business as well as staying in. Keeping on may lose a little. Getting out may greatly discourage customers, suppliers, and shareholders (and may cause some of them to sue the management for deserting them or letting them down on their interpretations of company commitments).

It can be true for a corporation, particularly one with diversified product lines and a long established period of doing business successfully in those lines, that a very large part of its sales volume yields return on assets employed below the returns that the corporation finds possible with certain new endeavors. It may also be that the new endeavors are only a small part of the total. Consider, for instance, a corporation with $5 billion of annual sales volume of which, let us say, $4.5 billion brings an R_A of only 10 percent, this from mature products. This company generates enough funds to make possible investments in new product areas. Having made such investments in recent years, it now has $500 million per year of sales in those added product lines. These sales, we imagine, provide a return on assets employed of 20 percent and the company sees the possibility of identifying and implementing more such product endeavors. However, such new products sales do not begin to compare with the $4.5 billion from mature products. The corporation may find it sensible to use a hurdle rate for new products of 20 percent for R_A, while at the same time believing that the established lines that now make up 90 percent of its business should be maintained even though their R_A is only 10 percent. The company could not contemplate divesting itself of these mature products without tremendous losses, perhaps on the order of a billion or two billion dollars. Furthermore, it would end up as a company one tenth the previous size with the severe problem of shrinking without coming apart.

Let us turn now to some qualitative criteria for product selection that relate to the corporation's goals and objectives. Suppose a corporation decides to expand internationally, perhaps to exploit existing products to the fullest. Or it plans to diversify into product lines that are extensions of or similar to existing ones to make the fullest use of the available know-how and capacity of the engineering, manufacturing and marketing organizations. Product launchings that enhance the chances of reaching those goals of international expansion and higher utilization of existing assets would appear to deserve a priority. Conversely, if the major objective of a company in the near term is to reduce the debt-equity ratio and improve earnings, then product line candidates involving large startup expenses and cash beyond the anticipated available cash flow would appear to be rather ill-matched to the stated objective. A corporation should have both well defined objectives and clear product line criteria. If it does not possess the former, it will be difficult to create the latter.

Because our interest is in technological corporations we must return in this brief overview to the technological aspects of product selection. (This matter will be developed more fully in the following chapters.) It is of fundamental importance that the product lines constitute a good match between the technological resources of the corporation and the market need, particularly that portion of the market really available to the corporation in view of competition. A product selection process falls far short of adequate, if it does not include assessing the important match of internal capabilities to the external market. Criteria for selection of products on a technological basis certainly must include adequate attention to the degree to which the product line approaches uniqueness and incorporates performance superiority and whether the corporation has a proprietary position. If a product itself is technologically only about on a par with everyone else's product, then the product's selection means the company must have special qualifications in some other nontechnological dimension. Something must be different or better to justify the entry of the corporation or the continuation of the corporation in that product area. Such possible advantages of the product line for the corporation may be based on diverse corporate strong points. For instance, the company might be blessed with as unusually strong marketing ability for that product, exceptional competence in manufacturing which shows itself in lower cost or higher reliability, or long and successful experience operating in the locale under consideration where labor is more stable and rates lower than that of competition producing virtually the same product elsewhere.

In making product selections some of the factors that must be examined can be elusive and misleading. A basis for the selection can be fickle. For instance, a competitor may be weak and the market highly attractive for the corporation's product, but only because the appropriate leading competitor happens to have made an error (maybe in product design, marketing approach, or pricing) which it can and will correct. The correction then may be made by the competitor and that will change the competitive environment entirely and turn the product selection from a good to a poor one in a short time.

Timing is a prime factor in sound technological product selection. There is a limit to the amount of new technological development the market can and will absorb, especially at prices that create satisfactory returns. Technological change needs to be timed right in order to be exploited. An awareness of this is part of competent product selection and will be discussed further in Chapter 9.

In a well run technological corporation, a substantial number of its products will be significantly related to one another. One technological effort will lean on and enhance another, or the manufacturing will share common approaches and facilities. Important applications of different products may be mutually supportive. All in all, selecting products requires analyzing their potential relationship with other products, either existing or contemplated. Everything else being equal, it would appear more sensible to put the investment of the corporation into product areas in which the various products supplement each other's opportunities for success.

Finally, one criterion for deciding on the best products should be that those products are the finalists after adequate contest and comparison among more than enough candidates. A corporation that, no matter how well endowed with available assets, does not possess enough practical ideas for product line extensions, and also does not have an existing product line worth keeping, is in trouble. There are always successful corporations that generate more cash than it makes sense to invest in doing more of what they are already doing. But, if a corporation is a successful technological one of any substantial size, it will have a high awareness of advancing technology and changing applications for existing technology. It will relate the company's technological resources to the market in such a way as to find attractive areas for investment and expansion of the product line. The usual situation is that the technological corporation must limit itself to only a fraction of the product endeavors that appear worth considering. The product selection process must inherently be a method for accepting some areas of activity and passing up others. In the process an abundant group of rejected product line activities should be uncovered which management greatly regrets having to forego. The well run corporation is disciplined to limit itself only to the better ideas and then only a reasonable amount of rueing the abandoning of the rest.

Selective Diversification

Good management of a company generally maximizes the market value of that company to its owners. This goal usually eventually leads a well managed technological corporation to become diversified and multinational. Of course, the route to such maximization may not be straight. Some long, winding, and even adventuresome paths may be followed, and the complexity of the detours can hide the ever present, straightforward maximization criterion. Other conditions may also confuse management. For instance, a very small technological enterprise, in its infancy and with a single, highly innovative and marketable product, may appear to call for a different strategy. In due time, however competent management will usually find itself seeking out those alternatives for action that will increase the worth of what the share owner owns. Such optimum values will not follow from reliance on the simple resolve, "let's stick with our successful product."

Management has available a set of resources—product development capability, manufacturing skill, financial and marketing know-how, facilities, people, funds, market position, overall image, and others. If these resources are to be exploited, considering fully their interactive strengths and weaknesses, it will prove only rarely or temporarily the right strategy to concentrate on a very narrow product line.

Products do not stand still. Market areas change. If the company does not change its product, its competitors will, developing a substitute for it, finding cheaper ways to manufacture it or make it smaller or lighter or more reliable or more rugged or with new features extending its applicability. Moreover, the product is only one element in some system that uses it. New systems developments will surely arise from changing requirements and potentials in an overall changing world, or from technological advances that alter other components of the system and make possible new and better systems. Any product's position as a system component changes with time. Good management of a technological corporation requires steady attention to all of these matters.

To retain competitive position in the long run the company must employ research and development specialists and provide them with facilities and support. When they tackle technical problems, their results will usually have broader possibilities for application than merely the narrow area of the company's present products. The company similarly must employ capable experts and innovators in manufacturing, application, marketing and distribution of the product line. Such a staff is expensive to maintain. Its output potential offers diversification opportunities quite automatically. These cannot be ignored without loss.

If a company has a good product for the domestic market, chances are it or a variation can be manufactured or marketed to advantage in other countries. Maximization of use of resources leads to diversification by geographic area as well as by product. This may appear minor when the company has a highly specialized and novel product, a very strong patent position, great economic payoff in its application compared with costs, and a hungry domestic market demand far exceeding the supply. It is tempting to recommend that in such a situation the management should simply relax and enjoy it. Such an uncommon and transitory situation has little relationship to the more prevalent real life one of a typical technological corporation.

In seeking exceptions to the rule that diversification and multinationalism should be the expected trend for well managed technological corporations, such companies as IBM, Xerox, and Eastman Kodak are often cited. Are they diversified in products and geography? Certainly, international opportunities unquestionably were grasped early and firmly by these companies. However, it might appear, superficially, that the managements of these highly successful companies have decided consistently against product diversification. This is not a proper conclusion. IBM at one point provided mechanical tabulating machines for business accounting by the use of punched cards. It was doing well in this field. A less alert management than IBM's might have decided to stay with the mechanical gear and leave electronics to electronics companies. As electronic technology took over, IBM embraced it. Product development for business accounting came to bear a close relationship to product development for scientific computers. It would have been surprising for IBM's management not to apply the extra resources needed in research and development, application engineering and marketing to diversify its product line into scientific computers as well as business accounting machines. Numerous other diversification examples, from military projects to typewriters, could be cited in IBM's activities. Similarly, Eastman Kodak has expanded into chemicals and information storage and retrieval. Its good management has not limited its activities to cameras, or even cameras and film. Xerox is finding that copying machines alone will not enable it to maximize its potential. Its management has redefined its field of endeavor to include a broader area of information handling.

Selective Diversification

We note, of course, that the diversification of these particular firms is highly related—IBM has not bought a car rental agency or an insurance company. Diversification leads to the highest return on resources employed—but not just any diversification. Success, granted diversification, is in the nature and degree of the diversification selected. Selective diversity is the name of the game. Good management will not settle on either extreme, zero diversification or arbitrarily widespread, random diversification.

One of the most powerful arguments for a technological corporation's diversifying in products and geography is that this very condition greatly enhances the number of available alternatives deserving investment, whether in existing or new areas. The best choices out of 100 good possibilities should lead to a superior average performance over the years, compared with the best of a small and narrowly restricted list of candidates.

Averaging Out Cycles and Mismatches

A specific product line that is presently very profitable may be generating more cash now than can be used well for the furtherance of the growth and profitability of that line. A company with such a condition has to make some choices. It can make the surplus earnings available in high dividends, forsaking growth, or seek new areas in which to expand (that is, diversify), or plow back to press its one product or one-country operation ahead, even though the incremental return on such incremental investment may be very poor. To take the other extreme, some single product line company may be able to justify investing funds for expansion well beyond the cash it is generating. It must accept a less than optimum rate of growth, or seek outside financing. Since varied product lines possess variations in their requirements for cash against time (even if they are all growing), a competently managed diversified company is in an advantageous position to optimize investment for growth. In fact, frequently, the mismatches of companies' requirements—one finding itself with expansion potential and no cash, and another having only modest needs but overly ample reserve funds—form the basis for sensible mergers. Why not anticipate the high probability of the occurrences of such mismatches over a period of time by the right amount of diversification within one integrated corporate entity?

The noncoincidence of cyclical effects among diverse product lines deserves special mention. A general economic recession, long-lasting and worldwide, will adversely affect the performance of almost all product lines. More common are the many smaller booms and recessions with great differences in timing of the peaks and valleys and consequent impact on individual product lines and geographic spreads in world markets. As one example, a low period in new car sales is likely to be accompanied by a rise, not a drop, in the sale of automotive parts in the replacement parts aftermarket. As another, the sales curves of electronic components for process-control computers, telephone systems, guided missiles, and home television sets will not cycle together.

Some ups and downs in activity of every product line are inevitable. The more severe the departure from orderly progress the more dislocating and difficult it is to provide unwavering support for a product line. Research and development, marketing research, manufacturing techniques improvement, financial analyses, and other vital functions are carried out best without sudden budgetary adjustments forced by swings in earnings or cash flow. The overlapping of noncoincident cycles of diversified lines yields a smoothed-out total against which steady supporting functions can be maintained.

Uncontrollable external parameters are at the least a nuisance to a company trying to develop and operate on an optimum plan. At their worst, cyclic variations force substantial deviations from preferred courses during the extremes of the swings. This can be true both on the rise and the fall sides of the cycle. With too narrow an operation, the worst of worlds may converge—at the same moment: an urgent need for capital for expansion, a temporary low earnings period, and a tight money and down stock market condition making borrowing expensive and new stock issues overly diluting.

Misconceptions Regarding Diversification

Understanding selective diversification's role in the success of a company is especially important at this time. Misinformation and misconceptions are being offered widely, suggesting that the narrow product line company should be favored. Most of the prejudice against diversified companies seems to stem from the record of a group of acquisition-conglomerate companies. These enjoyed a stock market fad position, peaking a decade ago. They were temporary darlings of the market for a number of years, for no substantive reason, and they were able to exploit blown-up multiples to acquire low-multiple companies for stock and increase earnings per share with each acquisition. Not surprisingly, the acquirees turned out most often to be second rate companies. The combine contained no ingredients for major improvement due to mutual association, especially in overall management (which for these companies was more often skilled in promotion than operations). Now, some years later, with the high-multiple + merger formula no longer credible and in justified disfavor, the acquisition-conglomerate company is poorly regarded. This sad situation for such companies bears little relationship to a well managed company that has diversified selectively.

Further misconceptions hide the real basis for success of diversified companies. Indeed, a substantial number of the "best companies" in the United States are diversified and yet are regarded falsely as specialized, single line companies. A Harvard Business School study of the 1950–1970 period for the Fortune 500 industrials in the United States and over 300 of the largest industrials of Western Europe showed that:

1. Almost all leading United States companies have diversified substantially, with 80 percent of them diversifying by at least 30 percent of their sales.

2. The number of companies with a single business is declining as a percentage of the Fortune 500 group. In the 20-year period, the fraction of single business companies in this top United States companies list (defined as having less than 5 percent of sales away from their traditional product line) decreased by a factor of more than three.

3. Top companies in the United Kingdom, France, Germany and Italy demonstrate a similar, pronounced trend toward diversification with a large decline in the proportion of companies in the list in only one business.

Alert managers all over the world have been diversifying to sustain the growth of their companies rather than limiting themselves to the destinies of a single industry or product line (such as coal, textiles, electric meters or whatever) or geographical area. Growth through diversification has become the most commonly successful strategy in Europe as it has in the United States.

Those who wish to judge whether a large technological corporation is well managed clearly should ask whether the company is diversified. Then, if so, they should seek to learn in what way it is diversified. How does its planning make visible to its management its alternatives for broadening its activities, either in product lines or by geographical area? What techniques does it use for making the selection of the best alternatives? Is it a leader in the specific areas it has selected?

Managing Diversification

The separate segments of a diversified company must not individually suffer from bureaucratic, overly coordinative, delaying direction from the corporate top. At the same time, the corporate management must be set up to perform comparative analyses in order to choose the overall projects that maximize the fit of that company's potential and resources with the outside world. If the selection of the kind, extent, and timing of diversification is part of good corporate management, then management must organize to make options clear. It must have means for evaluating them, comparing one against another and making the decisions about fields of endeavor. It must set up to fix the wheres and whens for startup and growth nourishment. For that matter, it must be equally prepared for sell-off, liquidation or harvesting when the preferred diversification is seen to be heading in new directions.

It is worth noting that the larger technological companies growing most rapidly are divisionally organized with very considerable decentralization of operating management responsibility and authority. At the same time, one finds, among the best performers, very few holding companies, whose top management merely watches the results as investors.

To realize the benefits of selective diversification of product endeavors within a single corporate entity, certain fundamental organizational approaches should be considered. Comparative analysis of alternatives for investment and decision-making must be accomplished at corporate level, while not interfering with the requirement for the decentralization of responsibility for operating management of the existing diverse operations. Within agreed upon goals and forecasts, the operating unit's managers should be allowed to manage without bringing back for approval to corporate headquarters the detailed, everyday decision-making that is the core of good operating management. Moreover, the operators should be allowed reasonable departures from plans to compensate for the inevitable real-life variations, the problems and the opportunities that were unforeseen when the budgets and forecasts were laid out.

Corporate planning, arranged to take advantage of the availability of many product options, is basic preparation for assigning specific goals and their accompanying budgets and detailed plans which then should be decentralized for execution. Good corporate planning requires that substantial deviations from the forecast for the decentralized activity (or the threat of such, either good or bad) be monitored continually. Alteration in the corporate plan or strategy may have to be considered, if the deviations are significant enough. The corporate management of a diversified company must employ an adequate staff for the task, if it is to be capable of making comparisons among the product line options for the use of corporate resources. The staff must have the time and ability to familiarize itself with the apparent potentials, costs, benefits, and risks associated with the many possibilities made evident by the existing diverse operating units and the additional ideas born outside the company.

Is it more important to put the corporation's chips behind the enhancement of an existing product line where only marginal growth might be expected, or should something very new, either in product or in geographical area, receive higher priority? Is a higher growth rate opportunity, albeit with more risk, better than a lower growth rate endeavor with less risk? How many babies can corporate management send to college? Is a somewhat higher debt-to-equity ratio justified in order to increase the number of projects in which investment can be made? What is the proper balance between highest earnings per share in the short term, attained by cutting down on investment for the future, on one hand, and increased earnings per share later, on the other? In a well managed, diversified corporation, such difficult questions usually will be dealt with at the corporate level. That is the proper place for generating the answers, hazardous as the decision-making process may be. Indeed, perhaps the leading measure of whether a diversified corporation is properly diversified is whether or not the corporate management is able to handle this kind of decision-making competently.

If the diversification of a corporation has resulted from a random, conglomerate-merger process, then no matter how well the alternatives are offered and described by the decentralized managers of the diverse entities, the corporate level will not have the knowledge and experience required to make adequate comparisons and decisions, let alone optimum ones. When the diversification becomes so great and unrelated that corporate management cannot integrate and lead the selection process, then the whole probably is described best as a holding company, no matter what might be its apparent modus operandi and organization chart.

A certain universal point of view must pervade the management of the corporation and its various diversified entities for selective diversification to be utilized to maximum advantage. This view is that the resources of the corporation—the people, facilities, capital funds, generated cash—belong to the corporation as a whole and not to the individual entities. The fundamental rule is that each operating unit is assigned specific resources and a plan. In a well run diversified corporation, these allocations will be part of a master strategy.

The roles assigned by corporate management to the operators of individual units may vary greatly. Some may expect a substantial period of losses while engaged in bringing into being a new product endeavor or an activity in a new country. Others may be entrusted with the generating of a maximum of cash with an established product whose period of growth has ended. Still others may be asked to liquidate or sell off a product activity or to restructure an organization or a new acquisition.

It is imperative, for success in management of a selective diversification corporation, that there be incentives for team play. The individual product manager must wear two hats, a parochial one for his defined area of responsibility, and a corporate one for his participation on the overall team working in a designated role toward overall corporate objectives. All operating entities' executives must be judged and rewarded on how well they perform against their individual, assigned tasks. They must believe that if all the separate product assignments are carried out well by each of them, it will yield the desired, overall corporate result that will accrue to the benefit of all.

Problems

6–1. A company has arrived at the point where its product line is mature, and it sees steady sales with constant margins for about a 10-year period ahead. At the moment it has total assets employed of $100 million consisting of $50 million working capital and $50 million fixed assets. Its long-term debt is $20 million and the book value of shareholders' equity is $80 million. It is considering several alternatives for the next decade:

    a. Stay in a no-growth position and pay out all earnings as dividends.

    b. Cut the dividends just enough to pay off the long-term debt by a constant payment each year reducing the debt to zero in five years.

    c. Create a new product development expense budget, enough to cut the earnings to one-half for each of the next five years.

    d. Keep the debt constant, pay out half the earnings as dividends and use the excess to buy back common stock at market price.

Compare these four alternatives, speculating as you deem sensible regarding other factors not mentioned.

6–2. A company has enjoyed a modest but steady earnings growth of 5 percent for over 10 years and has paid out 60 percent of these earnings in dividends. It has had a constant R_{DA}, R_V, and R_A. Empirical data analyzed by computer suggest that the multiple for the common stock of companies in its class, expressed as a ratio of the average multiple of the Dow Jones stocks, is approximately as follows:

$$M/M_{DJ} = K(1 + 24g_5)(1 - 1.7R_{DA})(1 + 1.6R_V^{1/4})(20R_{A5} - 1)$$

where K is a constant; g_5 is the average earnings per share growth over the previous five years; R_{DA} is the present debt to total assets ratio; R_V is the present dividend payout ratio, and R_{A5} is the average R_A over the previous five years. Suppose the company alters its pattern for the next five years and reinvests more of its earnings, dropping its R_V to 30 percent and its R_A to 10 percent. Assume R_{DA} remains unchanged at 20 percent and $i = .05$. After these first five years, the benefits are shown by the following performance for the second five years: $R_A = 14$ percent, $R_V = 40$ percent, and R_{DA} remains at 20 percent. Calculate the multiple and the expected common stock price for each of the 10 years compared with the original value at the beginning of the decade, assuming M_{DJ} remains constant.

6–3. A company's earnings per share have been going up steadily at a 5 percent per year rate for many years and are expected to continue to do so if no change is made. A change being considered by management is to impair earnings to introduce a larger R & D program to develop new products. The anticipated earnings per share growth pattern is as follows for successive years, the figure meaning the change from the previous year: first -20 percent, second -15 percent, third -10 percent, fourth -5 percent, fifth 0 percent, sixth $+5$ percent, seventh $+10$ percent, eighth $+15$ percent. Using 100 units for the earnings per share the year before the launching of this new program (hence, 80 for the first new year) list the anticipated earnings per share for the successive years after the installation of the new program. Assume the stock price-earnings multiple is

$$M = M_0 \text{ when } g = 0$$
$$M = M_0(1 + 10g) \text{ when } g > 0$$
$$M = M_0(1 + 5g) \text{ when } -.1 < g < 0$$

where g is the average earnings growth rate for the preceding five years and express the varying stock market multiples and the stock price over the eight year period as ratios of the values before the period started.

6–4. A technological corporation selling $200 million of products annually has divided these products into two categories, old which are declining in sales each year, and new which are increasing in sales. At the moment they are approximately equal in volume. The old products' sales are expected to decrease by 10 percent during the next year, while the new products are expected to be up in volume by 30 percent, for a net increase in total sales anticipated next year of about 10 percent. Suppose that a year later, if the same analysis is repeated, $110 million of sales are found in each category, old and new, for the predicted total of $220 million. How might it be that the total growth is properly predicted, while the division of the total between the two categories is not?

6–5. When it examined one product line's history, a company noted that for the first four years, starting 14 years ago, about $1 million per year before taxes was expensed against earnings for the initial R & D, product development and various production and marketing start-ups. Over the last 10 years of the product's history, which was the profitable operation period, $10 million of assets were employed on the average each year and an annual average of $2 million of cash was generated, 40 percent of it used to pay taxes on earnings. At this point the product line was halted and the assets, less a $3 million writeoff before taxes, were removed and used elsewhere. As an approximation, assume that the above average annual figures were the actuals for the specific years involved, and state whether the internal rate of return for this endeavor over its entire history met the company's hurdle rate of 16 percent. (Further assume the company has no capital gains against which the $3 million loss can be taken so that this entire loss must be absorbed.)

6–6. A new product program has the following history: In three start-up years before sales began, $1 million was spent each year before taxes on R & D, product design, and production engineering, assets employed being negligible. In years four, five, and six, the sales were $1, $3, and $10 million respectively; the R_A was constant at .14 and the turn-over was constant at 2.5. In years seven through 10, sales increased at the rate of 15 percent annually over the previous year, turnover rose to (and stayed at) 3.0 and R_A increased to .20. Assume that the value of the cash flow stream ahead measured at the end of 10 years was equal to the then book value of assets. Also assume that the start-up expenses were written off against earnings at the 50 percent tax rate. Further assume that investment equal to depreciation costs were made each year to maintain facilities and equipment in a like-new condition. Estimate the internal rate of return on investment for this program.

6–7. A technological corporation has been plateaued in sales at about the $300 million level. It employs assets of $100 million (book equity of $95 million and debt of $5 million) and reports $15 million of earnings, paying it all out in dividends. The management embarks on a new product development program estimated to have these consequences: Earnings in the immediate year ahead will fall from $15 million to $5 million as $10 million, after taxes, are expended in R & D and start-up costs; sales during that year will remain at $300 million; dividends paid will be held at $15 million; assets required will not be noticeably changed from the $100 million of the preceding year; equity will fall somewhat in order to pay dividends greater than earnings (we assume depreciation charges are equal to the investment made to maintain facilities and equipment); bank borrowings are adjusted as required. In the second year sales will rise to $305 million, earnings will be at $7 million, assets required will rise to $110 million. The third, fourth, and fifth year sales respectively will be $330, $350, and $380 million; the earnings $15, $25, and $35 million; the assets employed $120, $125, and $130 million. The dividend payout will be held at $15 million per year throughout the five-year period. Assume $i = 5$ percent. Draw up a chart of the operating figures for this company for the five years including sales, earnings, dividends, assets employed, book values of equity, debt, R_A, R_{DA}, and R_{ES}. Assume that before embarking on this plan the company had a stock market multiple of 4, which immediately jumped to 5 in the first of the five years when the new product development plan was announced, then went up in successive years as follows: 6, 7, 8, 9, and 10. Calculate the market value of the shares outstanding before the new policy took place, and then for each year of the five. Also calculate the ratio of market to book value of the common stock of the company for the six years.

6–8. Choose the annual report of a large and diversified technological corporation and identify any aspects of that company's situation which appear to you inconsistent with the line of arguments presented in this chapter regarding the need of a technological corporation for selective diversification. Describe the conflict you identify and take sides in a short essay.

7

RESEARCH AND DEVELOPMENT AND PRODUCT ENGINEERING

The Interrelationship of Product Design and R & D

Research, Pure and Applied

In a technological corporation, R & D appears frequently in a large fraction of all paragraphs, oral or written. The words Research and Development (R & D) are used with a variety of meanings, but most often research is reserved for basic explorations of science and technology, the pushing back of the frontiers of knowledge, while development suggests applying science and technology to create a useful device or system. When the two words are lumped together, that usually connotes the preparatory work a step away from the specific design of a product. The words product engineering and product design are commonly used to define the activity directly associated with efforts to bring out a product for manufacture and sale.

American technological industries spend some $20 billion a year (pre-tax) on R & D, which represents about 2 percent of sales and a third of the profits. In addition to this, a comparable amount of R & D is performed by industry for the federal government in military weapon systems, space technology, energy R & D and other fields. Market research of substantial volume accompanies the research and development in industry, of course, as does application engineering, follow-on effort for manufacturing methods and product improvements of an incremental nature, and for quality control and product testing. These latter tasks are often as high in technology as the initial R & D

185

that precedes or leads to a new product or technique but are not counted in the $20 billion figure just cited.

Basic or pure research is seldom performed in private industry. Such work has as its purpose the probing of those aspects of nature's phenomena not yet completely understood. This research usually provides theoretical and experimental results with potential value in many science and engineering applications. However, in pursuing truly basic research, scientists seek to learn the laws of nature with no direct interest in whether and how these laws will be applied. This kind of research is largely carried out in universities and nonprofit research institutions with the results expected to be given to the world for the benefit of all.

The research done by corporations is chosen particularly to boost the effectiveness of that corporation in the science and technology that apply to its product lines. The research is expected to turn up new knowledge, but in performing the work the ancillary, pure research fallout is incidental. To go beyond this, that is, to pay for broad research without regard to the missions of the corporation may be justified largely as philanthropy, sensible only up to a point. A large and profitable corporation equipped with unusual capacity for research should engage perhaps in some research beyond its highest priority needs and give the results out freely to everyone interested. However, this is akin to making money contributions to universities whose research and educational activities similarly will benefit the entire society. Most well managed corporations recognize an obligation to provide such eleemosynary contributions. However, if a corporation decides it should spend, say, a million dollars a year for such philanthropy to advance the base of science and technology for the general interest of all, then it generally is wiser for it to contribute that million directly to the universities. Pure research projects divorced from applications could be performed in an infinite number of fields. There is no reason to believe that the best selection of such efforts will be done by a corporation whose main mission in life is to be successful in certain, rather distinct product areas.

In judging the value to technological corporations of their sponsoring pure research (with the idea that it will eventually create new applications and therefore be valuable to its shareholders, even though the results will be available to all and not be the exclusive tools of the corporation), it is well to note that technological corporations have limited available discretionary funds for such efforts. It is not that there is little value in carrying on the purest of research and that philanthropy should be regarded as negative. It is rather that the corporation must put priorities on where its funds are spent. Thus, the purest of research is largely government sponsored and mainly the job of universities.

Suppose a corporation has a lion's share of the market in its field, say 75 percent of the sales volume. Its competitors split the other 25 percent. Then it can justify supporting broad, exploratory research in its product area through grants to universities, even though the results are made available to everyone, including its competitors. The whole field presumably will be broadened by this research and competitors will be riding free; that is, they will get the results of the research without having spent any money to perform it. However, if the research data lead to advanced technology, new applications, or cost reductions, the market leader will get three times as much benefit as his competitors combined. The ratio of three to one in market share will likely apply also to the market or profit increment stemming from the research. Putting aside such exceptional market dominance, the situation in a technological corporation is normally that the R & D is focused, as carefully chosen as the selection of a product area, and is carried on with the clear intent to improve the chances of success of the corporation in its area.

R & D and Innovation

Research and development has paid off heavily for the society in creating new products and new jobs, increasing productivity and economic growth and improving the quality of life. Many, in fact, think that almost any problem can be licked through R & D. Furthermore, it is believed widely that the secret of success in all pursuits is to innovate and thus arrive at better ideas and superior ways to attack and handle every need. Of course, a lot of evidence supports this view, but the generalization is an exaggeration. R & D is an essential function within every technological corporation, but its presence does not guarantee success or even innovation. The relationship among R & D activity, innovation and corporate success is hardly a simple and obvious one. R & D is essential for many purposes, including adding to the available stock of the company's innovative ideas, background data and understanding fundamental to further innovation. R & D ordinarily will provide a basis for incremental improvements in the company's existing product endeavors, distinct from originating new product ideas, but even here it is difficult to generalize, because some product areas will exhibit a declining return from R & D expenditures. And for R & D intended to provide radical innovations, it is necessary that such innovations be well-timed and have a strong practical fit with the society's requirements. On the whole, matching the R & D effort to the company's specific opportunities and needs is a difficult and complex management task.

Even where it is clear that the objective of the R & D efforts of the company is to provide technological innovation along certain well established directions, that innovation cannot be taken for granted merely because the company employs well educated, experienced scientists and engineers. Universities do not train their graduates directly to be inventors. Research directors in industry cannot command their technical staffs to be creative and inventive. However, it is both necessary and possible to provide an environment that encourages innovation, and that is what the management of a technological corporation should seek to arrange for its R & D teams.

For one thing, some funds must be readily available for at least initial explorations of an idea by the idea's originator and appropriate expertise for the critical facets of such explorations should be assigned, if only for a small effort. Preliminary market research competence should be available to accompany the early R & D explorations. This is partially to find the evidence quickly, if it exists, that the idea is a poor one from a market standpoint and to halt further effort. More especially, however, it is because a small amount of market information considered early may focus, guide or alter the embryonic idea so that it has a better chance of success. The management should arrange that reward, both recognition and financial remuneration, is associated with successful innovative effort. Of course, useful innovative results are not always synonymous with brand new, basic ideas. Invention and originality can be required for the development and introduction of mere refinements and improvements in existing products and methods. Here, a corporation can establish the practice of capable cost-performance-sales tradeoffs carried out promptly and efficiently. Saving funds leads to added profits, and improved earnings should provide direct heightened return for the originators as incentives for continued outstanding performance.

Not all innovations in complex technology come from large technological corporations with their array of experts and large, well equipped research facilities. For instance, the key ideas for the following fields came from individuals who were not employed in large organizations: atomic energy, advanced electric batteries, computers, cellophane, color photography, the cyclotron, DDT, FM radio, foam rubber, inertial guidance, insulin, lasers, the Polaroid camera, radar, rockets, streptomycin, the vacuum tube, Xerography, and the zipper.

Of course, large corporations lead in reducing innovation to its final, practical mass-produced form. Between the original idea and its full utilization by society, numerous innovative experts in large corporations are often involved. Also, for projects of especially large size, a proportionately large organization is needed for integration of the efforts of the multidisciplinary teams attacking the problem as a system. Such a systems program has vast opportunities for innovative effort during every step, but the fact that so much complexity and interaction exists means conspicuous single inventions do not stand out. Rather, innovation is very much a team effort and often a very large team at that. Thus, a rocket to the moon, an ICBM system, a nuclear breeder reactor or a facility to generate electricity from ocean-thermal effects would each depend on thousands of inventions and other innovative R & D effort all brought together in a harmonious, coordinated ensemble.

A technological corporation's R & D program must be balanced between needed profitable improvements in existing products and other short-term projects, on one hand, and long-term or strategic efforts on the other. The latter may have the objective of innovation to provide radically new products to end-run existing approaches and give the company a strong advantage over competitors. This strategic effort may also exist to explore pertinent technology to broaden the base of technology available for the other short-term innovation, as well as new product possibilities. Generally, it is well to arrange a deliberate separation of these two kinds of R & D programs, because the results obtained need to be rated so differently and the mechanism of use of results and the organizational control are both different. Usually, a short-term project has clearer and more readily quantifiable objectives—for instance, to cut costs by 10 percent while retaining the performance or to find ways around critical materials in short supply or to introduce a feature needed to be competitive without violating a competitor's patent.

In many corporations, the technique of control from top management is such that the entire R & D budget may be assigned to short-term projects, or at least readily identifiable and thoroughly describable ones, particularly those with a high probability of reaching the hoped for accomplishment in time and expenditures. This tendency must be noticed and resisted when it occurs. The long-term activity may go on for years without clear cut benefits. Indeed, the results may always turn out to be indirect, mainly serving to lay a foundation for superior innovation on the shorter term projects.

Managers of R & D in United States corporations have been reporting in recent years a heavy shift in emphasis to short-term programs aimed primarily at safe incremental changes and to provide compliance with the new government regulations about environment and safety. As we stated earlier, basic research has been virtually disappearing from private United States industry. In the decade of the middle 1960s to the middle 1970s, real dollar funding for R & D by United States industry fell by about 20 percent and federal support for basic research in industry dropped by over 75 percent. However, we should note that, in one field alone, namely solid state physics, four Nobel prizes have been awarded in the past to industrial scientists. It is also to be noted that the United States is dominant in solid state technology with the transistor, the large scale integrated circuit (LSI) and many other dimensions of the multi-bllion dollar semiconductor industry attesting to the value of the recommendation that basic research should not be dropped in its entirety by private industry.

Not all R & D effort can be thought of as focused on attempts to be innovative, either to create entirely new products or to improve existing ones. The R & D effort is needed also as a defensive measure, to assess new technology as it is announced on the outside or possibly as it appears imminent or as it is developed internally. This assessment is necessary to determine what effect the new technology might have on the existing products of the corporation. What does the new innovative technology make possible in performance and costs of systems that use the company's products? Might entire systems, of which the company's products are components, be replaced by entirely different and better ones? What are the implications of the use of this advancing technology by competitors? A technological corporation preferably should not be caught by surprise. The selection of new product endeavors and the adjustment of existing ones are difficult enough tasks even when technological change is adequately followed and its innovation implications properly anticipated. A balanced amount of defensive or assessment R & D is accordingly a necessary accompaniment to the R & D that primarily seeks innovative advance.

Frequently, when studies are made by a technological corporation of failures in its innovative effort basic to a new product, that failure can be traced to an inadequacy in the R & D program. Other conditions may be even more important in many instances in causing failure, but when the R & D effort is found later to have been insufficient, it is quite often because the technological difficulties were underestimated. Sometimes so long a time and so many dollars are seen later to have been necessary to eliminate the remaining unforeseen obstacles that the original market analysis proved no longer applicable, the time of entry became too late, and the costs became too high. Also, in competitive industrial innovation, it has not been uncommon in the history of each technological corporation that a competitor's technical approach was superior and was not soon enough recognized as being such by the R & D organization that pressed forward with its own approaches.

Concern about competitive innovation is not a factor alone among technological corporations of any one nation. Recently, in the United States a great deal of concern has been expressed regarding the failure of the United States to build its R & D activities rapidly enough to retain leads over other nations. Total funding for R & D by industry, government and universities has dropped in the United States as a percentage of the GNP from around 3 percent in the middle 1960s to just over 2 percent in the late 1970s. A National Science Foundation study suggests that the ratio may decline further during the 1980s. After adjusting for inflation, the real dollars being spent for R & D in the United States have been declining. Meanwhile, Japan, Germany and the USSR are devoting an increasing proportion of their GNPs to R & D. Of course, the pace of innovation is not determined alone by the R & D budget. Innovation is affected also by the state of the economy, the profitability of investment and government policy about patents, taxes, antitrust and regulation. These nontechnological factors are usually regarded as the real bottleneck to innovation. If the government could operate to halt inflation, more funds would be available for investment in innovation through R & D and other routes. Science and technology are not being used to the fullest to provide beneficial innovation for the society, but the bottleneck is not science and technology per se.

In summary, if a corporation has a strong, well manned R & D effort, it is not a guarantee of successful innovation. There are so many other factors that enter the equation. However, a strong R & D effort is essential for a sound technological corporation, one with continuing successful performance.

Relation of R & D to Other Company Functions

Research and development work in a technological corporation has to be closely related to marketing, product design, and manufacturing. As to marketing, the R & D effort must include continually surveying what is new in science and technology, particularly outside the corporation. No matter how large a corporation is, more will be happening in the much larger collection of other corporations, universities, governmental laboratories and various nonprofit institutions than within that one corporation. It is also necessary to audit what is new, proprietary, patentable and patented in the science and technology developed internally. These advances in science and technology must then be coordinated with the marketing research effort of the corporation to seek the unusual matches, those weddings of technological potentials to market needs in which the corporation can have a lead over competitors and be in an especially strong position to supply the market with a cost-effective product meeting the return on investment standards of the corporation.

The teaming effort of R & D with market research to establish the potential of further R & D in its application to the product must be both analytical and creative. To perform it effectively may require a good deal of laboratory experimenting and the creation of prototypes, embryonic physical embodiments of the new ideas used to test performance or obtain design data.

The tie of R & D with product engineering is twofold: R & D sometimes gives rise to product engineering and R & D always must support it. To begin with, the necessary knowledge needed for the design of the product may be lacking in some key aspects. Whether the task under consideration is a completely new product or just an improvement in an existing one, some unknowns will exist in the scientific and technological underpinnings. The R & D support will include tracking down the necessary data. Some research should be devoted to ferreting out the state of the art advances made outside the company and not readily available to it. Sometimes the additional R & D will extend the art and give rise to patentable, proprietary advances. The corporation may elect to use these developments exclusively to get an edge on competitors and accomplish a market success that could not have been attained without the R & D effort.

The third area of close relationship of R & D to the other vital functions of the corporation is with manufacturing. The R & D may have made possible a new product which could not have been designed or perhaps even conceived without the R & D. Or the R & D effort may affect the way an existing product is designed, giving rise to improvements either in performance or in the ease and cost of manufacture. In any case, once the product is headed for manufacturing, one might at first assume the R & D phase is finished. But if it is a new product of considerable complexity, which happens often in technological endeavors, or if the modifications that R & D has brought to bear on existing products involve a wide departure, then the later step of manufacturing of the product may be in difficulty unless the R & D talent remain interested, involved and available. The product may have to be debugged; the manufacturing process may need to be altered; compromises among performance, reliability, life, cost, size, weight and appearance may have to be considered. For the manufacturing effort to be successful a need may exist for digging back into the fundamental new science and technology that is being applied for the first time. In a technological corporation, the R & D effort cannot be too far removed from manufacturing, just as it must stay close to marketing and product design.

R & D in technological corporations is most often identified closely with the product, that is, its design and performance, and rather distantly with the manufacturing process. This is unfortunate. Usually the R & D effort is inadequate for the materials and techniques of manufacture and assembly. Whether the manufacturing involves the processing of materials or use of both mechanical and informational automation, a border exists between the recognized and commonly used art and the wide world of potential improvements. We need more often to cross that border. Numerous unknowns and possible breakthroughs await investigation and discovery about materials, production processes, concepts of assembly and test, control of information flow, and optimization of the entire manufacturing system from scheduling the incoming materials and labor operations to the delivery of the finished product. These problems require for their handling a degree of analytical talent and imagination totally comparable with the envisaging of a new product or system. Thus, obtaining a good yield in semiconductor manufacture, or in precision casting or forging of exotic metals, to cite two examples, requires deep knowledge of the physics of the solid state. This is hardly different from the degree of scientific and engineering sophistication required to make decisions in the R & D process about the use of specific semiconductor configurations or metals having particular internal molecular make-ups.

The Technological Evaluation of New Ideas

Let us return now to the direct relationship R & D has to the design of the product. In many technological corporations it is not easy, and very often not desirable, to attempt separation of the R & D activities from product design. Both functions may be in one organizational unit or in a project organized as one unit to handle a specific product line.

The unit may include fundamental science experts in various disciplines who provide advances and know-how to support product design activities, while engineering specialists are engaged in performing and integrating the design of the product. Most often the closest relationship is needed between those who are providing basic knowledge and conceptions and those who are trying to apply them in detail to achieve specific performance and physical characteristics of the product.

In the previous chapter, we emphasized the product selection process from the standpoint of potential return on investment. Within the R & D and engineering organization of the corporation there also needs to exist a deliberate evaluation process that provides for technical soundness. Many product ideas will be technically sound in some ways, and unsound in others. The part that is sound may dominate, because it may be the focus of attention. It may involve the new, the answer to a market need as a result of the perceived, inherent performance the product is capable of. The unsound aspects may be discovered too late if not sought out diligently. An electrical product, for example, may perform perfectly electrically but be weak mechanically or have problems dissipating the heat generated. A complex system may work well but not if the human components behave differently from the prescribed instructions. Equipment may not perform in the extremes of the environmental conditions under which it must survive. The performance requirements may be met when various components are tested separately, but not when all are combined.

Many other elements of unsoundness may surface. The technology fundamentally may not lend itself to design for appropriate costs, or pricing, or reliability, or practical maintenance in service. Perhaps too great a dependence may exist on critical items to come from others. Perhaps the early samples of such critical, externally developed components may not provide proper indication of how those components will perform when they come off a large scale production line. The list is not endless, but for every product, possibilities of unsoundness abound.

In design of a product, technological risk must be considered as a factor in deciding whether it is going to prove sound. With a innovative product it is not easy initially to put down all of the specifications to describe a practical success. Some product requirements will not be discovered until the product is in the customer's hands. If the product extends the art in a big jump, then it is more likely that unknowns exist concerning how the product will really work out. Problems that were initially unforeseen probably will surface later and not all of them will have a practical solution. Perhaps the product will work fine with PhDs available to keep it in adjustment, but will be too complex for the customer. Whatever the reasons, the risk of technical problems is greater with great advances, and when the degree of departure from established product areas is greater.

Cost of the product is, in many respects, a technical evaluation item. The cost of the product must be in the thinking of the R & D and the product design teams from the very beginning, and should never go away. It is not satisfactory in a technological corporation for the product engineers to believe that a product may be sound, though it might be too expensive to manufacture, arguing that the cost problem is for the manufacturing department to solve. They should think rather that it is sound only in some technical ways. Unless the engineers have a solution to the cost problem, the design is not yet complete. They have not yet really established overall technical feasibility. They must ask themselves whether there exist different ways of doing the same thing that will ease the problems of manufacture. It may take more inventing, analysis, and experiments to come up with the basic facts, more negotiating with marketing to understand the tradeoffs of performance requirements against the sales potential, more cooperation with manufacturing to create lower cost approaches.

Technological evaluation requires a combination of the services of the inventor and the analyst, the creative type and the practical one, the determined optimist and the skeptical pessimist. Technical evaluation is partly relative. With what does the product compete? What is the whole system of which it is a part? How does the product interface with other components? Is it understood what the system and the product do for the customer in a technical sense, quite aside from economic and competitive aspects?

If the product is highly technical, the design should not be considered sound unless appropriate application engineering has been carried out with the customer. The design is not right unless it does the job for the customer that he expects it to do. It is not a practical design if useful life, reliability and ease of maintenance are not satisfactory. Accordingly, technological evaluation and the product design effort are neither complete until the interface investigation with the customer has been dealt with.

Risks in Technological Product Engineering

Any corporation putting out any kind of new product incurs risks, and the assessment of risk is often difficult. Experience may be needed before facts are available to enable risk assessment. But with complex, high technology products the risk can be very high. Risk can come from inadequate matching of product to need, premature technological obsolescence of the product, technological breakthroughs by competitors, advances elsewhere in the system of which the product is only a part, and changes in market demand. These are sample dangers of the environment in which product engineering takes place. Risks are attached to this environment.

Risks can be minimized by the company's engineers being more ingenious than the competitor's, being ahead with advanced concepts, and, almost conversely, by concentrating on making overlooked improvements in old products. Similarly, risk can be minimized about wrong timing in an era of rapid technological change by causing R & D to be very close to marketing and having good intelligence about competitors and the customers' needs. Risk can be cut down by deliberately having a policy of designing products and choosing product lines with flexibility for change.

Technological products usually are dependent in part on components from outside suppliers. The risk of failure in a product line can be reduced by being sure there are always two sources for everything bought from the outside.

Another risk is that of underestimating all the costs of bringing a technological product into being. The risk that costs may escalate as the product is taken safely through debugging, production and adequate application engineering can be reduced by great emphasis on limiting the corporation's endeavors to products where it is believed large margins can be realized between the sales price and the overall cost of producing the product. The rule would be simply to stay away from products that appear marginal.

But these things are easier said than done. A well run, large, diversified multi-national corporation has advantages in minimizing risks. It can afford large R & D, engineering and manufacturing staffs with many specialists and interdisciplinary experts, and has broad visibility of technological and market changes. Such a company can be close to government, academia and the professional societies. It is true that some of the great technological breakthroughs and the most profitable inventions are regularly accomplished by single inventors or small teams working in small corporations. However, the chances of minimizing risks on a continuing basis are better for a stronger, broader, larger technological corporation than for the small, narrow one—assuming the same general level of competence for management, technology and the other aspects of a functioning organization. This is because the factors that stand in the way of success are so many and so diverse.

The biggest risk in technological product developments, as experience has shown again and again, is that of simply underestimating the funds and time required for success. The more complex the product, the more advanced it is in its application of new science and technology, the more likely it is that cost and time estimates will be difficult to make and will turn out approximately wrong. The old axiom in engineering "if something can go wrong it will" is more a real life commentary than a facetious remark. Over a period of time, with many new product developments, occasional bad estimates will not do a corporation in. But this assumes it is strong and adequately diversified, not only about variation of product lines but also in the spread of products from the mature, bedded down and nonrisky to the new groundbreakers. The way to minimize the risk of a corporation's becoming financially in over its head in a technological development is to be mindful of this possibility.. The principle is to be sure to have ample financial reserves or else not start the development at all and regard the product instead as unsuitable for that corporation.

A final risk in product development for technological corporations can result from excessive pride and isolation by the scientists and engineers at work on R & D and product design. In many technological groups a powerful N.I.H. (Not Invented Here) factor is at play. The team may fall in love with its own ideas, its own techniques of design and manufacture, and ignore the superior parallel developments of others. Eventually such characteristics will exact their penalties in the failure of products. To cut this kind of risk, management must institute a process that forces adequate challenges and reviews of its internal R & D and engineering operations.

The managers of R & D and product design should arrange for outside evaluation on occasion. If they do not, the general managers above them should. They must look for indicators in the technological fields that dominate the products. What is going on in the professional societies related to the company's products? Who gives the leading papers in professional meetings describing advances of the art, the company's engineers or those of its competitors? Who is filing the patents, the corporation or outsiders, in the areas that relate to the company's products? Are the company's key scientists and engineers being sought out by competitors who try to persuade them to change jobs? How long since the corporation lost a good researcher or product engineer to a competitor? If the manager has no recollection of such a transfer ever taking place, then maybe the company does not have the best scientists and engineers (or perhaps it is paying far too much compared with what the competition believes these experts are worth).

One of the dilemmas about risks is that for advanced technology products the time span can be many years from conception and the initial market research that suggests a market for the basic idea to the full blossoming of profitable products delivered to happy customers. It is not only that the corporation has to be patient so long to get its financial return; equally important is that technology may advance either for the product, meaning it can be replaced or its work done in some better way by a competitive approach, or for the system of doing things into which the product goes. Thus, risk in carrying out high technology product development is lower for products with shorter development times.

Technically Trained People

Scientists and engineers are no different from other people, in some respects. They do a better job and are happier, if the environment is stimulating and motivating. Everything else being equal, they prefer generous compensation and favor fair treatment, reasonable security, and opportunities for career growth. But the culture of scientists and engineers makes technical accomplishments and the recognition by peers for those accomplishments exceptionally important. Scientists and engineers have high professional pride. The pride in accomplishment and in stature with peers creates a tendency in science and engineering personnel toward perfectionism and independence. The latter characteristic, a desired quality in many respects, tends to bring with it a preference for attacking each task in an individual, personal way, starting from scratch rather than making use of the results of others.

The scientists and engineers of a technological corporation, for the most satisfying individual careers and effective productivity at their work, must somehow find it possible to combine individual and team efforts. They need to be understood and recognized in both kinds of efforts. Good managers of R & D and product engineering will find ways to break the anonymity screen that can cover individual efforts in a large corporation and encourage independent, innovative thinking while still organizing effective teamwork. The technical professionals whose efforts are behind the success of R & D and product engineering must cover a wide range of skills. The specialties and contrasting talents should overlap and supplement each other. For the team to create a harmonious assembly of ideas, analyses, concepts, and follow throughs, theory and experiment must be mixed and balanced. The same must be true of combining the synthesist and the analyst, the inventor and the highly disciplined evaluator. There is room and need for them all. The trick is to get them to work together.

Inevitably, a substantial fraction of the research and engineering staffs of a technological corporation will be specialists. Specialists can frequently underrate the importance of issues that lie beyond their fields of endeavor, and some specialists do not communicate well with others outside of their specialties (including management) even when describing their own efforts.

As a product progresses through its various phases, from initial market research, raw technological ideas and product conception to product design, production, application engineering, and customer service, the kind of technical specialist assigned to each step will change. Some aspects need to emphasize creativity and originality; others, efficiency and cost consciousness. Some parts of the required effort may profit from informality to stimulate innovation while others will demand rather precise control and adherence to rigid plans. At the same time, there must be overlap, follow-through and communication or the product cannot move successfully through its various phases. As the product matures, emphasis on conception will shift to debugging and refining, of the product itself, the way it is manufactured, and the manner in which it is applied. But how the product works, is made and is used should never be too far from the minds of all the specialists. This is what they have in common.

Effective results in R & D and product engineering require respect for the necessary administrative procedures even as an atmosphere of free thought, uninhibited ingenuity, and courage to challenge company approaches are also fostered. As to administrative controls, the budgetary ones are often annoying to some technical people, but obviously necessary. Also, there must be neatness and completeness in records. Good communications include the engineering and scientific descriptions of what is being learned and done so that others will be able to incorporate those results in the parallel and later steps of overall tasks.

A large technological corporation will have a substantial number of scientists and engineers with a need to keep up and improve themselves in their specialty fields. There must be allowances for participation in professional societies and in continuing higher education. In fact, a well run technological medium or large corporation will probably have its own internal colloquia and educational programs and will subsidize added formal education for its employees in nearby universities.

Preoccupation with executive status and perks (perquisites) in a corporation is a disease which also can infect high grade technical experts. Many employees in a corporation will measure their success by how rapidly they are moving up to positions of higher executive responsibility and some of the scientists and engineers will pick up and be influenced by this pattern. Those engaged primarily in marketing, manufacturing, accounting, labor relations, and so forth, can advance to executive ranks without such a radical a change in their professional work content as is true, say, of a physicist who shifts from the laboratory to the executive suite. A scientist who is directing the efforts of a large corporate unit is no longer a scientist. Some scientists and engineers happen to have the particular attributes essential to being an excellent manager and the ability to encompass a broader range of disciplines, experiences and challenges than the specific technical specialty in which they were originally trained and worked. However, if does not follow that an outstanding scientist or engineer can be an outstanding supervisor of scientists and engineers, not to mention a general manager over a variety of functions. Even if he has what it takes, he may find a few years later that he will regret having left his first love for an entirely different kind of life's work.

It is obvious that an outstanding individual salesman is not necessarily a good supervisor of other salesmen and an expert accountant is not necessarily suited to managing an accounting department. But if in these two categories the ability is there and the change is made, it appears natural and hardly a change of profession. With the scientist and engineer the shift to management tends to be profound, and hence, before the shift is made, a more careful consideration of this factor by top management is needed than with most other professionals in the corporation.

Patents

If this book had been written decades ago, it might have been justified in saying that the R & D and product engineering effort of a technological corporation goes hand in hand with a conscientious, thorough and zealous policy to file for a patent on nearly every conceivably new and patentable aspect of the science and engineering work covered. At that time, experience and promise suggested that with a patent position a company could hope to dominate a field of endeavor, keep others out or extract high royalties from those who used the patent, and have a highly advantageous profit position. Today, one would have to qualify greatly such a summary.

The general value of patents is changing, in the down direction. The complexity of the patent process, the huge scale of patent operations and the vast library of patented art have produced devaluation in the worth of a patent. But what has really hurt the value of a patent to a corporation as a practical asset is the mood of the United States government. By trying to ensure that no improper monopolies exist, the government finds it difficult to view strong patent positions with favor. To stop someone else from using your patent requires that you have a strong case. This means ample and positive evidence of infringement. It sometimes takes years and substantial funds to investigate, bring to trial and enforce a patent, even if the patent is clearly sound in the first place.

When you are issued a patent, it does not mean that you have control over the area. First of all it is not clear that your idea even deserved the patent you have obtained. You may not have been first, your idea may not be new, the claims you have been allowed may not be justified, or they may need revision. For the minor portions of your claims, others will find alternatives and for your major claims others may challenge you. Patent ownership, or the value of a patent which a corporation may own, sometimes is decided only after long and expensive court trials or the settlement by the government of interfering claims to a given patentable idea before a patent is issued. The way the government operates the patent system, resolution of an interference between conflicting claims of two would-be patentees may go on for ten or even twenty years. Thus, an inventor finally may receive a patent in the end that is then worthless. Conversely, the patent may be so dominant that it will control a field of endeavor in which he has not even been involved for a decade or two and where the entire succeeding development may have been in the hands of others.

Because of the overlapping of a large number of patents relating to specific product lines, many corporations, knowingly or unknowingly, are in violation of the patent rights of others. Sorting it all out is a very difficult process requiring large staffs and detailed effort legally and technologically. Most often corporations will negotiate among themselves to arrive a what they regard as fair deals in exchange of patent rights, each corporation interested in minimizing court costs and delays.

In addition, as already hinted, there is confusion today between the whole concept of monopoly which a patent grants the owner of it and the antimonopoly laws of the nation. The government is unclear on this issue. The net result often is that a corporation that owns a patent is for all practical purposes better advised to allow others to manufacture under that patent, with only a small royalty payment in return for granting this privilege, in order to avoid difficulties with another part of the government over violations of antitrust laws. Although the owner of the patent is thus able to receive some royalty revenue in addition to what he generates by manufacturing and marketing under the patent, he cannot be assured of dominating the market. Indeed he may have competitors who succeed in paying him only a modest royalty and hog the market because of their other strengths (say, in marketing and manufacturing) so that he cannot operate profitably even with his own patent.

Most importantly, almost any substantial technological effort will involve many, many patents, not merely one. Something about a corporation's new product may indeed be new, but more of it may be old. The corporation may simply have made an improvement on technology covered by patents of others. The improvement may be such that it greatly changes the cost-effectiveness of the product and its market acceptance in the near term. It may behoove the original owner of the patent—that remains basic to the product, although partially outdated by the improvement patents—to offer a deal so that the corporation with the patented improvement is able to produce the product and the owner of the earlier, and still binding, patent is also able to do so.

To hold patents is to possess assets, but the returns on the investments needed to acquire the patents may not be good. From the beginning of the idea, the keeping of records of conception and the reduction to practice, through to the filing of the patent and then perhaps defending it, funds are constantly being invested. All this is to obtain a legal paper that it is hoped will represent a considerable benefit to the corporation but may turn out to be of little value. High selectivity is needed to decide which patents to go after. It will hardly pay to file patents on every minor improvement on a minor product. Conversely, it will be rather important to file broad claims, and even narrow ones, on a product line that is of maximum importance, where the company enjoys a strong market and profit position. Amplification and leverage are involved. The cost of obtaining a patent may not be great when compared with the overall investment in that product and the profit stream expected.

It is important to use the patent system, for whatever it is worth, to try to keep competitors from disturbing a favorable market position.

Minor patents can be bypassed by the market leader. He can often expend some R & D funds to find an alternative around the patent, which then could become almost worthless to the market lagger.

A corporation whose products do not lead the field may have to look at the patent situation in an entirely different light. The corporation that is well behind in market position had better have a policy of filing patents only on major new claims.

As we discussed earlier, the United States government R & D expenditures with private industry are of the same order as the industry's own funding of R & D. Thus, it is important what the policy of the government is for the situation where the government pays for R & D that results in a patent. Most often, the government takes the rights to the patent and makes it available to everyone, usually at no charge. The rationale is that since the government funded the invention, it cannot give the commercial rights to one company, even the one that created the patentable idea.

However, a patent available to everyone is no more than a piece of paper. Without the protection the patent provides, investors are reluctant to put money behind exploiting an invention, and the government owned patents are usually neglected. The result has been that government sponsored R & D results in less applications and benefits than if some scheme of motivation for further investment were provided through a different procedure. The government might take a free license for its own use, as one example, but assign all other rights to the inventor or the company that employs the inventor. Through a 50 percent tax, the government gets half of any profits that any inventor would make from the invention anyway.

Granted all of the foregoing commentary, a technological corporation, nevertheless, must maintain an active patent activity. It must do it for defensive reasons, if for no other. It constantly must be looking at the patent situation in its field. It must gather strength for its patent position to be able to negotiate with others. Then it will be able to pay out the least as it trades patents and arranges for licenses to use the patents of others, and it will be in a position to make counterthreats when it is threatened because of a claimed strong patent position by a competitor.

The function of research and development for some technological corporations could be described simply by saying that it is to give the corporation a proprietary position. Technology that is radically new, advantageous, and readily protectable by patents constitutes an example of a proprietary lead. But this is not the only kind of such lead. An unusual combination of information and skilled people who know how to use it, whether the data contain patentable ideas or not, can constitute a strong proprietary advantage for a corporation. Again, these highly technological factors are not the only basis for a proprietary position for a company. Nontechnological factors can sometimes be more important in a corporation's having a lead position. Thus, sometimes to have a superior marketing organization and a stronger image for quality, cost effectiveness and service in the minds of the customer, may be more advantageous than a technological lead.

R & D Startup Costs in Relation to Total Investments

We had occasion in the previous chapter on the product selection process to point out that the marketing research and R & D startup costs are only the beginning of an overall risk-investment scenario in bringing a new product line into being and that a typical forecast of events usually has to embrace a number of phases. It is useful to project the cash flows in and out throughout these periods in order to assess overall investment fund requirements and returns. It will be timely now to illustrate this process with a group of examples.

In each of four cases, starting with a highly simplified one labeled Scenario A, we will seek to relate the allowable startup costs in the first period to the investment required to launch and maintain the product line and obtain financial benefits in time from it. The three scenarios will differ in the histories they project of progress of the product line versus time, that is, the buildup of volume and cash flows. After we have set down the basic assumptions and consequences for each example, we shall attempt some additional conclusions on the product selection and the role of R & D in that process.

Scenario A

This example will comprise only two periods. The first, we shall imagine, lasts only one year. E_0 is expended during the first year on R & D, product design, market research, and manufacturing startup expenses. (Assume E_0 is an after-tax figure because the corporation has total earnings against which the before-tax loss, $2E_0$, is taken, for a net of E_0.) Starting with the second year, and continuing for a total of 10 years, steady annual earnings result. At the end of 10 years the activity is halted. Assets, A, to provide facilities and working capital are invested at the beginning of the second year and remain constant throughout. The constant annual after-tax earnings are $E_1 = R_A A$. The depreciation expense is exactly equal to the capital investment budget each year. This is the amount of funds required annually to keep the facility in fit condition. Thus E_1 is also the annual cash flow back to the corporate coffers from this activity.

The cash the corporation will have put into this development, discounted for present value at the very beginning of the first year at the hurdle rate of the corporation for investments, R_1, is

$$\text{CASH IN} = E_0 + A/(1 + R_I) = E_0 + Ax \qquad [1]$$

where

$$x = 1/(1 + R_I)$$

We assume that the full amount, E_0, is made available at the beginning of the first year and, even though it is spent gradually during that year, no interest income will be earned meanwhile on the unspent amount.

Now, we further assume that at the end of the 11th year, when the operation is liquidated, the assets then employed (still A) are returned to the corporation as cash for use elsewhere, the facility, inventory and other nonliquid assets being sold off at book value. Then the cash flow from the activity is

$$\text{CASH OUT} = E_1 \sum_{n=2}^{n=11} 1/(1 + R_I)^n + A/(1 + R_I)^{11}$$

which can be rewritten as

$$\text{CASH OUT} = E_1 \sum_{n=2}^{n=11} x^n + Ax^{11} \qquad [2]$$

Recall

$$\sum_{n=1}^{n=n} x^n = n \frac{1 - x^n}{1 - x}$$

Hence

$$\sum_{n=2}^{n=n} x^n = x \frac{1 - x^n}{1 - x} - x = \frac{x^2 - x^{n+1}}{1 - x} \qquad [3]$$

which, when substituted into Equation 2 yields

$$\text{CASH OUT} = E_1 \frac{x^2 - x^{12}}{1 - x} + Ax^{11} \qquad [4]$$

Setting the discounted CASH IN equal to CASH OUT to make the net present value zero at discount rate R_I, we have

$$E_0 + Ax = E_1 \frac{x^2 - x^{12}}{1 - x} + Ax^{11}$$

which, using $E_1 = R_A A$, leads to

$$E_0/A = x^{11} - x + R_A(x^2 - x^{12})/(1 - x)$$

or

$$E_0/A = R_A x^2(1 - x^{10})/(1 - x) - x(1 - x^{10})$$
$$= x(1 - x^{10})[R_A x/(1 - x) - 1] \qquad [5]$$

But

$$x/(1 - x) = 1/(1/x - 1) = 1/(1 + R_I - 1) = 1/R_I \qquad [6]$$

So

$$E_0/A = x(1 - x^{10})(R_A/R_I - 1) \qquad [7]$$

This tells us, as we might expect, that if the cash flow is to be able to fund any start up at all then

$$R_A/R_I > 1 \qquad [8]$$

Let us take a specific example: $R_I = .15$ and $R_A = .20$. As a fraction of A, how much can we spend on start-up in the first year, that is, how large can E_0 be, for the scenario assumed and have the project still pass the hurdle for internal rate of return?

$$x = 1/1.15 = .8696$$

from which the calculator applied to Equation 7 tells us

$$E_0/A = .2184$$

The startup cost must not exceed about 22 percent of A to produce an R_I of 15 percent with an R_A of 20 percent. If E_0 were to exceed 22 percent of A we would need an even higher R_A than 20 percent. As it is, R_A must substantially exceed R_I for the project's return to meet the R_I hurdle, not surprisingly since there is an important initial loss year whose results must be compensated for by later flows (and, moreover, when the A we put in comes back to us whole, it is an eleven-year discounted shadow of its original self).

Scenario B

Let us alter the previous story in only one respect. We assume the product line does not get shut down and the assets liquidated at the end of the 11th year. Instead, we imagine the assets hold constant as do annual earnings, E_1, and the cash flow to the corporation, also E_1 as before, all three doing this forever. The cash put in, discounted at rate R_I is again given by Equation 1. The discounted cash out viewed at the beginning of the second year, the first profitable one, is the then present value, call it P_{r1}, of the constant stream of annual payments of E_1 cash each, or

$$P_{V1} = E_1/R_I \qquad [9]$$

When this is discounted to the beginning of year one, the result is

$$\text{CASH OUT} = xE_1/R_I \qquad [10]$$

We now equate cash out to cash in to obtain

$$E_0 + Ax = R_A Ax/R_I$$

or

$$E_0/A = xR_A/R_I - x = x(R_A/R_I - 1) \qquad [11]$$

Again assume $R_I = .15$ and $R_A = .2$. Then

$$E_0/A = .8696(.2/.15 - 1) = .2899$$

which is an improvement in the allowable startup. Again, as a check, we note from Equation 11 that unless R_A exceeds R_I we have no coverage of (that is, are permitted no) startup costs at all.

Scenario C

Let us depart from the previous scenario by assuming that the cash flows grow at a constant rate g rather than remaining constant. The cash in will still be as given by Equation 1. To obtain the cash out we first again set the earnings for the second year as

$$E_1 = R_A A$$

Then the cash flow for this (second) year, returned to the corporation at year end, will be $R_F R_A A$, where R_F is the fraction of earnings paid out. The scenario will assume that the growing earnings provide for the financing of growth. Thus, again, only A is put in by the corporation (at the beginning of the second year) and R_F is given by

$$g = (1 - R_F)R_A \qquad [12]$$

or

$$R_F = 1 - g/R_A = (R_A - g)/R_A \qquad [13]$$

The present value of the growing flow P_{V1}, as seen at the beginning of the second year, is given by the familiar equation

$$R_I = F/P_{V1} + g \qquad [14]$$

where F is, of course, the flow at the end of this first year of flows, that is, $R_F R_A A$. So that

$$R_I = R_F R_A A/P_{V1} + g$$

or

$$P_{V1} = R_F R_A A/(R_I - g)$$

Using Equation 13 we obtain

$$P_{V1} = A(R_A - g)/(R_I - g) \qquad [15]$$

and, the present value at the beginning of the first year is

$$P_{V0} = xA(R_A - g)/(R_I - g) \qquad [16]$$

Setting CASH IN equal to CASH OUT, we have

$$E_0 + Ax = Ax(R_A - g)/(R_I - g)$$

or

$$E_0/A = x[(R_A - g)/(R_I - g) - 1]$$

or

$$E_0/A = x(R_A - R_I)/(R_I - g) \qquad [17]$$

from which

$$R_A - R_I = E_0(R_I - g)/xA$$

or

$$R_A = R_I + E_0(R_I - g)(1 + R_I)/A \qquad [18]$$

As g approaches R_I, the second term is seen to approach zero. This means that regardless of the start-up cost (measured by E_0/A), the hurdle rate will be attained through the growing, discounted cash flow if only R_A exceeds R_I by a vanishingly small amount. For lesser growth ratios, R_A will have further to exceed R_I. To illustrate, suppose $E_0/A = 1$, $R_I = .15$, and $R_A = .20$. What g is implied? In Equation 17, we have

$$1 = (1/1.15)(.20 - .15)(.15 - g)$$

from which $g = .107$. To attain a g of 12.5 percent and still meet the hurdle rate of $R_I = .15$, we would need an R_A (from Equation 18) of

$$R_A = .15 + .025 \times 1.15 = .18$$

Scenario D

Now let us complicate the scenario, but do it in such a way that the development described is closer to the typical real life pattern. First, let us extend the start-up expense period into two years with $E_0/2$ spent each year. Second, let us follow this by a period of investment to provide for sales buildup, again lasting two years, with $A/2$ invested each year. During this second two years we shall assume no cash flow back to the corporation. There may be some earnings during this period and accompanying cash generation, but all the cash available has to be reinvested to finance the growth. A third period starts at the beginning of the fifth year. It lasts six years, we shall imagine, and generates enough cash each year so that the corporation has to add no more cash, but all cash generated must be reinvested in further growth. The development is thus self-supporting in this third period, but it pays nothing back to the corporation. During this period the assets build up, we shall suppose, from an initial A to $3A$, a compound average growth rate of about 20 percent per year for the six years.

Finally, a fourth and last period starts. This is after a total of 10 years. It is a steady growth period with a constant fraction of the cash generated paid out to the corporation and the rest reinvested to maintain the growth which we shall assume remains steady forever.

Let us now set down these assumptions and the pertinent relationships in quantitative form. It will be easier to start with the last period first, to obtain the present value of the stream of cash flows back to the corporation. The cash flow generated at the beginning of the fourth period will be R_A times the assets then employed, which we have said will be $3A$, plus the depreciation expense. However, we assume that cash equal to depreciation must be spent each year to keep the facilities and equipment in an as-new state of continued efficiency and usefulness. Thus $3R_A A$ is the total *available* cash generated. Of this, a portion must be plowed back to maintain the growth, g, where, from Equation 13,

$$R_F = \frac{R_A - g}{R_A} \qquad [19]$$

Also, because R_F is the ratio of the first cash payment, F_1, to the total available cash, $3R_A A$, we can write

$$F_1 = 3R_A A R_F$$

or

$$F_1 = 3(R_A - g)A \qquad [20]$$

Now, since the present value, P_V, of a growing stream of cash payments, starting wih F_1 at the end of the first year and discounted at rate R_I is given by

$$P_V = F_1/(R_I - g) \qquad [21]$$

then, from Equation 20, we obtain

$$P_V = 3\frac{R_A - g}{R_I - g} A \qquad [22]$$

This, discounted 10 years to obtain the present value at the very beginning of the scenario, becomes

$$P_{V0} = 3x^{10}\frac{R_A - g}{R_I - g} \qquad [23]$$

We are now ready to equate discounted CASH IN to CASH OUT.

$$\text{CASH IN} = E_0(1 + x)/2 + A(x^2 + x^3)/2 \qquad [24]$$

$$\text{CASH OUT} = 3x^{10}\frac{R_A - g}{R_I - g} A \qquad [25]$$

If we are to meet the hurdle rate, R_I, and still cover the startup cost, E_0, (that is, for E_0 to be positive when the two opposing cash flows are equated) then

$$3x^{10}\frac{R_A - g}{R_I - g} > \frac{x^2 + x^3}{2}$$

or

$$\frac{R_A - g}{R_I - g} > \frac{1 + x}{6x^8}$$

which can be written as

$$R_A > g + (R_I - g)(1 + x)/6x^8 \qquad [26]$$

As g approaches R_I, the second term approaches zero and R_A approaches $g = R_I$. Again the growing stream of discounted cash flows will cover the start-up cost if only R_A exceeds R_I as g approaches R_I. This is, of course, an extreme or theoretical limit. Suppose $R_I = .15$, then $x = .8696$ and

$$(1 + x)/6x^8 = .953$$

Then, in Equation 26

$$R_A > .953R_I + (1 - .953)g = .953R_I - .047g$$

It seems we just happened to have picked parameters that lead to the relation that if R_A is about equal to R_I, then at least some E_0 expense can be tolerated. Had we chosen, say, a ratio of two, rather than three, times for assets growth during the third phase, then the second term on the right side of Equation 26 would have been much larger and R_A for the fourth period would have to substantially exceed R_I to provide startup coverage expense. Conversely, had we been more optimistic and assumed the growth in the third phase to be even greater than three times, then the whole project could meet the hurdle rate and also cover some startup costs E_0, and yet the R_A during the fourth period could actually be below the value of R_I.

Let us introduce specific values for R_A and g, namely $R_A = .15$ and $g = .10$, and see how big an E_0 as a fraction of A this assumed scenario could cover. Equating CASH IN to CASH OUT from Equations 24 and 25, and using $R_I = .15$ as in the previous scenarios we have

$$\frac{E_0}{2}(1 + x) + \frac{A}{2}(x^2 + x^3) = 3x^{10}\frac{.15 - .10}{.15 - .10}A$$

or

$$\frac{E_0}{2}(1 + x) = A\left(3x^{10} - \frac{x^2 + x^3}{2}\right)$$

and

$$.4348E_0 = .0350A$$

or

$$E_0 = .0805A \qquad\qquad [27]$$

This is an impractically low value and results from our having been too pessimistic in choosing R_A (or too demanding in the hurdle rate, R_I).

If this scenario is to be a practical one we need to generate cash flows sufficient to neutralize a larger E_0. Let us try $R_A = .20$. Then

$$E_0(1 + x)/2 + A(x^2 + x^3)/2 = 3x^{10}A(.10/.05)$$

and we find that

$$E_0 = 1.79A$$

which is in the ballpark of ratios that more often characterize starting a new product line.

These scenarios are merely illustrative, of course, and an infinite number of them can be invented. However, a few conclusions can be stated with little risk of overgeneralizing. From inception of R & D to mature profit operations and positive and available cash flows, many years may pass. To cover startup costs, which can be high, both the growth rates and the returns on assets employed are powerful parameters. The compounding and thus penalizing effect of necessary discounting of cash flows received late in time is also powerful. Often the newer the product, the greater the time for full development to a profitable position and the greater the startup costs. So, correspondingly, the stronger should be the evidence of high- and long-time growth and high returns on employed assets before the project is launched.

Problems

7–1. The total start-up costs for product engineering, production and marketing usually exceed greatly the R & D costs incurred initially. In view of this and the critical importance of new products to a technological corporation, why are not R & D budgets very much higher? That is, if the R & D expense is a small part of the total, would it not be better to have for selection for production and marketing the best of a larger number of entries as to potential products?

7–2. Choose three technological corporations, study their annual and 10-K reports and list the sizes of their R & D programs as a percent of sales and a percent of earnings before taxes. Where this information

appears to be not adequately available, make some speculative estimates and explain the assumptions you used in making your estimates. Comment on whether the magnitudes you have listed appear
to you adequate and suitable.

7–3. A company's history tends to indicate that for every successful
product that goes from R & D into production and satisfactory profit
performance, two other projects are started but then dropped. Using
this chapter's Scenario A for a typical successful product with R_A =
25 percent during the 10-year profit period, what must have been the
first year's expensed R & D before taxes? Express this as a ratio of the
assets employed during the profit period, if an internal rate of return
of 15 percent was attained? What will happen to the internal rate of
return if this initial R & D expense is tripled to cover two unsuccessful
projects that are halted after the first year and R_A is not increased?

7–4. Using Scenario B, show that

$$R_A = R_I[1 + E_0(1 + R_I)/A]$$

and plot R_A versus R_I for these three values of E_0/A: .5, 1.0, and 2.0.

7–5. In Scenario C, what R_A is needed to yield R_I = .15 if E_0/A = .5
and g = .10?

7–6. Discuss what happens to the relationship between R_A and R_I in
scenario C if g exceeds R_I.

7–7. In Scenario D, assume the estimate for g comes from market
research and for E_0/A from analysis of the R & D and assets required
to launch the new product. Express R_A in terms of these two parameters (g and E_0/A) and a specified hurdle rate R_I. If E_0/A = 1, g =
.12, and R_I = .16, what R_A must be attained?

7–8. In Scenario D, rederive the relation of R_A to specified values of
R_I and g if the growth during the third phase is four to one, rather
than three to one, and a given start-up ratio E_0/A is to be covered. If
R_I = .15 and g = .10, what is the least R_A can be and still cover some
start-up costs?

8

MANUFACTURING; PRODUCTIVITY

Manufacturing as the Corporation's Central Function

For a technological corporation producing hardware products, the actual bringing into being of those products will certainly be thought of by some as the heart of the corporation's activities. In the end it is these manufactured items on which the sales, profit, reputation, and payroll depend. By this way of thinking, everything else done in the corporation, however vital it may be, is supporting to the central manufacturing function. If making the product is the focus of all effort, the design of it and the selling of it after it is made are merely beginnings and ends of the core of the activity, to produce the item. The design process, in this view, would be dominated by the objective of arranging that the product be manufacturable with ease and reasonable, or preferably, lowest cost to beat out competitors. The performance of the product and an adequate life for it free from undue maintenance problems would also be associated with skill in manufacturing.

Some manufacturing entities, of course, will be categorized correctly by all as having a narrow assignment. For instance, a factory might be operated as a second or third source of certain component parts. The designs of the system of manufacturing and of the product itself will have been done elsewhere in the organization. There all of the refining and debugging of the product and the production process also will have been accomplished. All that is expected of this addidional factory is that it make to print—turning out parts precisely as specified, processing metal, incorporating purchased parts, making assemblies, running tests, packaging and sending off the produced articles—

in accordance with carefully laid out detailed plans. Under these circumstances, that particular isolated factory is not involved in manufacturing in the deepest sense. It would not be regarded as the key to the overall success of the corporation.

In this chapter we shall discuss manufacturing with the broadest definition of the function in mind. We shall liberally hold the job of manufacturing up to the level that the most capable and ambitious overall corporate vice president for manufacturing might seek. In part we shall do this because there is a good deal of truth, and only some exaggeration, in this view. Also, we seek to compensate for a common imbalance in the way manufacturing is too often regarded, particularly in a technological corporation. The function is not neglected but is frequently underestimated and undermanned for managerial talent and attention and investment in analysis and innovation. We shall have more to say about this shortly.

To begin with we shall note the very important and yet ambiguous boundary between product engineering and manufacturing, and for that matter, between market research and manufacturing. The technologies of both the product and how it is to be made overlap in this gray area of responsibility. It is possible that a corporation may have such advanced techniques for manufacture of certain classes of products that this alone gives it an edge on competitors. These technological processes for manufacture may thus represent valuable, proprietary assets. The manufacturing know-how of the company in those circumstances can be an important parameter in the selection of products to manufacture and market. If one corporation is ahead of most others, for example, in forging and casting certain rare metals, then its marketing and product engineering organizations should be looking for products to design and sell that have a strong dependence on such techniques. If the factory employs an unusually expert team of technicians in the assembly and test of intricate, miniaturized electronic componentry, then the marketing and product engineering groups of the corporation should be looking for products the world needs that are replete with intricate microminiaturized electronics. It also follows that if the corporation is ahead and in a position to exploit its lead in specific manufacturing processes, and if this is the foundation of the market position of the corporation in its product endeavors, then the corporation's R & D budget should be allocated in part to maintaining and extending this manufacturing technology lead lest competitors catch up and the strong position deteriorate.

It behooves us at this point to repeat what has been said before in connection with the role of product engineering. The product is not engineered unless it is satisfactory from the standpoint of manufacture. Decisions on how to make a product go to the detailed way in which it is designed and to the volume, both of which affect manufacturing cost, which affects selling price, which influences sales. A policy that manufacturing does only what it is told—it makes the product drawn up by the product engineering organization—is generally a bad approach, especially for a technological product. Yet, this is allowed too often in technological corporations. The product engineering groups usurp the company's engineering strength and the manufacturing organization have experts only on tooling, machinery prices, time and motion studies, scrap reduction, labor rates, labor unions, labor grievances, fringe benefits, and raw materials purchasing. It is difficult to justify a marketing effort that does not include working out with manufacturing the relationship of cost to price to sales volume. However, this also has happened in technological corporations.

A product may be envisaged initially between the R&D and marketing groups with manufacturing not initially involved. But when a new product is seriously being considered, or modifications are being planned to extend the market for an existing product, then manufacturing should be brought in immediately as a full partner. For any other approach to be tolerable it would have to be true that the manufacturing department is too weak to participate, and that situation itself should be regarded as intolerable. It will be rare that a manufacturing organization can be rated as competent and yet unable to contribute to how the product should be designed, how many units should be built at a time, and how much each will cost.

Manufacturing as a Combination of Innovative Art and Technological Discipline

It is not usually adequately appreciated that manufacturing involves a broad array of technological facets. The intellectual breadth required for adequate attack on all of the problems of manufacturing, putting aside the even more difficult people problems (motivation, training, labor union relations, environment, safety, job security, organization, communication, assignment of responsibilities, etc.), is as great as that for R & D and product engineering. Unfortunately, in science and engineering educational institutions, and in technological industry itself, the manufacturing function does not always attract the talent required for the highest quality results.

A product is made of pieces. These ultimately come in a variety of raw and finished materials. The manufacturing process is the first firing line of real life hardware experience, where the specified performance characteristics will be built in, if all goes according to plan. Data that tell how the product will be produced can only originate with engineers who understand both the product and the process of making its parts and putting them together, using people and machines. Design modifications will be introduced both into the product design and the manufacturing technique as a product is brought into a mature production phase. Manufacturing improvements are likely to originate during the manufacturing operations, because the opportunity should exist often at that point to perceive improvement possibilities. Such potential benefits will not be worked into the product design and the method by which it is being manufactured, unless people are present in manufacturing who have the ability to make such contributions. They have to combine opportunity, perception, tools and know how. They must be able to integrate experience into intellectual disciplines. They must be full-fledged professional engineers.

Manufacturing engineering seems often to lack glamour. It generally lacks support in its R & D aspects both in industry budgeting and in the government funding that supports basic R & D. Manufacturing, like product design, rests partially on underlying science. For those who excel in creative and analytical techniques, great opportunity exists in a technological manufacturing operation, because it is a vantage point for beneficially influencing product research and development. At the other end, the market for the product is affected and thus the success of the entire corporation. This potential should be exploited. It is not always easy to break down the detailed manufacturing costs, or foresee where the difficult fabrication and assembly and test problems will be. It takes a developed skill to examine the manufacturing process for a product in great detail and find the clues on the basis of which the product design should be altered and the production process improved. Market success may hinge on doing this extremely well.

The tradeoff problems that must be dealt with in the manufacturing operation are many and go well beyond the volume-versus-cost relationship. How far to automate, whether to make or buy certain component parts, how much inventory of raw materials to carry, how far to go in detailed checkout of each step before going on to the next one, how to schedule all of the test operations to balance lower costs with quality control, how extensive a training program, what kind of a pay structure and motivation approach should be used for the employees in the production operations, how deep to make the accounting for clear breakdowns and lower costs—these and many other tradeoffs and optimization opportunities need a combination of innovative and analytical approaches for best results. Modern manufacturing organizations use advanced computer technology to provide constantly updated data bases and to construct computer models to aid in decision making. Nowhere in a technological corporation that is managed well is one likely to find better payoffs in using modern analytical tools and computer-aided operations management.

The manufacturing organization of a high technology corporation has to contend with an extraordinary degree of obsolescence. The product itself defies stabilization as it continues to be altered by technological advance and is ultimately replaced by a still newer technological product. The technique of manufacturing, involving dealing with a complex physical article, is itself dynamic as advances in technology make possible improvements in the manufacturing approach to reduce cost and improve quality. The tools of manufacturing, such as the computer to handle manufacturing information or to control a process, will advance for nontechnological product manufacture as well as for producing high technology products. However, in a high technology corporation, one would expect a greater appreciation of the impact of technological advance on the manufacturing process itself. At the least, it should be assumed that unusual sensitivity and perception will exist on the part of competitors of the potential of technological advance. This makes it incumbent on the manufacturing leadership to be strong in the technological dimension.

Productivity's Many Dimensions

Definitions of Productivity

A principal example of difficult problems to be handled in the manufacturing function is that of designing and operating the activity to make it productive in its use of facilities, equipment and human assets. The commonly used measure of productivity is the amount of goods and services produced per worker in a given time, say, an hour or a year. To arrive at a specific number for the United States for a year, for example, one takes the GNP and divides it by the number of workers. The population and number of workers rise year by year and this growth alone could increase the GNP. If the productivity also rises, the GNP will rise for both reasons, and, on the average, the standard of living should also rise, if real dollars remain constant. GNP could rise because of inflation, but it would not be a real increase.

All quantitative concepts for measurement of productivity in use by economists and others concerned with production involve a ratio of some kind of output to some kind of input. These quantitative measures of productivity are all closely related to the concept of efficiency. Numerous productivity indices are computed, such as the amount of grain grown per acre, the number of automobiles produced per thousand worker hours, or the amount of a given chemical obtained per ton of raw material. For the purposes of our discussion, such definitions of productivity will be inadequate, and we shall often be broadening them. The values of any kind of quantitative measures of productivity hinge on what uses are made of these measures once obtained. There is a big difference between employing productivity indices for judging how the nation as a whole is doing—in economic competitiveness, or in providing for the material needs of the population, or in relation to consumption-investment ratios and the policies of government—on one hand, and the assessment of productivity for an individual firm or, for that matter, for a single individual, on the other. The manager of a corporation is interested in the macroeconomics of productivity, the workings of the nation and the entire international community, but largely because his company and he are parts of the society and are affected by the dynamic changes in the overall economic structure. He is probably somewhat more interested in the microeconomic aspects, the productivity of his own company or an individual plant or division of that company because he is more likely to be able to do something about those productivities.

The usual productivity definitions, and even the GNP definition, tend to be simplistic. For example, we could increase the GNP by taking in our neighbor's laundry, serving each other dinner, cleaning up each other's houses, mowing each other's lawns, and receiving pay from each other for all these services. These dollars would add to the GNP, as it is now reckoned, while not increasing the real production of these same services we now produce for ourselves (without pay). There is no agreement on how to measure productivity. Hence, it is difficult to generalize about whether it is really declining or rising when the increments are small. There is not even agreement that it is good that all productivities, as sometimes measured, should increase.

Some advocate that certain productivities ought to go down, that decrease being an inevitable consequence of the preferred increase in the quality of life. For example, improving the safety of workers and stopping factories from producing impairments to the environment may produce less goods for each employee hour (lowering the GNP) and, for the matter, may produce less employee goods for each dollar of capital invested in the plant—but yet, this can constitute a good for the society. Which is better, to be able to afford another pair of shoes because a productivity increase lowers the price or to have the privilege of walking barefoot on a clean beach? Which is to be rated higher, to produce more goods accompanied by more cancer, or enjoy less production but better health? Which constitutes the higher level of quality of life?

When technological advance makes long distance calls quicker, more reliable and cheaper the society gains in quality of phone service, but the GNP covers only the price of all the phone bills, the amount of dollars spent on phone service per year, not its quality. GNP similarly lists the sales in dollars of the automobiles produced but does not account for the effort to make them safer, less gas guzzling, and lesser producers of air contaminants. It is not adequate to measure production of goods and services by dollars spent without clarity about the qualities and values of what is being produced.

A technological corporation manager will distinguish between productivity per person in his company and productivity per person in the total population. For the population as a whole, government employment is part of an overhead that has been increasing rapidly, causing a decline in productivity for the economy as a whole. About 30 percent of the population is now working for government, supported by tax payments, not adding to the GNP, and thus contributing in some respects to the poorer productivity performance. We also have a rising overhead in corporations (the overhead on direct labor often runs between 200 and 300 percent), since the companies must hire more to interface with government workers engaged in monitoring and regulating industry operations.

A corporation will be interested most often in how productive it is in utilizing its assets, and the return on assets, R_A, will be the end figure that it will seek to maximize. One route to accomplish this maximization is often to increase the productivity of the labor. Given the same physical assets, machines, computers, laboratory space, factory area, and the like, if all the employees were to work more ingeniously, harder and generally more effectively, make fewer mistakes, learn the new parts of their tasks as these arise with greater speed, be more highly motivated and ideally suited to the task, the productivity (measured, say, by the output per employee per hour) would rise. It could also be made to increase by investing in new tools to make each worker more productive or in further automation that eliminates some of the labor.

A company that uses 10,000 employees to turn out 100 million dollars worth of products might later turn out 200 million dollars worth of products with the same 10,000 people. This would mean an increase in productivity, the ratio of output to employees, of two to one during that period. However, this increase may have been primarily the result of investing many, many millions of dollars in the design and purchase of automation equipment. Without analyzing the numbers carefully we cannot say whether this big investment paid off in terms of lower labor costs versus higher capital, depreciation and maintenance costs.

Obviously, it will not necessarily always be in the best interest of the corporation to automate to increase productivity. The decision is based in part on tradeoffs analyzed by the criterion of optimizing return on investment, attaining lower prices and a stronger position in the market, and other factors of that kind. Automation could be overly expensive. The corporation could get down to very few workers but still have a much poorer return that it was realizing before it embarked on an extreme over-automation of the process.

Lagging United States Productivity

In the United States, productivity increases have lagged in recent years, and there is much concern over this. The reasons are only partly understood. They are complex, interconnected in ways not clear and vary from one to another industry group. For today's economic environment some industries are overexpanded. The existing manufacturing capacities of many industry groups are not being used as close to 100 percent as in previous times. This hurts productivity, of course. In many plants the output could be relatively easily boosted by the addition of comparatively few workers, but the market demand does not justify the higher output.

During the first half of the 1970s, compensation per hour increased about 8 percent per year, while productivity increased about 1.5 percent per year. Salaries, wages and fringe benefits account for almost three-fourths of all income produced. They are the major component in the cost and price of goods and services produced by the technological industry. As labor costs rise faster than productivity, the difference must find offset in price. Improving the rate of productivity advance thus would reduce inflationary trends. Unfortunately, for several years, the United States has witnessed a rather drastic decline in the economy's rate of productivity growth. The United States output per-man-hour has been growing only slowly and is now down to about half the rate of increase that the United States averaged over the preceding century. The output per dollar's worth of capital input (with inflation taken into account) has actually been declining, in contrast to its growth in other industrial countries.

A typical United States family had $5,000 less income in 1978 than it would have had if the growth in productivity had not slowed from historical levels. The total loss of goods and services to the citizens of America was $300 billion in 1978 alone. Between the mid-1940s, and mid-1960s, productivity increased at an annual average rate of 3.2 percent; however, from mid-1960s to mid-1970s, the annual rate of increase dropped to 1.6 percent, the lowest rate among leading industrial nations. In the last two decades, the average annual productivity increase figure was almost 6 percent for West Germany and over 8 percent for Japan. The slowed rate in the United States undermines the domestic economy and its competitiveness.

Increasing Productivity—General Approaches

Four ways to improve productivity are often mentioned: (1) technological innovation; (2) heightened capital investment; (3) better training, education and higher motivation of workers; (4) improved government-business relationships. Some studies have indicated that about half the past increase in productivity in the United States has been attributable to technological change, that is, to a combination of scientific and engineering advance that yielded improvements in the way we produce goods and in the know-how of management. Some 15–20 percent of productivity growth is attributable to capital investment in further automation. The remainder of productivity improvement has resulted from scale economies, education of workers and improved allocation of resources. In general, it is felt that R & D and worker training must accompany capital investment to get the full benefit of it.

In the high technology industries a continuous and deliberate effort to increase productivity, through technological innovation spawned by research and development, has been particularly effective. During the past quarter century, productivity in the high technology industries has increased at an annual rate of over 4 percent, this compared with 2 percent and below for lower technology sectors. In some technological fields annual productivity gains have been phenomenal. For instance, in semiconductor operations, gains of 200 or 300 percent from year to year are quite common. In contrast, in steel making two or three percentage points have been considered excellent for productivity gains. We should keep in mind that semiconductor manufacturers can keep installing new machines radically better than earlier ones, as they create new production plants in which they are able to justify investment, because their markets are continually expanding at a tremendous rate. Also, their machines tend to cost only a few hundred thousand dollars each. Steel makers are expanding little, if at all, and a new installation may cost a few hundred million dollars.

In the semiconductor industry, microprocessors now are used to control almost all processes from beginning to end of the production cycle. In the steel industry, microprocessors and computers save fuel for the furnaces, cut time and product waste in rolling mills, and keep track of tens of thousands of pieces of steel in various stages of production as they proceed through a plant. Though both industries use these latest techniques, the other and differing factors of market volume growth, capacity growth, and inherent technological advance in the product account for the large difference in productivity gains.

To illustrate further the relationship of R&D to improved manufacturing, it will be helpful to quote from a recent advertisement of the Western Electric Company:

"In the last ten years, the costs of labor and raw materials that go into the telephone have skyrocketed. And yet, the price of the finished product has risen only 18%. The explanation is really quite simple. During the same period of time, the telephone has been redesigned literally dozens of times. Western Electric engineers kept discovering ways to make it a little more efficiently. So while our materials and labor costs were going up, we've been able to hold our manufacturing costs down. Not a bad way to cope with inflation. At Western Electric, cost reduction and other improvements in our productivity don't just happen. They're the result of a systematic and formalized program which has existed for years. One of the key elements in this program is our Engineering Research Center (ERC). Western Electric is one of the few corporations that has such a facility. Unlike most research and development centers, its primary purpose is manufacturing research. In 1977, the net effect of our cost reduction program was a savings of over $200,000,000. With cost reductions like these, no wonder our rate of productivity improvement is well ahead of the overall U.S. rate."

Equally, we can quote excerpts from a recent IBM advertisement:

"A set of computations that cost $1.26 on an IBM computer in 1952 costs only 7/10ths of a cent today. That's because IBM scientists and engineers have put their imagination and intelligence to work to create and improve information technology. The computing power of a machine which filled a large room 25 years ago, for example, is contained in circuits that now can be held in your hand. And the computation speeds are over a thousand times faster. With every innovative advance, and every resulting reduction in computing costs, the advantages of information technology become available to more and more people. Advancing technology increases productivity. And greater productivity can indeed help bring costs down to size."

These examples might indicate that all the United States needs to do is increase R & D to increase productivity. Even if this were true, it is easier said than done. As we discussed earlier, inflation and government requirements for environmental controls improvement have hurt earnings and discretionary funds available for R & D. Also, R & D is only one of many facets influencing productivity. As a matter of fact, United States productivity has been lagging behind other industrial nations, even though, as shown by studies on data from the mid-1960s to the mid-1970s, United States intensity in R & D compares favorably with that of other industrial nations. United States privately funded R & D in these years exceeded that of all other nations in its intensity (with one minor exception, the Netherlands). Intensity is measured by comparing the R & D funds with the dollar value added by the manufacturing industry carrying on that R & D. In only one year (1973), Japan surpassed the United States in the ratio of R & D expenses to value added in manufacturing. For four major industries (chemicals, metals, electrical machinery, nonelectrical machinery and instruments), growth in output per unit labor was compared in the studies with average R & D intensity for that decade. In only one instance, namely, chemical industries, did there appear to be a direct correlation between total output and R & D intensities.

Some of the other factors important in productivity increase are capital investment, energy costs, government regulation and employee education. Since a major element in productivity improvement has always been capital investment, it is not surprising that the productivity improvement lag in the United States has followed a capital investment lag. Moreover, the composition of capital expenditures in the United States is shifting markedly. Of the total dollars invested, a large fraction now is earmarked for meeting environmental and occupational health and safety regulation requirements. Thus, the investment for productivity increase has been declining. The ratio of capital to labor (that is, the ratio of the net stock of fixed assets to total employee hours) increased at an annual rate of 3.3 percent in the decade from the mid-1940s to the mid-1960s but declined to well below 2 percent for the following decade. (These figures exclude the investment to meet environmental standards.)

Another deterrent to capital investment has been the declining return on investment. The rate of return in the late 1970s is substantially below those in the two preceding decades. This trend is particularly bad for capital investment to increase productivity because, as most managers would see it at the present time, there now are greater risks and uncertainties for all investments.

One reason for our declining productivity is that we simply have too large a capital investment for the demand in many industries. By the end of World War II, there had been enough delay in capital investment, what with a depression followed by a war, that great economic payoff resulted from increasing the amount of capital invested to back each worker. We apparently thought this was a fundamental trend that should be followed indefinitely. That was wrong. Industry overshot in expanding capacity versus market requirements in many areas. Hence, those industries suffered a decline in return on investment in recent years.

The present higher energy costs and potential shortage of fuel have together pushed industry toward different productivity priorities and options, compared with the previous period in which energy was a cheap input and labor was a costly one. During that earlier period, industry substituted machinery for labor. Even machinery that was a high energy user generally would increase productivity and improve return on investment. Now the situation has changed. In some industries, notably chemicals, energy has become the highest cost factor. In others government regulations alone are forcing a change in the trade-off among energy, machinery and labor. When wages increase more rapidly than energy prices, which was the pattern until 1973, then both energy and capital spending are substituted for labor. Now labor is being substituted for energy. Also, higher energy prices tend to depress the rate of capital formation and thereby reduce the rate of substitution of capital for labor. With the new tendency for rising labor use, the long-term outlook for labor productivity is a slowdown in its rate of growth.

Probably the greatest handicap to productivity increases in the

United States at the present time—at least when productivity is defined narrowly—is increasing government regulation. Government requirements on industrial operations are now diverting capital expenditures to meeting much stricter environmental and safety rules. As we already mentioned, these capital investments do not increase the output per labor hour. Furthermore, the funds used to meet these regulations are not available for R & D to improve the production technology or to invest in further exchange of capital for labor to produce the same output. Also, the production processes must be changed away from the most efficient (by conventional definitions of efficiency) to means that will meet the new regulations.

Finally, as to United States productivity lag, it is important to note the lack of a close relationship between our universities and the manufacturing industries for the laying of a proper base for productivity improvement. Only about 15 universities have strong departments in manufacturing or production technology. For example, in metalworking (where Japan and Germany are excelling over the United States), greater use of computerized control and other advanced technological techniques could help raise productivity. However, graduates in engineering are not given a background to permit them to work in this field effectively. Also, only the very largest corporations typically have on their staffs engineers thoroughly able to adopt new techniques, that is, capable of analyzing the operation, estimating the costs versus benefits of new equipment for making products, and designing the complex systems required to increase productivity by use of the latest tools.

Summarizing the United States productivity lag, inflations and recessions have hurt earnings and cash flows so that less funds are available for R & D and capital investments to improve manufacturing methods and thus realize productivity gains. The new regulations requiring more environmental protection and higher standards of worker safety have forced higher capital investments to meet these rules with no higher outputs. Some approaches to productivity increases are hampered by being energy dissipators. With potential energy shortages and higher energy prices, these approaches have been held back.

Productivity Increases in a Technological Company; Use of the Computer

In a given technological corporation, the general, national trends of productivity growth are not necessarily controlling. The manufacturing head will pursue routes toward productivity gain he thinks right for his company. When he chooses to invest in improved methods he looks for lower costs and higher returns. He expects to increase the degree to which his labor and capital assets are productively used.

To improve productivity of labor, the manufacturing manager must focus on precisely what it is that the workers do in performing the various operations. Perhaps a better balance or partnership of hand and machine, or human brain and computer, would achieve an improved result. An increasing part of manufacturing cost is in the handling of information, a critical function in which today the human beings doing this task are usually found in close collaboration with computerized information systems. Great increases in productivity, in the amount of production accomplished and pertinent information handled per employee per hour, have come from automating control of manufacturing processes. This means automating the acquisition, processing, flow and utilization of information with electronics, including computers, intelligent terminals, and digital data communications systems. Computer programmed systems are used in manufacturing for scheduling, costing, machining, measurement, motion, and inventory control.

The greatest increases in productivity in manufacturing in the future may well result from further advances in electronic information technology. One problem for management of manufacturing operations in applying these electronic systems is working out the tradeoff of the annual expenses for planning and designing the information systems and the capital to buy them versus the cost of the labor replaced. The problem is made less straightforward and more complex by the fact that rarely is an operation left untouched when computer control and electronics information systems are introduced. The combination of people and computers in accomplishing manufacturing operations and in handling information basic to those operations is more efficient only if the partnership is designed properly, that is, if the installed system is right for the task. The increases in capacity, accuracy and speeds of flow and analysis of information the new computerized electronic systems bring when correctly applied to manufacturing operations makes it possible to use machines and human labor with higher economic return. It is not then just a question of replacing a human operator; rather, the hybrid man-computer-robot system is superior and brings the operation to a plateau of effectiveness that could not have been attained without the entry of electronics.

Today, with the availability of low priced and reliable computers, microprocessors and increasingly sophisticated systems and programming concepts, it is theoretically possible to replace or parallel humans in virtually any manufacturing operation, and worth serious consideration as a practical step in such operations. For industries requiring many assembly steps like the making of automobiles, total automation is still a long way off but already some manufacturing operations could not work well without computers.

Where the processing involves a variety of both batch and continuous flow operations, modern systems of manufacture are particularly dependent on computers. Technological industries, as a broad generality, are becoming more and more skillful in their use. Robots that easily handle mechanical motions and transfers automatically are now becoming programmable with good cost-effectiveness. Computerized systems for machine tools minimize in-process inventory, lead time, direct and indirect labor, and changing of tools and setups, and, at the same time, they maximize equipment flexibility and utilization. Computer control is in place in controlling steel furnaces, rolling mills and continuous casting as well as in industries such as paper and pulp and in such continuous flow industries as petrochemicals. The use of computers in these industries has brought about better product uniformity and smaller inventory levels. The computers are employed for management information handling, production scheduling and integrated control of operations in an area all the way down to supervisory control by digitalized signals applied directly to individual machines. Computerized manufacturing systems vary in approach with each machine tool builder and with each factory that uses these new methods. But all have the same general purposes: to cut lead time, inventory, direct and indirect labor and to minimize tool changing and setups while maximizing the flexibility of utilization of the equipment.

The digital computer has found increasing use over the past two decades in the numerical control (NC) of machine tools. Some 50,000 NC machines are in use today with machine tool builders now including NC equipment in about half of their total machine tool output. The previously hard wired NC controls are giving way to computerized numerical control (CNC) using microprocessors. Still, in the entire United States metalworking industry, only about one installed machine in fifty is of the NC variety. Some factories are now moving to the concept of a computer integrated manufacturing system (CIMS), where a whole group of general purpose machine tools are integrated with materials-handling equipment to perform machining operations on sequenced parts with all parts of the system operating under computer direction. In contrast, most machine shops in the country have no computerized control whatsoever.

The International Institution for Production Engineering Research conducted a survey in 1976 among its worldwide members on the impact of advanced technology on the future of manufacturing over the next quarter century. It was predicted that by 1990 more than 50 percent of machine tools will not have a stand-alone use but-will be part of versatile manufacturing systems featuring automatic parts handling between operations and control from a central computer. Today less than 25 percent of United States industrial output is the result of mass production. The rest is produced by batch manufacturing with long-lead times, high inventories in process, low machine utilization and very little automation. On the average today, a part in production spends less than 5 percent of its time on a machine. The rest of the time it is moving or waiting between operations. Of the time spent on the machine, only a third is in a cutting mode. It is widely believed by manufacturing experts that use of the digital computer's potential to improve these ratios is as yet largely untapped, but imminent.

The manufacturing of technological products is highly dependent on precision mechanical equipment to process materials, to move and position parts for processing and assembly and to perform measurement and tests automatically or to assist a human operator in such activities. Some of the machines are standard available items used in the manufacture of quite diverse items. However, in technological product production, a large fraction of all of the machinery used, whether mechanical or electronic, has to be custom designed to the individual product and its specific production techniques. A typical machine may involve at least 100 independent design parameters, making the best design of the machine or setup a major engineering challenge. When products must meet strict quality specifications regarding geometric dimensions, finish and cleanliness, the overall design of the manufacturing process may exceed in its complexity the design of the product itself. Superior engineering applied to the production activities may be as much or more of a key to overall corporate success as R & D and product engineering.

Despite the foregoing, mechanical design science has been badly neglected in the United States over recent decades. The sum of all basic research in this field has been, at most, only one or two percent of the research funds spent in physical science. The wedding of innovation and mechanical design technology with advances in information automation or computerization could have important productivity improvement benefits and represent a most unusual challenge.

As an example, consider the robot, so-called because it constitutes an equivalent of the human system through use of computers, sensors and actuators. Today it can be said that no production line for the manufacture of technological components is up to date if, in its design, the engineers involved have not considered the production system as a man-machine partnership. With the appropriate use of robots and computer programmed processing machines and computer controlled information gathering, processing, dissemination and overall control, higher quality at lower cost could result and the return on investment could be enhanced. Robots can move materials and parts, load and unload processing machines, sort, store and assemble parts, rivet, weld, paint, sand, and grind. They can do all of these things with greater safety than can human operators, in environments unsuitable for humans, and with far less errors and down time of the production line.

Intelligent robots, in view of the present availability of microprocessors from the computer industry, can be designed for reprogramming to new tasks and literally can be educated to take on new motion and action sequences once they are led through the new programs by human intervention. Some 10,000 robots are now at work in the production world and the number will doubtless be in the millions by the end of the century.

Social-Political Factors

Let us turn now to influences on productivity that have little to do with improving the manufacturing process but are rather political in nature. Productivity is complicated by many distortions from the political-social arena. As an example, consider that regularly Congress increases the minimum wage in the United States. When this happens the productivity-automation tradeoff curves of corporations are altered. A corporation may have, for instance, a group of old but satisfactory elevators operated by young, unskilled operators. When the wage they may be receiving is increased substantially by law, then it becomes sensible for the corporation, as it seeks to minimize its costs, to junk the old elevators and buy new automatic elevators. The elevator operators are laid off and the corporation has less employees, although it is still turning out the same production output. Its productivity will have increased (at least by the narrow definition of productivity).

The same social-political dynamics of the nation that causes us to raise minimum wages increases unemployment. The unemployment relief budget must be raised when minimum wages are increased.

(Those unemployed elevator operators must receive a stipend on which to live.) It must be paid for by taxes, which in part are paid by corporations, which now have less funds available to invest in manufacturing methods improvement or in new products that might produce more jobs.

The overall system that relates production technology to government policies regarding taxation, minimum wages, unemployment relief, and the like, is most complex. It is beyond what any one corporation is going to do much about as it goes about its own narrow optimizations. The only point we wish to make here concerning the impact on management is to further illustrate why productivity analyses that simply compare automation costs with labor costs are not always definitive. We cited a case where United States law on minimum wages causes actions that create unemployment and increase productivity, at least temporarily. We could have suggested an example on the other side, in which a corporation makes a capital investment decision to increase productivity and return on assets and lays off (now unneeded) workers, but runs into immediate labor union problems that are settled only by increasing wages of all its retained employees.

Personnel Needs for Manufacturing

Let us now discuss the various presonnel requirements for manufacturing of highly complex products. We first recall that for successful manufacturing results, some of the R & D and product design talent must lock in closely with manufacturing and cooperate in ensuring quality performance. This must continue until the product that comes off the production line gets debugged and confirmed about its workability and refined to cut costs or to attain the promised performance. Too much segregation, particularly in the early stages, between the designers of the products and the manufacturing principals may doom the product. Manufacturing, if left alone, may make many improper and inadvertent design changes to make it possible to produce the product. On the other hand, allow too much domination by the R & D group that invented the product, and the design may never get stabilized so that the product can be manufactured in quantity. Its cost will be too high and too many engineers may be needed, not only for initial assembly and test but also in the field with the customer to keep the product working.

If it is a low volume product endeavor, a model-shop factory may sometimes be the best for a technological product. The trouble is that little effort goes into manufacturing engineering in a model shop. Usually this situation does not last for long, because, if the product is any good, competitors will arise. If they then do an effective job in designing the manufacturing activity, they will come out with a lower cost, more reliable product.

Choosing approaches to productivity improvement involves the workers, to say the least, but when scientists and engineers consider productivity in their firms, their tendency often is to over-focus on innovation and capital investment to increase automation. There is a tendency to ignore the problem of the human worker in his interface with his job, his equipment, his environment and the management. In a technological corporation particularly, the manufacturing workers as well as others are likely to be well educated. These employees expect good working conditions and, more particularly, conditions that would make the most effective use of their own abilities, ingenuity and creativity. They want greater flexibility in work patterns, high health and safety protection on the job, and substantial personal control over the performance of their work. New techniques such as group incentive systems. flexible work schedules, autonomous work teams, and goal setting by the team are being tried in some companies. Government rules and regulations are increasingly important in how industry attacks all these issues.

If the technological product is complex enough, the tradeoff between labor costs and automation to eliminate labor is not initially at the top of the list for attention by the manufacturing management. Usually only if a substantial volume of production is involved do the matters of modifying the process and the design to get the benefit of automation come into the act. Before automation enters in a high technology product production plan another tradeoff is usually handled first. This is between using engineers or technicians who have participated in the design, or, instead less skilled, regulary factory workers for the assembly, checkout and test activities when the factory first gets started. Usually a very high understanding of what goes on with the product, and the meaning of the performance specifications are highly advantageous to make the early production line work. It should be an objective of the production activity, however, that it remove the engineers, scientists and highly trained technicians on loan from the product design department from the factory line as soon as things bed down. At this point it may be sensible also to introduce additional (partly automated) equipment on the production line to go with the lower skilled workers who take over.

For highly technological products, an automation process usually requires ingenious devices. They are combinations of mechanical and electronic components, and their design should ideally take place within the production engineering activities of the manufacturing function. This effort should involve considerable consultation with the R & D and product design talent of the corporation, ones who are familiar with the detailed workings of the product and the reasons for the specific tests, checkout steps, manufacturing tolerances and other requirements that are specified and must be adhered to.

Attaining lower cost fabrication and higher volume usually involves breaking the tasks down so that the individual steps can be done by less-skilled, lower-paid workers, with the operation nevertheless constituting a completely controlled one for quality. If a first class job has been done to automate the production of highly technological products, it is usually only partly automated. The design process to create the right kind of production operation is one that looks upon the availability of people of particular categories of skills, on one hand, and machines, robots and computers with certain mechanical and information handling potentials, on the other. The optimum system is a balanced hybrid of human being and machine.

No one engineer alone is generally capable of conceiving and laying out in detail and then implementing, refining, debugging and ensuring the success of such a hybrid operation. A system team is needed that knows intimately the production processes, the product itself and the factory workers. This systems engineering group of the manufacturing function must understand people as well as machines, or at least almost as well. In their repertoire of proven talents, the production system engineers will have to be familiar with the process of selection of appropriate factory workers and their training. They will also have to be concerned with their motivation. No system of production requiring people as participants will work out well if it turns off the necessary participants.

Product design and R & D engineers are quite likely to be less interested than the manufacturing management in the importance of motivation of the factory workers. For instance, the other departments might regard the unions who represent the production employees with only passing interest. But the executive responsible for production knows that interest in the workers and their unions, the needs and aspirations of both, is vital. He will have an objective to design that human dimension into the picture from the beginning, because doing so is fundamental to success for a manufacturing operation.

Depreciation

We have already had occasion earlier to call attention to the importance of depreciation as an expense. Depreciation is involved in every fixed asset, in every tangible piece of equipment that the corporation has acquired, and in much of the inventory of parts and materials. So it is of concern to all parts of the corporate activities that utilize such assets, product engineering, for example, as well as manufacturing. Quite typically, however, manufacturing has the bulk of the depreciation expense. It has the biggest investment in total facilities, the most machines, and the largest inventories. (At any rate, this is enough of an excuse for us to decide to incorporate in this manufacturing chapter additional depreciation discussion which is necessary for the overall objectives of the text and which has to be put someplace.) Let us discuss the varying ways in which the depreciation expense can impact both earnings and cash flow.

The cash flow from depreciation will be real. Presumably, in taking the funds from the sale of a product and using them to payoff all expenses, a portion to cover depreciation is set aside. These funds become available to the corporation as much as any other cash. It may be that the cash is not available for very long and, instead, is almost immediately used up to buy replacements for worn out equipment. But how much cash is generated through depreciation expense depends on how depreciation is reckoned. Both the earnings reported for any period by a corporation and the amount of cash produced are determined by the particular historical patterns used to depreciate an asset, to change it from its original listed value on the books to periodically lower ones. Since the annual depreciation expense can be altered by altering the schedule, then the cash flow and the reported earnings can be altered.

So-called straight line depreciation is commonly used. In this method the original ccost, C, is amortized in N years at the rate of C/N per year. For buildings, N is typically 20–30 years and for equipment it is 5 to 10 years. Both the IRS and the standards set by the certified public accounting firms are involved in judging a corporation's depreciation practices in the choice of the number of years, N, to use in figuring depreciation. Historical, actual costs are always used even if, because of inflation, the replacement cost is higher. Reasonableness and consistency are basic here. Some facilities and apparatus are very special to a specific program which may have only short duration, while others are of general purpose and have long life. Past experience shows what life expectancy is to be, and whether the items being depreciated may be expected to have resale or liquidation value after usefulness to the corporation is ended.

In some instances, not uncommon for technological corporations, accelerated amortization appears proper and is accepted by the IRS and the public accountants. Suppose, for instance, that automation equipment is purchased with the knowledge that the technology is moving so rapidly the equipment will be out of date and probably replaced by superior equipment in, say, four years. Then it would be justified to write off the cost in four years and take a bigger depreciation the first year than the second, and so on. One neat way to do this that is employed often is the sum of the digits method. This is best defined by an example. For a total depreciation write-off of the original cost in, say, four years, the sum of the digits is $1 + 2 + 3 + 4 = 10$. The depreciation expense for the four years will then be 4/10 of the cost the first year, 3/10 the second, 2/10 the third, and the final 1/10 for the fourth year. If C is the cost and the number of years is N, then the depreciation in the first year will be

$$\frac{N}{1 + 2 + 3 + \cdots + N} C$$

In the last year it will be

$$\frac{1}{1 + 2 + 3 + \cdots + N} C$$

and in the nth year it will be

$$\frac{N - n + 1}{1 + 2 + 3 + \cdots + N} C \qquad [1]$$

Table 8–A shows a depreciation and cash flow schedule for a machine costing $50,000 which the manufacturing department has just placed in operation. It is anticipated it will cuts costs by $20,000 per year, will last five years, and be junked after that with no residual value. The Table assumes that the firm's average cost of capital is 10 percent (and this is used as the discount rate), that its income tax rate is 50 percent, and that the firm employs straight line depreciation over the tax life of five years. The table shows the net present value of the investment and indicates that by the standards employed it was a good investment.

Table 8–A

Depreciation = $50,000/5 = $10,000 per year
Annual earnings improvement = $20,000 − depreciation
= $10,000
less tax = $ 5,000
Cash flow (add back depreciation) = $15,000

Year	Net cash flow	Discount factor	Present value, P_V
0	$(50,000)*	1.0	$(50,000)
1	15,000	.909	13,635
2	15,000	.826	12,390
3	15,000	.751	11,265
4	15,000	.683	10,245
5	15,000	.621	9,315
SUM:	$ 25,000	Net P_V:	$ 6,850

$$\text{Profitability index} = \frac{P_V \text{ cash benefits}}{P_V \text{ cash outlays}}$$

$$= \frac{56,850}{50,000} = 1,137$$

* Parentheses denote negative values.

In Table 8–B two changes are made in the situation. We assume an additional $20,000 charge for transportation and installation of the machine. We also assume that after five years the machine can be sold for $20,000. Now, as the table shows, the net present value of the investment is negative, and by the same financial criteria as before, it was not a good idea to invest in the machine.

Let us generalize this situation somewhat. Suppose we make an

Table 8–B

Depreciation = ($50,000 + 20,000 − 20,000)/5 = $10,000 per year

Year	Net cash flow	Discount factor	Present value, P_V
0	$(70,000)	1.0	$(70,000)
1	15,000	.909	13,635
2	15,000	.826	12,390
3	15,000	.751	11,265
4	15,000	.683	10,245
5	35,000	.621	21,735
SUM:	$ 25,000	Net P_V:	$ (730)

investment, A_o, in new machinery and realize annual earnings benefits, after depreciation expense is taken and taxes are paid, of $R_A A_o$, with a depreciation annually of A_o/N. With the discount rate R_I let us write down the cash invested (CASH IN) and the cash benefits (CASH OUT) properly discounted.

$$\text{CASH IN} = A_o \qquad [2]$$

while the cash benefits are

$$\text{CASH OUT} = A_o(R_A + 1/N) \sum_{n=1}^{N} x^n$$

or

$$\text{CASH OUT} = A_o(R_A + 1/N)x(1 - x^N)/(1 - x) \qquad [3]$$

where

$$x = \frac{1}{1 + R_I}$$

Equating to make net P_v equal zero, we obtain

$$1 = (R_A + 1/N)x \frac{1 - x^N}{1 - x}$$

or

$$R_A = \frac{1 - x}{x(1 - x^N)} - \frac{1}{N} \qquad [4]$$

Illustrating, with $N = 5$ and $R_I = .15, x = .87$ and

$$R_A = .10$$

This says that in buying machinery costing A_o we must realize earnings increment of $.1A$ each year in order that the investment meet the corporation's hurdle, in this case 15 percent.

Suppose now that we do indeed realize this increment ($R_A = .10$) from the new machinery. Then let us look at the annual reported incremental results for the earnings each year by the corporation as a result of this investment and the ratio of those earnings to the book value of the employed assets at the beginning of the year (Table 8–C). (We shall call this ratio R_A' so as not to confuse it with the previously defined R_A). It is interesting to note that three different ratios have some pertinence to the investment and that they are not identical. The annual earnings or savings per year to the manufacturing operation realized through the purchase of this machine, expressed as a fraction of the machine's cost, was $R_A = .10$. The internal rate of return used as the hurdle rate for this investment was $R_I = .15$. The reported annual return on assets employed, R_A', grows as the book-value of assets employed are depreciated and seems to average over .20.

Table 8–C

Year	Earnings	Book value of assets	R_A'
1	$.1A_0$	A_0	$.1$
2	$.1A_0$	$.8A_0$	$.1/.8 = .125$
3	$.1A_0$	$.6A_0$	$.1/.6 = .167$
4	$.1A_0$	$.4A_0$	$.1/.4 = .25$
5	$.1A_0$	$.2A_0$	$.1/.2 = .5$

Learning and Experience Curves

The more a corporation produces a product, the better it gets at producing it. The more that products of the same kind pass down a production line, the quicker the employees get at completing every task, and, at least up to a point, the less errors they will make. As time passes and as the experience of producing a given product accumulates, the supervisory people will have a steadily increasing opportunity to observe and eliminate shortcomings of the process, and invent shortcuts, machines and procedures to cut costs. Other parallel developments can be expected to impinge in time to make possible the improving of the production process as experience grows.

The learning and experience pattern is complex and not linear with time or with the number of products produced. However, generally, in a competitive situation, the company with the head start and the largest share of the market may be expected to have substantially lower costs. It has the best potential for getting those costs down as it learns how to manufacture that product through the experience of doing just that. It will be farther along on the learning curve compared with competitors, because it will have built up more experience. As the volume of products it has produced rises with time, reaching levels more and more beyond that of its competitors, the gap in costs should increase.

In trying to match the technology to the market, good planning includes understanding the concept of the learning curve, in which costs decrease with units produced, and keeping it a conspicuous factor in production, product design and market strategy. The initial cost of manufacturing is hardly the whole story when the cost is expected to come down during the life of the product, particularly if it is likely to come down rapidly as the production experience escalates with increasing volume, and even more particularly if such a learning curve scenario can be pulled off with a lead over competitors.

In highly technological project activities, the idea of a learning or an experience curve is made more complex because the product does not stand still. It is one thing to estimate and take into account the experience curve for a product, if it is the same product after three years as it was at the beginning, and another if it changes greatly. While production activities are building and experience turning out a quantity causes the costs to move down the learning curve, the application engineers are also developing a better understanding of how the product is faring in the field and how the customer is using it. Meanwhile, parallel developments take place in the system of which the product is a part. The manufacturing and design engineers are introducing changes to improve performance, to give marketing an edge and to ease manufacturing difficulties. The technology is all the while advancing and competitors are introducing new features, and the threats those actions imply must be answered. These conditions will conspire to cause the product to be moving on its own curve of modified specifications, appearance and detailed makeup as a production assembly and sometimes as to the materials, purchased parts and components that go into the assembly.

Controlling Design Changes

In fact, it is important that the change in the product be controlled. Here again we have tradeoffs that will involve negotiations among the various functions affecting the product. It is necessary to improve the product, if it is in difficulty; but a habit should not develop in the corporation to incorporate every new idea. If this is allowed, and along with it every desire of the customer is catered to immediately, the product can never settle down. The volume will remain too low and the learning curve will hardly be recognizable as a meaningful concept. The learning curve's specific shape and degree of advance of cost reduction versus number of units produced depends greatly on a high degree of cooperation between engineering, manufacturing and marketing. One of the issues that the managers of these functions would be expected to have in mind as they negotiate the best plan for a product is to balance the value of a flow of changes, which frustrate the learning curve, against the benefits of stability, which will militate toward moving on a good learning curve in production.

The realization of a beneficial learning curve in which costs decrease with the number of units produced is dependent on employee stability. This is especially true of highly technological, complex products. Experienced employees who leave impair the learning curve. Or perhaps we should say that they take some of the learning with them and the replacement employees have to go back to some earlier region of the curve.

The shape of specific learning curves, even if the product remains stable for a reasonable period of time, will vary with the product and the circumstances. However, all learning curves will show a degree of compounding, a rapid decrease in costs in the early life of the product. Thus, for example, a full detailed checkout of every aspect of a product may be necessary during the early part of the production experience to catch faulty components before they are shipped to the customer or before the whole product goes into final test. Later on, the production team will make fewer mistakes, allow fewer bad parts into the system, and be guilty of fewer instances of failure to notice and report something that is not going right. The re-do costs will go down, but also the final checkout and test procedure will be truncated and still yield the necessary overall final quality required. The lower the foul-ups and the smoother the production line (and the lower the costs), the more the personnel will have time to invent improvements in the process.

This compounding effect of learning affects not only the corporation's internal operations but also that of its suppliers. Generally a product depends not only on raw materials coming from the outside but also on some externally furnished components that become part of the final assembly. Each source of items from the outside should have a similar kind of learning curve experience so that with the producing of more and more units, the cost may be expected to diminish from outside sources as well. In addition, the sources become more reliable. A larger fraction of what they deliver will meet the specifications and will no longer cause costly delays and re-work. So, not only will the price paid to the supplier come down because of his learning curve, but also the improved performance of the supplier's products will lower the costs of handling and incorporating his component into the final assembly.

Both the time elapsed and the number of units built are proper parameters to examine for influence on the decreasing cost the learning curve represents. It might appear at first that the only learning curve to have in mind is one that merely shows the cost of producing a unit versus the number of units produced to date, the actual number of units produced being the measure of the experience. However, the time that passes during which this production takes place is a factor. If two identical products are made by two virtually identical companies with one turning out 10,000 copies in one year and the other turning out the same 10,000 copies in two years, they will not reach the identical cost of production as they each pass the 10,000 unit mark. Because one takes two years and the other takes one year to reach that same total of experience, measured by number of units produced, something different will occur in the ability of the production system to learn. Depending upon the circumstances, either time frame might be advantageous over the other. Building a huge number of units in practically no time at all, to take an extreme example, may not provide ample opportunity to incorporate the valuable experiences and inventions, because of the time delays and lead times that go with the flow of the information representing the experience and the way it affects what everybody in the process does. On the other hand, if it is going to take forever for an organization to digest and use the experience of a given number of units, then the erosion with time of the experience's value before it gets applied, will have an effect.

It is not practical to detail this further in this text. It is sufficient only that we be aware of the fact that there is an important learning curve phenomenon at work in all products. The exact pattern and the degree of learning will vary and do so in a rather complex way difficult to generalize about. The leadership in manufacturing must exploit the learning curve. It also must participate with marketing and product engineering in making the learning concept in manufacturing a key parameter in planning a product strategy.

The Volume Parameter

Unless the manufacturing organization of a corporation is against making a specific product in the first place, it will usually favor the marketing organization's selling a lot of those products to get the manufactured volume up. Generally high volume means lower costs, accelerated learning, and superior market position. It provides a base for more R & D, deeper market research, and more generous contributions to overhead costs. Through all this it improves the company's financial position. Usually, if high volume can be considered seriously for a product, then whole new approaches to manufacturing become possible. The product design is different for high volume than for low volume. New applications, and hence whole new market potentials, are opened up by the lower prices.

The manufacturing organization is interested in volume from the standpoint of producing a lower cost product, knowing that this will benefit the corporation as a whole. But there is the other side of the coin as well. Marketing and some of the other corporate entities will put special pressure on manufacturing to get the cost down, so that the price can be lower and the volume up as a result. The issue of what volume to plan for is a key parameter determining the market strategy for the product. It may dominate the design of it and the risk of investment in facilities to make possible the manufacture. We might better put it another way. A product is not understood for its practicality for investment by a corporation unless the volume is taken into account in all of the analyses as a major factor.

Many products have to be produced and marketed in high volume or they are not practical at all. Telephones, automobiles, television sets—all of these are sensible only in terms of very high production. Otherwise the high manufacturing costs and resultant high prices would make them totally impractical. The whole system of distribution, maintenance and service would be quite inconceivable at low volumes. Basic associated subsystems, like fuel supply and roads in the case of automobiles, and broadcasting programs in the case of television, would be out of the question to finance. Many new technological products for the future are in this category.

Of course certain highly technological products are inherently low volume, like communications spacecraft, nuclear installations, or a plant to produce synthetic fuel from coal. The output of a plant changing coal to gas may be high in volume, but if a corporation is in the business of constructing such plants, its volume will be low in units produced per year. Citing these examples reminds us that we are not seeking to make the point only high volume technological products will in the end be successful. For some successful high technology products, suited to specific corporations as their preferred product lines, the volume level will have little significance.

Overall the importance of the volume question is relative. The comparison really is against leading competitors. If a product is cost-effective to the customer and offers a good return on assets employed for the corporation producing it, the desire for higher volume in general should still be there. Higher volume might bring the price down, and this will probably lead to more applications for the product line and a better return on investment in that product area. But a conspicuous test of strategy is the corporation's volume against its leading competitors. If others have larger volumes, then it is vital to examine the question of how best to compete, granted that disadvantage. If a corporation is well ahead of its leading competitors in volume, then, although it will certainly still be interested in volume, the issue will be less critical for it in the short term.

Quality Control

Manufacturing operations tend often to be dominated by the need for very precise scheduling and strong control over the operation to keep it on schedule. The schedule usually is tight, the operations strained. It is inherent in the pattern of production operations that the plans do not include large cushions to provide plenty of time to make up schedule slippage. Moreover, since cost is almost certain to be a major issue, there are again not wide safety margins for turning out pieces and assembled products that will meet all of the cost specifications. The pressure and the motivation is to get the product made and out of the door. In view of this and the overall interest of higher management of manufacturing in turning out a quality product, independent inspectors are needed throughout the manufacturing operation. They will have as their assignment catching deficiencies, stopping the product from continuing on into further steps of manufacturing and assembly, if it is faulty, and, especially, stopping the shipment to the customer, if the product is not right as defined by objective criteria.

This quality control operation must not report to the heads of those manufacturing subdepartments that are making and assembling the product for shipment, but rather to top manufacturing management. The independence of the quality control function from the fabrication organization is necessary because of human nature. The quality control department is a critic, engaged in a check on the production process, and that means on the work of those who are operating it. Quality itself must be inherent in the production operation. Quality is not produced by measuring and sorting and rejecting. If the quality has not been built in, that is, if the production process has not provided parts up to specification, quality control can prevent their getting shipped to the customer but cannot correct the faulty production process that produced the rejects. However, quality control, properly executed, can lead to knowledge of where the production process must be improved. The savings can be large, if effective quality control is employed to reduce the penalties to the operation of looseness, incompetence and waste.

For technological products, quality control can represent a very difficult, highly professional and challenging field of endeavor. If it were a case of simply looking, measuring, and separating the good from the bad, it would still be a difficult technical task to perform for technological products. But more than this is involved, because in manufacturing operations sophisticated techniques of testing, analysis and rejecting are preferably to be used. Most often, with a substantial volume level, the parts that are manufactured are within tolerances, the pieces and the finished items have been appropriately assembled and are worth shipping to the customer. The problem of quality control then comes down to inspecting only statistical samples and being able to interpret deviations from the acceptable range through these samples as an indication of how much further checking there should be, how deep the inspection must go.

The availability of computers has made possible a major breakthrough in measuring and reporting on quality performance in manufacturing operations. Acquiring daily data in measurements of tolerances, precision of performance, adherence to specifications, scrap, movement of inventory through counting points, shipping data, and the like, has traditionally presented a problem in an attempt to get good quality control in manufacturing. It used to be extremely difficult to make appropriate analyses without virtually real-time data on inspection reject rates, problem part numbers and locations flowing to quality control personnel. With computerized systems, product performance data now can be made readily available at any moment. Percentage defective and number of pieces inspected and rejected can be called up for viewing on a video screen at will. The computer can produce daily reports for the quality control and manufacturing supervision. Such a computerized system can create a practical tie between quality control management and the control of all gauges, meters and other equipment in use by quality control.

It is a sophisticated engineering job to figure out what to check on, how completely, and how often. Statistical analytical methods and common sense are both necessary, and so also is an understanding of the design and performance of the product and the techniques of production. Quality control generally can benefit from having available experts in statistics and probability theory but not in the abstract and theoretical sense alone. Statistical analyses of what is happening in production operation, if they are to be useful, cannot be performed in isolation from an intimate knowledge of the workings of the product and of the manufacturing operation.

Quality control is very different between high volume production and low volume, almost custom production. Quality control is also vastly varied for production of integrated semiconductor circuits produced by the millions compared with production of a single nuclear reactor. The formal organizational requirements to have quality control function smoothly must be different from one technological product to another. Manufacturing leadership must organize quality control with these distinctions in mind.

Problems

8–1. A company's product appears to have another seven years of constant market demand. Incorporated into the product is a component from a single-source supplier whose poor quality performance has penalized the product's before tax profit by $200,000 per year and, it appears, will continue to do so. The company buys $500,000 per year of this needed component. The company's engineers estimate that after one year of expensed start up cost before tax of $600,000, and with a capital investment for equipment of $300,000 at the beginning of the second year, they could produce the components at a cost of $550,000 per year for the six then remaining years of product life, with a quality high enough to eliminate the present $200,000 per year penalty. Assume the average cost of capital, 10 percent, is the company's hurdle rate for investment, that the capital equipment will be written off straight line in the six years and that the tax rate is 50 percent. As far as meeting the hurdle rate is concerned, should the company go ahead with the project? What are some of the risks inherent in doing so, even if the net P_V turns out positive for the assumed scenario?

8-2. A manufacturing department uses a small computer as an aid in optimum scheduling of machines for fabricating parts and assigning skilled manufacturing personnel. The department manager has proposed expansion of the computer installation, arguing that with even more precise manpower and facilities optimization, he can reduce costs further. The request is turned down. Speculate on some of the reasons why this rejection may have occurred.

8-3. Re-do Table 8–A with an investment hurdle rate of 12 percent instead of the 10 percent used. Also, calculate at what hurdle rate the net P_V is zero.

8-4. Assume the parameters of Table 8–B remain the same except that the new machine replaces an old machine that has today a salvage value of $20,000, although a book value of zero because it is fully depreciated. Thus, if the new machine is bought there is a $20,000 cash in-flow from sale of the old machine, which also means a taxable gain of $20,000 (assumed taxed at a 50 percent rate) in year zero. What are now the cash flows, and the net P_V? Is the investment project acceptable now?

8-5. Re-do Table 8–B assuming that the old machine being replaced has a tax book value of $20,000, but no salvage value. This means that if we substitute the new machine to obtain its benefits we must junk the old machine and sustain a $20,000 loss. Assume a 50 percent tax rate applies to this write-off and that the hurdle rate and other conditions of Table 8–B still apply, except only one, namely, the incremental profit improvement resulting from use of the new machine. What would it have to become annually, in place of the $20,000 before tax figure of Table 8–B, so that the project will meet the 10 percent company hurdle rate specified?

8-6. A product line manager wishes to compare the use of funds for manufacturing methods improvement to cut the cost of his product (and thus increase his sales margin assuming the same selling price) or for redesign to increase the performance of the product for the same manufacturing cost (making possible a higher selling price and profit). If in both instances the profit increment compared with the expense to create it is the same, consider qualitatively what circumstances might prompt one or the other decision for the best use of available funds.

8–7. One of the major components of a new product was to be received from an outside vendor. The first ten of such units received were tested thoroughly. When no flaws were found the manufacturing manager decided to sample check only one of the next ten. When again no flaws were found he decided to assume the purchased components were all coming in good. After 100 units of the product had been assembled four only of these components were found bad, all in the process of final test when, not knowing what component was at fault, it was necessary to do a thorough test on all components in the failing assembly, as well as to disassemble and reassemble the entire combination. The manufacturing head felt he had won his gamble, since the total cost for the 100 assemblies, including the handling of the bad units, was less than if he had held to the original plan of testing every incoming component before assembly. After more thought, he decided otherwise and directed a return to a thorough test of each incoming component. Guess at some of the reasons why the department head might have been right in reversing the decision.

8–8. A product line is in a loss position, the total costs to produce at the present sales volume exceeding sales revenues by 5 percent. The marketing department says the problem is the price has been set too high. They believe they could get a very large increase in sales with a 10 percent reduction in price. Assume that fixed costs are about equal to variable costs (varying directly with the number of units produced). To attain a breakeven situation, by what percentage would the number of units sold have to rise at the new proposed lower price? By what percentage would the overall sales revenues increase?

8–9. Suppose an investment in manufacturing equipment of A causes a profit improvement of $R_A A$ annually for N years during which time the equipment is depreciated straight line to zero book value and then junked. Derive an expression for the minimum value of R_A, if the project is to meet the company's investment hurdle rate, R_I. Show also that as N becomes very large this minimum R_A approaches R_I.

9

MARKETING—THE CUSTOMER AND THE COMPETITION

The Broad Range of Marketing's Importance

It is possible for the manager of any essential function in a technological corporation to make a credible case that his function is the most important and that all of the others revolve about his and are merely supportive. Thus, the product engineering group could claim with considerable conviction that the essence of the corporation's activity is found in the product. Without it to manufacture and sell there is no corporation. Manufacturing equally can see itself as the heart of the corporation, doing the substantive work, the making of the product to be sold. Granted, a design function is needed, but if manufacturing can really make a needed product better and cheaper than the competition, the company can probably arrange for the necessary product design effort.

If the marketing function in a technological corporation is understood properly and implemented successfully, then it is perhaps more forgivable than for most other functions that marketing be perceived as containing the center of success of the corporate endeavor. Marketing in the large, as we shall discuss it in this chapter, must embrace a very broad range of operating functions and management duties. Given the boldest invention and a fully staffed factory suited to production of it, success is not at all guaranteed. It must be true that the market for the product exists and that the competition does not have a better chance to fill that market. This must all be known, or a calculated risk decided upon, ahead of committing the company to the product. In this sense marketing is ahead of engineering and manu-

249

facturing about the time phase of decision. Before designing, and even before doing most of the R & D, marketing research is in order, and even some hard selling may be required. The marketing head-start is needed to provide the critical impact on product selection or that choice may well be wrong.

Usually other companies can do what you can do, and they will do so rather soon, if your product is a good one. Since it is on the firing line, marketing often is the key initiative and leadership group in arranging for an optimization in the match of the company's specific R & D, product design capability and manufacturing innovations to the market need. The closer the corporation can come to optimizing the relationship of its resources to what the real market opportunities are, the less likely it is that a successful competitor will arise.

Marketing Research

Even after a product is successfully established, manufactured and sold, marketing constitutes the main source of intelligence regarding the cost-effectiveness of the product, the potentially competitive ways of filling the same need and the insight about what improvements or extensions of the product are needed for it to hold its position. Marketing, if carried through as a full blown, strong function in a technological corporation, includes not only assessment of competition, but the relating of the product line to other products and to the system for effecting benefits for the customers of which the product is only a subsystem or a component. Marketing must chair the matching of the technological capabilities of the company and the company's other resources to the customer's desires, getting the timing right, and working out the right strategy and communications to connect fully with the customer. Marketing must arrange for effective application engineering.

Cost and price, performance and reliability, long life and ease of maintenance, versatility in the customer's hands, the potential for growth and flexibility to serve his needs—these are part of the systems problem that must be worked by a number of organizational groups within a technological corporation. However, because a large fraction of all of these issues goes directly to the customer, with which the marketing organization is the main interface, an outstandingly run marketing group will very often have a dominant position in these systems problems. There is another way to put it. If, as often happens in technological corporations, the R & D and product design units preempt the main decisions for product selection, assignment of resources, priorities for areas of activity, and the like, it means either that the marketing organization is not as forceful as it ought to be or that the corporation is not fully exploiting its potential. The R & D staff and the product engineers must live and breathe the market and customer environment. It is more likely they will do so in a sensible and compatible way, if the marketing organization is strong enough to provide adequate leadership and communication.

Looked at in this broad way, the marketing function of a technological corporation is tremendously challenging and stimulating. As the principal function relating the corporation's technology to the society's needs, it requires great breadth of understanding of economic, political, and social factors, not to mention the business parameters of the corporation and the technological fundamentals. Even aside from this systems part of a strong marketing organization's responsibilities, there is always room for practical innovation in the way the straightforward parts of marketing, such as sales effort, are accomplished. Conceptions not only on how to do the selling are involved, but also what to try to sell, when and where.

To put technology to work to the greatest advantage of potential customers, marketing must constantly inventory what the corporation can or should be able to do technologically and compare that with a constantly updated list of what potential customers need. Then marketing must find areas where these two lists coincide, and the corporation comes close to being uniquely qualified to exploit that coincidence. Such lists will always be too big in an active, successful, alert technological corporation, and marketing must take the initiative to refine the areas of the corporation's abilities and resources. Where the corporation might have proprietary know-how, market domination could result, if, for that product endeavor, the corporation is also particularly strong in understanding the customers and the economics of applying this product line to the customer's interests.

From time to time studies have been made of innovative efforts that failed, to find out why they did. Often these studies have shown that the failure was not specifically technology-related, but rather resulted from a marketing problem. Usually the market was overestimated or the cost-effectiveness to the customer was not high enough at a price representing profitable performance. It does not follow, since the burden of responsibility for failure is frequently marketing, that a mediocre R & D effort is therefore adequate. Rather it means that technological corporations seeking to innovate find it easier to produce a first rate R & D effort than to make adequate product selections with an eye to the market and then integrate R & D, manufacturing and marketing endeavors to bring off a total success.

Some of the most successful inventions have really resulted from the inventor's having had the creative ability to perceive the need and then to relate it to the existing technology. Other technologists, candidates for making the same invention, might have been more expert in the technology that was applicable. But they could not see the invention, because they were not talented in matching the technology to the application. They did not understand the specific key elements that would have made for a payoff in filling the need.

Of course, from time to time there are scientific discoveries and technological breakthroughs that occur with no relationship to a perceived market. When these events happen it is not obvious the scientists and engineers in a corporation will see the market. They may only have an awareness of the breakthrough, may be captivated by it and want to explore all aspects of the inherent science and technology that are new to them. The R & D staff may possess a strong hunch that there ought to be some important profitable applications out there, but their understanding of the market may be too poor to make the connection. Thus, still required is a marketing organization to step in and work with those who understand the new technology, to pin down the market, if it exists, and to lead in the decision about what to do about the possible openings.

A corporation may prosper by creating a market that did not previously exist. This is done in part by perceiving a need ahead of everyone else. Studies have shown that more successful products arise from effort at innovation to fill a perceived need than result from new technology seeking a market. Successful innovations tend to be stimulated by the market. By interfacing with engineering and manufacturing, a way to fill that need may be worked out earlier than a competitive approach. Here again the leadership and the synthesizer position is often in the marketing organization rather than in engineering or manufacturing, this if the marketing organization is of proper strength.

Suppose a corporation spots an area of endeavor that appears to offer a good match to the company's technology and resources. The corporation appears to be in a position close to unique and ahead of the competition and to have the financial strength to enter and grow in that market and perhaps dominate in market share. How close can the corporation come to making sure of all this? How can analyses be best performed? Can the market be tested? Can some partial steps be taken that will provide good indicators? Can some milestones be set up which, if not passed successfully, might indicate that the analysis has been wrong? In setting up answers to such questions the marketing organization is an essential participant, and it is often in the chairmanship position.

Even if existing products are highly successful, it is continually necessary to reevaluate the present and future position of the company in those product areas. What is happening to the technology that relates to that field? Is obsolescence setting in? Are competitors finding new approaches either to performance or to cost? Are the applications moving away from the past and present dependency on this particular product? Is change coming in the social, economic, or political environment that may alter the system of which the product is a part and thus impair the future success of the corporation in producing that product? These questions can only be answered by information from many parts of the corporation and from the outside. The general management must arrange that there be these separate inputs and that they be integrated into overall corporate positions about the product areas. However, again, marketing not only participates, it is very often the prime organization in arriving at the answers.

Marketing research ranges from general surveys to highly specific studies for the contemplated product entry or modification. A number of private organizations in the United States provide general market extrapolations in high technology fields. Others sell services for more detailed market surveys of individual endeavors. Professional societies, agencies of the government and a number of nonprofit organizations also provide information that can be valuable. Large industrial corporations dealing with consumer products often test market, that is, launch a limited sales effort as an experiment to provide more definitive information about a specific new product to which they are contemplating making a major commitment.

For most high technology corporations, the evaluation of the market must be done in substantial part by their own marketing organization. This usually means working directly with potential customers in assessing whether the contemplated new product or product change will find a favorable response in the market.

In assessing the demand for a product, sophisticated analysis must be done that separates the initial surge of product demand that may have built up over many years and awaits fulfillment through the new development, on the one hand, from the steady annual requirement for replacement and extension in the use of the product, on the other. Thus, if you invented and produced a good, radically low priced, broadly useful chemical laboratory instrument, you might be busy for a year or two filling a pent-up demand by all chemical laboratories. The sales then settle down to an annual volume based on the slow growth of chemical laboratories. On the other hand, if you invented a new cheap fuel for automobiles, it would be the continuing market with which you would be concerned from the beginning.

In making market surveys for technological products, particularly very new ones, the difficulty is not mainly in obtaining and discussing technological facts concerning the product endeavor and its potential with the customer. The technological performance information, that is, the various characteristics of the product itself and its application, are usually expressible in numbers and most often the overall economic effectiveness is similarly quantifiable and analyzable. The difficulty is more likely to be that if the product is unfamiliar to the customer, the precise way in which he will apply it and in which it will affect his activities is not easy to predict. This is because many nonquantifiable factors are involved. Thus, it is readily understandable that it would have been difficult for a horse and carriage customer to anticipate adequately how a horseless carriage based on an internal combustion engine would affect his life. Similarly, a department store chain does not find it simple to assess the impact of installing electronic point-of-sale devices for sales registry, charge authorization and inventory control. Initially the chain is not sure how it should best modify its operations and what the overall consequences will be. The same applies to an airline contemplating the market for a supersonic airplane with its characteristics of very different performance and price.

Marketing Strategy and the Competition

The marketing organization of a technological corporation should be the prime mover in the creation of marketing strategy. Prices should be set in part by starting with costs and adding an appropriate return-on-investment profit factor. This is a step in setting prices, but it is hardly adequate. Two other factors, at least, are of extreme importance and marketing should be the initiator on both, because it has the most direct opportunity to analyze the situation and make the appropriate recommendations. One is the competitive situation. It does little good to set prices based on a corporation's cost and investment-return goals in disregard and ignorance of competitive pricing. The other is best described as the cost effectiveness to the customer and the relationship among pricing, the benefits to the customer and the total volume that can be marketed to the family of customers that will find the product cost-effective to them at the price. Making these tradeoff decisions requires understanding of how the customer will use the product and what will be the consequences of that use. For this, the marketing organization has primary responsibility.

Unfortunately, a rapid technological advance does not always make marketing easier, even when the advance takes place within the corporation rather than in a competitor's laboratory. Some technological products, to be cost-effective for a customer, require a number of years of his use, this so the initial cost of purchase, installation and learning to use the new development can be spread over a substantial period and volume of his operations. A new product coming on the market that does the job even better presents the customer with a dilemma, or at least an optimization problem. Should he throw out the existing equipment that he counted on to help him for several years when he purchased it, take a book loss, and buy the new system that looks as though it will do even more for him, or should he ignore the new development and continue to benefit from his present investment?

A similar dilemma exists for the supplier of the equipment. The supplier corporation will have startup costs to write off, preferably against a reasonable period of profitable sales on the original product, a writeoff that will be accelerated (hurting annual earnings) if he brings out the improved product too early. Meanwhile, of course, there are competitors for both the supplier and the user of the equipment, forcing their strategies by independent actions.

Competing to a competent marketing organization is not viewed merely as a contest between salesmen seeking the order by out-talking, out-presenting, and out-advertising the competitor. The total position of a corporation in a particular product area relative to the competition involves an array of elements. It is the job of the marketing organization to separate these elements and continually evaluate the company's strengths and weaknesses in each dimension against those of the competition. Perhaps a corporation is ahead today in the basic technology inherent in the product. If so, what can be learned about the R & D efforts of competitors? Are they likely to pass the corporation? Looking at the narrow side of marketing alone, what can be said of the strengths of the company in sales, application engineering, service after the product is sold, maintenance, spare parts, and the like? What is the overall image of the company against competitors and what does it stem from? What can be done to emphasize the positives and remove the negatives in the competitive reputation aspects? If the corporation's manufacturing endeavors are apparently very successful, fully up to competitive standards or superior, is there a chance that this happy status may erode? What of the labor situation and the dependence of manufacturing on suppliers whose situation may be doubtful?

The resources available to a competitor need continual assessments about their significance. It is one thing for you to be battling a small or medium sized corporation whose continuity may be very dependent on the product line and whose pricing policies, R & D budgets, and overall marketing effort may be relatively predictable based on knowing they are dependent on the earnings from this product line to finance their future efforts. It is another to take on a division of a very large corporation, with the parent perhaps putting an imbalanced magnitude of resources behind that division competing with you. From your standpoint some of your competitors may do crazy things, and you have to give some attention to predicting what those might be and when they would be timed. The international position, the degree of head start, the various other interests of a competitor, his habits of investment and implementation, his priorities and alternatives—all of these things must continually be pondered. Again and again the job of marketing is to create a credible though changing plan to get ahead of competition and stay ahead, or close the gap and catch up if behind.

Market Share

The most important aspect of all is to follow the way the market for the product area is divided up among the competitors, both existing and potential ones. Your corporation's market position must be realistically evaluated. Whether you are first, second or third, you ought to know where you stand and why you are in that position. Being first is extremely important both in time and in volume. It enables the exploitation of the learning curves and the use of pricing as a weapon to improve earnings and increase the gap over competitors. If the position of the corporation in that product area is first among competitors, then the strategy goes to maintaining that position and exploiting it. If the corporation is second or third, then the strategy needed is on how to get out of that unfavorable position or, if this is not possible and the situation can be lived with, to minimize the disadvantages.

Market share is so important a strategy factor that the motivation of employees, from the highest levels down, must be geared to recognition and performance relative to it. Often a sales executive's salary and bonus, and even the financial compensation and stature of a product line general manager, are tied too directly to the sales and earnings performance of the immediate period. Market share has the characteristic that it affects not only the immediate results but also is fundamental to superior accomplishments for a substantial period into the future. Market share cannot be built overnight, because it evolves around so many aspects of the product (performance, cost, availability, reliability) that require time for planning, development and implementation. On the other hand, market share can be lost in a hurry, if the competition has performed all of these time-consuming tasks better. Thus, market share for the future must be analyzed and related to the near-term activities of the organization.

Performance on those functions intended to enhance and maintain market share must be related to compensation and, in general, to motivation of the performers. Reported sales and earnings for a period do not automatically disclose market share and market share trends. When actions are taken, or deferred, to increase margins and improve financial results for a period, the manager should examine those actions carefully before they are taken to see what the effect might be on the future market share position.

Although this is not true in every instance, those companies that have the largest share of market most often also have a higher return on assets employed than their lower market share competitors. This is a generalization and can only be the beginnings of strategic planning for specific product line businesses. A really useful strategy has to be very detailed and specific. Perhaps the most important single aspect of strategy for success is to segment the market carefully, picking out those aspects in which the corporation can be outstanding. Superficially, the company may be far from a leader in market share in the general product area. But in the segment of the market in which the company has chosen to specialize, it may be first, and that is what counts.

For success it is necessary that management attention, R & D budgeting, manufacturing technology efforts, and (perhaps more important than any of these three) highly focused marketing be applied to the chosen market segment. The company must be precise in definition of the market segment and know the real competition in that segment. The segmentation can constitute highly narrowed-down product characteristics (performance, price, energy use, maintainability, life, etc.), geographical area of marketing, distinct kind of customers, custom versus standardized units, or a combination of these and other concentrations.

Timing

The strategy used to market a product will certainly vary from one product to another and may vary over time for any one product. Timing is of critical importance in a marketing strategy. It is a parameter both obvious when mentioned loosely and difficult to define quantitatively without taking very specific product examples and following them through in great detail. As a generality, there is a sort of absolute timing regarding the market for a product involving an economic and a social acceptance. Is the world ready for your product? Has the system of doing things in which your product would be a subsystem arrived or is it yet to develop? If it does develop, on what time scale and with what rapidity? And how does the entry of your product affect the timing of the development?

A different kind of general timing question worth mentioning is the timing of the availability of the corporation's own resources: financial, management, skilled factory personnel, location, relationship to other product commitments and the status of the technology. Is the corporation's own team ready and anxious? Does it need and want the work? To produce the product the corporation will need suppliers for certain materials and components. Is the timing right for them?

Timing is often a critical issue with regard to competitors. Sometimes a new product must be introduced, or a series of improvements made to an existing one, at a particular time because of what is believed to be the competitive strategy and timing. In other instances, it is well to delay the entry of a new product or major improvement precisely because the competitor's performance is such that it is unnecessary and costly. Premature launching of a new product could threaten the return on existing products and the value of the associated inventory of partly finished goods and spare parts.

One of the most fascinating, difficult to handle, and yet often highly exploitable timing issues relates to the general economy and often the social-political environment for a product endeavor. Some product launchings should be deferred if a recession is threatening, when the customers will be unable or unwilling to make the additional investment, even though in the long run their buying of your products may aid their overall position. In other instances, the onset of a recession may play into your hands and may suggest your product should hurriedly be put on the market. This, in contrast, would imply that your product might enable customers to cut costs quickly and maintain their earnings position in the face of decreasing sales. Obviously many variations are possible, and it is not sensible to discuss this in detail without taking up in great depth very specific examples of products and overall national or world economic-social-political conditions.

Mutual Support of Product Lines

A product line rarely exists successfully in isolation. It relates to all the other components of the system of which it is a part (a transmission is part of an automobile and a digital switching network is part of a telephone system). Moreover, successful new product endeavors very often are mere improved versions or extensions of existing product lines. The broadening of a product line to handle other applications very often might not meet the company's R_A standards, if the product item were purely on its own. The returns become satisfactory instead because not much in the way of incremental assigned assets are needed. The new products share resources with older, established products. Moreover, extended products might share the market organization and sponge on the market position which the corporation already has (and would find far too expensive to bring into position from scratch to back up these product extensions alone.)

Marketing strategy very often hinges on whether a product can be fully supported by the present product organization, that is, on whether product engineering, marketing, manufacturing and application engineering will be adequately behind the product. The strategy always requires understanding what needs to be changed about the company to cater particularly to the proposed product line, how profound such change is and when and how it can be made. Sometimes a corporate strategy is based on believing that the corporation has an unusually good opportunity because of the way a product ties in with other products, while the competitor will find this same product poorly related to his other activities. He will have only a hodgepodge of unrelated products trying to compete with your rather nicely interrelated, mutually supportive set of product lines.

Exploiting the relationship among the various products of a corporation has virtually no end of possibilities. Since large technological corporations tend to be diversified and multinational, they have widespread sales, customer service, and application engineering organizations. A corporation should always be continually asking itself what other products it could equally well market at low incremental cost. These should then be given priority in product design and engineering as well as advanced R & D. As a matter of fact, in principle there is no reason why the marketing organization of a corporation should not market products engineered or manufactured by other corporations.

A marketing resource should be used to the fullest when it already exists. There are successful corporations whose marketing organizations do just that.

A marketing strategy is not complete without including the customer in the act. This is not to say he directly sits with marketing to figure out what the corporate strategy should be. But it does mean that marketing should go out and ask the customer questions to find out how he feels about the product, the benefits and difficulties he sees in use of it, the timing, the idea of this corporation as the one to supply him with the product, the competition, and overall, what conditions would make for the most success in marketing as seen by that customer.

The Marketing Manager

In order for the marketing strategy for a product line to be meaningful it must be thought of as an all embracing plan that includes everything from R & D through to the buildup of production and the assignment of the salesmen and maintenance engineers. If the strategy is to be so encompassing, it is quite clear that the head of marketing must report to the highest integrating management level, to which engineering and manufacturing also report and where the profit and loss responsibility for the product exists. If what we have already listed as contained within the marketing function is topped by the marketing strategy, the overall manager of the marketing function must be a broad gauged individual with very considerable interest in and knowledge of the external economic-social-political environment into which the corporation must sell. In a technological corporation he is unlikely to be successful without a substantial science and engineering background as well.

Profit Impact of Marketing Strategies (PIMS)

From the previous descriptions of the marketing function, and the broad role we have outlined for the function, it is seen that under the aegis of marketing we have placed a considerable load of strategic planning for the profitability of the company as a whole, a task we can properly say belongs to overall corporate management. Admittedly, marketing is not the equivalent of general management and is only one of the inputs to overall strategic decisions concerning the selection of product lines and the planning of courses of actions to build or drop those lines. Still, marketing is so close to the action and the heart of such decision-making that, here, in the marketing chapter it seems appropriate to place some further generalizations about corporate strategy in which the emphasis is on the product lines (rather than, say, on corporate financing of growth).

Specifically, for an existing product line the strategic questions are such as these: Is the performance satisfactory? If not, what can and should be done to alter it? Should the line be eliminated, extended, or used to generate cash with no growth goals? Should more R & D be done on the line? Should the marketing effort be increased? Should the sales price be raised or lowered?

For a candidate for a new product line the strategic questions are: Does the corporation have special leads or a combination of advantages, talents, and position that will make for long term success? What are the risks? How are the risks of failure and success related to the size and nature of the program planned to launch and build up this line?

In considering questions such as these, two kinds of efforts are going to be conspicuously at play. One is to garner answers from experience. The other, with experience in the background, is to work the problem of the moment from scratch on its own apparent merits. All of these questions will have been raised in the past on the various existing product lines of the given corporation and of many other corporations. Similar decisions have been made and acted upon many times before. On those occasions how did things turn out? Suppose the top executives of a corporation noted that whenever they had a strong technological lead on competitors the product line flourished. Conversely, when they went into a product that was behind technically, or lost the lead, the product line failed. Then it is to be expected the company those executives manage will have a strong bias when making strategic decisions to associate success with technological lead as an empirical relationship derived from experience.

Every company has experiences and empirical laws, written and unwritten, that guide company strategy. But the management of every well run technological corporation knows the available laws are inadequate—not really proven, perhaps the result of accidental, unidentified company, competitive, or external environmental actions that greatly influenced success or failure in individual cases. Thus the second kind of effort is always carried on, in which the facts, potentials, and alternatives are built up for each product line under consideration from the very bottom. Here an effort is made to include everything (known, estimated, or, if nothing better can be done, guessed) that can make for success or failure of a product line strategy, without reference to general empirical laws from past experience. Then it is seen how the product line's forecasted scenario looks.

The importance of strategic planning and decision making for technological corporations is difficult to exaggerate. It is not surprising then that over a hundred top companies have jointly become sponsors of an activity known as the PIMS program (Profit Impact of Marketing Strategies), which is the actual title for a program at the Strategic Planning Institute, Cambridge, Massachusetts, in which each participant furnishes data from experience to provide a broad data base for business planning by all. Since each contributing company has clearly defined experiences on 10–100 product lines, the combined data base can incorporate thousands of individual cases.

The Strategic Planning Institute assembles, edits and maintains the data base. It then conducts research to discover the general empirical laws, where they appear to exist within the data base, that govern profit success and other outcomes resulting from various strategic actions or changes in the external environment in which the product lines have operated. The information on each business consists of about 100 items. These describe the market, competition, technological status, cost structure and other characteristics, the strategic steps taken in managing the product line and the results obtained in terms of profits, returns on investment, growth, and so forth.

From this source of data and laws useful answers can be obtained (about what the past experience adds up to) on such questions as: What profit rate is par for a product line given certain facts regarding market position, technology, costs, and the like? If no change is made in strategy what are the likely results? What strategy might improve the forecast? How might a shift in strategy influence profitability versus time?

The research already done on the available data base shows certain high correlations, meaning that at least some empirical laws are suggested by past experiences and should be taken seriously. If you are violating them you had better convince yourself your case is an exception. PIMS have found that nine influences constitute the main determining factors of a business. Some businesses are good and others are not. If an attempt is made to list how these business differ, 80% of the variance is explained by (i.e., contained in) these nine influences. These characteristics constitute the empirical behavioral laws of the marketplace, the business itself, and its competitors. Unknowns (and/or luck) thus appear to have constituted only 20 percent of the influences on the businesses in the data bank. Being in the right business and running it the right way, according to the distilled experience on the thousands of cases in the PIMS data base, is 80 percent of the key to success.

The nine influences in brief abstract follow:

1. The higher the investment base (high capital intensive, high inventory) the lower the R_A.

2. Profitability is higher when productivity is higher (i.e., when the value added by the company per employee to the input material and components is higher).

3. Profitability and cash flow are higher with higher strength of market position compared with the largest competitors.

4. Growth is accompanied generally by higher profits and lower cash flow.

5. Quality, as judged by customers, relative to competitive products, goes with better financial performance.

6. More R & D improves financial performance for a company with strong market position to begin with; otherwise, usually not.

7. In stable, mature product lines, vertical integration (make rather than buy) helps profitability. In changing (growing or declining) markets, the opposite is true.

8. Cost pushes (wage increases, labor union presence, inflation in material costs, etc.) have complex impacts depending on the ability of the company to pass along increases, and the like.

9. Change of strategy temporarily can create opposite effects to the long term effect of new strategy. For instance, increasing market share may use cash; when the higher market share is reached, higher positive cash flows will then result.

To give one or two brief examples of the applications of these nine laws, consider first a product line for which the market position is weak. The generally safest strategy based on many experiences is this: hold down R & D; eliminate expensive marketing drives; use suppliers instead of making components in-house. Must you always follow these laws? Of course not. If you perceive a technological breakthrough that you are confident will alter your market position then by all means consider putting funds behind R & D and marketing and even making your own components perhaps. But remember, most often experience shows that route fails. Perhaps the market leader copies your new technology and quickly passes you. So you better be sure you really have a brilliant new invention, patented and exclusive and you are ready to keep the top competitor from using it.

As another example, don't automate a successful operation without a very careful assessment of the consequences. The investment may be higher than you think relative to the incremental cost reduction and the benefit from pricing/volume changes. Will you get the cost benefits or will most of it (because of factors beyond your control) go to customers and employees?

Application Engineering and Customer Support

We have already emphasized that a technological product cannot be designed and marketed successfully without a close relationship with the customer. Application engineering is of fundamental importance to achieve a successfully designed product and to create the beginnings of a good and close relationship with the customer. The customer, even if it is another high technology corporation, cannot be expected to comprehend fully what the product you wish to produce and sell to him can do for him. Conversely, it is not automatic that the product-producing corporation will understand the needs and alternatives of the customer. What application engineering is about is creating a real understanding on the part of the corporation's customer of the present product, and of the corporation's future product potential to do something beneficial for him. It is equally important for the corporation to understand what the customer's needs are, and how the product, or what the corporation can create as a product, will meet his requirements or give him some previously unperceived advantage. You must match your technology and resources to his needs and opportunities for gain.

Sometimes the customer will articulate so completely what he needs or could use with great advantage that the task is done for you. You can then concentrate on trying to see if you can meet the detailed specifications he has called for. Some corporation customers, such as chemical companies contemplating further use of electronic instruments, or large department store chains considering automation of information flow, take the initiative on occasion. They may expend a great deal of funds to bring in experts to work in their system, come to understand their existing or future activities, and do at least the beginning design of improved systems. Out of such in-house studies may arise detailed specifications of the component parts of the systems they are devising. The customer has then created a market for those components.

Most often, however, for the creation of a new ensemble of hardware and software and the specification of the elements to be produced joint effort is required. The resulting product is something that neither the customer nor the supplying corporation could alone have invented. Very often it is not properly described as an answer to a problem the customer has, but rather it is the exploitation of an opportunity for the customer and hence for the supplying corporation.

Application engineering is essential to market the product from the market research stage through to making the sales. It continues to be vital to keep the product sold and prepare for its extensions, improvements and ultimately its replacement. During all of this time, application engineering greatly influences the design of the product and the marketing strategy and lays the groundwork for a good deal of the facts needed to set up a scenario for investment in the product or in the extension of the facilities to broaden the market for it.

In addition to application engineering, another important engineering task properly may be considered as part of the broad marketing function in a technological corporation. This is customer maintenance service. A large technological corporation typically has many products that need this servicing, and it markets these products over a wide geographic area, nationally and often internationally. It involves maintenance of equipment, repair, and supplying of replacement parts, and that usually means the creation of an organization specifically to carry out this function. A very small technological corporation with a narrow product line often finds the customer maintenance function a very difficult burden. As a result it subcontracts this service to a larger company that has the necessary organization for it.

A large corporation usually has many different products and may use the same customer service organization for all of them. Of course, the unit needs engineers experienced in handling those products, who are able to diagnose failures and direct technicians trained to make modifications or repairs, install new parts and otherwise ensure that the equipment works properly in the customer's hands. Typically, large corporations employ thousands of people in such organizations. With products coming and going, a constant training program is needed even if there is no turnover or expansion requirements for the personnel.

In addition to personnel training, there are interesting questions pertaining to the geographical distribution of the personnel and physical resources of a maintenance organization. Always there are tradeoffs about whether to concentrate the people in a few larger cities and have them travel out to service equipment at some distance or to distribute them more widely to give more rapid service when a fault occurs. Optimization of the inventory of spare parts is required. How much inventory should be carried and where should the parts be warehoused? A luxurious inventory, high quantities available and a multiplicity of locations, can be far too expensive. It is thus a matter of balancing the advantages of rapid service against reasonable costs for the maintenance operation.

The importance of service and maintenance on technological products is obvious for some of them. Often the importance is made evident by the fact that the cost of maintenance over the life of the product is substantially greater than the first cost in purchasing the unit. On this basis alone the related matters of maintenance, reliability and working life of a product should be very influential for product design, pricing and marketing strategy.

The service and maintenance experience must feed back to product improvement and indeed should be in the picture from the very inception of the product at the R & D phase. The tradeoff problem of price of product versus cost of maintenance must be handled both as a product design problem and as a marketing problem. Increasing the cost of the product would appear to be justified if the service and maintenance cost to the customer is decreased over the life of the product more than the added cost required to provide better reliability. But the customer will not always appreciate this. The first cost the customer is certain about. If your price is higher than that of your competitor, it will be of concern to your customer. The fact that he might make up the higher cost in lower maintenance cost may sound credible, given the detailed arguments in support of such a claim, but the scenario is still speculative to him and will require years to prove. It becomes a function of marketing to work out a proper relationship between this kind of logical optimization, on one hand, and the understanding by the customer and his willingness to consider higher priced products whose cost in the end will be lower, on the other.

The excellence of customer support over a period of years does more than anything else to establish a good image of your corporation with its customers. If a customer believes he is receiving prompt, efficient, economical service and if the products, improved in their performance by this service, do the job for the customer, then he is going to be favorably inclined toward doing business with you again on his next purchase of products. The customer comes to know you well as he deals with your corporation through your service organization on a

frequent and intimate basis. Good performance by your service organization means you likely will be privy to the thoughts of the customer
about his future plans and will learn what competitors are offering
him. The customer will be more generous in offering his expertise
about his needs and perceived opportunities. You obtain through good
customer service the equivalent of free expert consulting for development of your own marketing strength.

In view of the importance and the challenging difficulties of creating
and operating a top grade service operation for technological products,
it is regrettable that this is an underestimated field in engineering
circles. University engineering schools and their top technical graduates tend to regard career opportunities in service and maintenance
as mundane. Actually, just as is true for manufacturing, the effort
requires for its management and planning the high technological and
managerial skills that not every engineer possesses. Done right, customer service and support engineering can have a powerful influence
on the success of a technological corporation's products. Performed
poorly, it may have an even greater influence, but in the wrong direction.

Selling and Leasing

The art of selling appears to be a multifaceted one about which many
books have been written and many more will be. We shall in this
textbook hardly get into the problem at all. Many of the organized and
described sales approaches do not apply well for technological products. There are some obvious generalizations that can be made, of
course. For technological products the salesman need to be adequately
prepared in the technology underlying the product and its application.
Application engineering and customer service support organizations,
although not basically in the sales business, are very important to
creating the atmosphere for a sale and to eventual success in getting
the order. Advertising brochures and the sales pitch itself for a highly
technological product, particularly one sold directly to a high technology industrial customer, must avoid the exaggerations, the illogical,
overpowering and mind-bending ploys, so commonly used for many
mass-consumption, nontechnological consumer products.

Distributors and Sales Representatives

An important decision that typically must be made with regard to
technological products sales is the degree to which that sales effort

must be handled by an in-house staff. The alternative is for the products to be sold and distributed by independent organizations that make marketing their specialty. Small companies often have no choice but to partly use independent distributors and sales representatives or they will miss full exploitation of their product in widespread geographical markets, particularly in foreign countries. An in-house effort sufficient to reach the whole market would require an organization quite disproportionate to their overall corporate position in view of the narrowness of their product lines. Generally, whether the corporation is large or small, it may find that full reliance on in-house marketing and distribution versus the partial use of outside distributors involves both benefits and negatives. The question must be studied in great detail. The answer may vary from product to product for the same corporation.

A company can often learn a great deal from independent distributors that it would never learn through its own organization. Typically those independent distributors have a different, sometimes more objective, view and contact a much broader range of customers and competitors. Through their experience with the products of other companies as well as yours they can provide comparative assessments and intelligence information on forces and trends in the market that otherwise would not be so readily available to the corporation.

It is very important to consider independent distributors, if a corporation is in the components business. Here typically there are a large number of different products and a high volume is required to keep the price down. This high volume of sales may be much easier to realize by using a network of independent distributors who can find customers in every nook and cranny all over the world.

However, after citing these possible advantages to the use of distributors it must be said that they are rarely satisfactory for a company's entire sales and distribution activity. Even a small corporation will find it preferable to do at least some of the selling with its own staff. Otherwise it will not be close enough to the customers to comprehend the market well.

Leasing

It is important in marketing highly technological products, particularly those involving a price tag in the hundreds of thousands of dollars or more, to note that leasing may be preferable to selling. To a first approximation the choice of one approach over the other should go basically to the matter of how to realize the greatest return on investment, how to finance at the lowest cost of capital, and to balance both the return on assets and the cost of capital against the risk.

When a corporation engages in leasing its products rather than selling, it is in the banking business, even if only indirectly. It is necessary to be certain that the return on the capital invested in the leased equipment, and carried on the corporation's books as depreciating assets, is greater than the cost of capital, particularly in today's inflationary times. (We shall discuss inflation as it relates to this question somewhat more specifically in Chapter 12) Even if the present value of the stream of committed rental payments by the customer implies a satisfactory return on investment and, let us say, is at least the equivalent of obtaining all the money at once in an outright sale, it must be noted that there is a risk as long as the assets are carried on the balance sheet. Although a firm contract may be held with the lessee, the possibility of default on the contract may still exist. In contrast, a sale means the money is in hand at the outset, with all of the risk removed.

Beyond these basic financial considerations, marketing strategies enter the equation. By leasing equipment rather than selling it the corporation may secure the advantages of greater volume and a larger fraction of the market. Many customers feel more comfortable equipping themselves with certain technological products, and obtaining the annual bennefits therefrom, if they reckon those benefits against the annual payments on a lease basis. It should be true for the customer, of course, that he also looks at the return on investment if he makes a purchase and compares it with the equivalent cost of a lease operation. Still some customers prefer a very straightforward comparison merely of annual benefit against annual expense and are unable or reluctant to finance the purchase themselves.

Of course, there are instances where corporations will provide equipment on lease without duration-of-lease commitments, offering the lessee the privilege of turning the equipment back at any time he wishes (perhaps with a small penalty) rather than being bound to hold the equipment and go on paying the lease price each year for an extended period. Under such circumstances, the company producing and leasing the product takes all of the risk. It is understandable then that for some customers it may be much more attractive to lease. Even if they understand they are paying a penalty equal to the cost of capital and perhaps substantially more, they are often attracted to the idea of removing at once and totally any concern about inflexibility, technological obsolescence and later dissatisfaction with the product.

They know that if they can turn the leased equipment back to the supplier, they can avail themselves at any time of a still better proposal by a competitor during the entire period ahead.

Although it may at first seem foolish for a corporation to lease its products without the guarantee of a stream of payments that will write off the assets with an appropriate return on the investment, this overlooks two or three related possibilities. It may be the producing corporation feels it is in position to assess the market for its products and to put a limit on the risk involved, that is, the probability of the customer's returning the product in the short term. The leasing corporation may feel quite comfortable in its assessment that the average actual lease time will be substantial, that it can re-lease the product to others if it is turned back (albeit perhaps at a lower leasing charge) and that the leasing income properly discounted to cost of capital for the life of the average lease is very attractive. It may even prefer to lease rather than sell on this basis.

To decide on leasing versus selling requires comparative analyses in each individual situation, and generalizations are not too sensible except perhaps the one that merely says leasing should be considered as a means of enlarging the market when dealing with very new, technological product endeavors. If the product is regarded by some customer's as unproved, and the corporation producing it has high confidence in what it will accomplish for the customer, the leasing route may be a very valuable route against competitors. Of course, at times a company may have to consider leasing as a defense against a competitor who already has started to use leasing against the company to take over its market position.

Granted leasing as a possibility, it is then necessary for a technological corporation to master the technique. For example, carefully worked out contracting relationships are required about leasing rates versus time with cancellation possibilities and inflation properly brought into the picture. Leasing plans also are not complete unless the lessor has adequately considered the impact of technological obsolescence. This may cause the products under lease to be returned because new products may arrive on the scene and be superior for the customer. He may then even be willing to pay a penalty to return the products.

Problems

9–1. Your product will provide a typical customer with 10 years of service before it must be discarded. It sells for 20 percent more than a competitor's product that yields identical performance but will last for only five years. What is the overall financial advantage to your customer in purchasing your product against your competitor's if the customer's average cost of capital is 10 percent? Answer this by figuring the net P_v for the cash in and out for the customer in the two cases. Speculate on why many prospective customers appear to prefer your competitor's product over yours.

9–2. The established competitor in a product line has 100 percent of the market you are thinking of entering. He will have more salesmen, be better known in the field, and be able to produce his product more cheaply than you will initially, not only because of the advantage of higher volume, but also because your product will be more complex. However, your product will be superior in performance and hence more cost effective to the customer even at a higher price. Your marketing department says that the best strategy is to spend heavily on customer education about your superiority in performance and to hold the initial sales price down to a modest increment over the competitive product, absorbing the losses as inevitable start-up expense, and to increase prices later as the volume increases. What do you think of this strategy? Do you have any better ideas?

9–3. Your company proposes to add a product line by licensing the rights and know-how on an existing product from another company. It is estimated that start-up costs before taxes will be $100,000 during the first year. In the second year and thereafter a sales volume of $500,000 per year will be expected for a total of 10 years with a sales margin after tax of 10 percent. Assume that after these 10 years the product line is dropped and the assets then employed, without gains or losses, are diverted to other things. The licensor receives a royalty on sales of 6 percent and a $100,000 initial payment for the license. Company engineers meanwhile estimate that with a modest program for one year an equally good product can be developed internally. How costly an internal program for that year can you afford if the approach is to represent an equal investment opportunity to your company? Use an average cost of capital of 10 percent.

9–4. Your proposed product is the equal of an existing one of a competitor but, because of its advanced design, will cost you 30 percent less to produce, assuming you and the competitor will share 50 percent of the steady total volume the market will require. The plan you submit to management follows: (1) enter the field the first year with a 10 percent lower price, acquiring immediately 15 percent of the market; (2) increase market share from 15 percent the first year to 50 percent the fifth year on a straight line basis; (3) increase price to equal the established competitor's price the fifth year, the increase per year being again straight line; (4) break even the first year ($R_A = 0$), R_A rising straight line to a fifth year value of 20 percent (after tax); (5) assets employed during the fifth year, $5 million, having risen straightline from $2 million the first year; (6) fifth year sales, $12 million. Produce a five-year chart of sales, assets employed, R_A, earnings (after 50 percent tax) and cash flow (assuming depreciation just equals replacement). Management asks: since during the first five years the return is low, what is the internal rate of return if the fifth year performance is continued steadily for another 10 years, the assets then removed without gain or loss? Also management wants to know what you think the competition will be doing all this time.

9-5. A multi-billion dollar corporation owns a novel process for generating liquid fuel from coal. Estimates suggest that after reaching a high sales rate (over a billion dollars a year) the company will be able to produce this synthetic fuel with satisfactory R_A and R_I at a sales price roughly equivalent to the 1979 price of purchased and refined foreign crude oil. However, the corporate chief executive office decides against an entry into this field. Think about this and try to explain why this decision by the CEO might be a correct one.

9-6. Three companies share the market in an advanced technology field that is moving rapidly so that all three competitors feel compelled to spend about the same amount each year for R&D and marketing research. Their fixed expenses are close to the same. For the market leader these fixed expenses are about equal to the variable expenses, and the variable expenses are roughly proportional to the sales for all three competitors. The market is divided among them as follows: 40 percent, 33 percent and 27 percent. If the leader has a sales margin before tax of 22 percent, what are the before-tax sales margins of the other two?

9-7. Two competitors share the market on a 70/30 basis with the same price per unit. For the market leader the variable costs are twice the fixed costs. The other competitor has fixed expenses only 65 percent of the leader's, because he does less research and development and has substantially less investment in facilities and in complex and expensive capital equipment. Furthermore, the variable costs per unit produced for the second company is 150 percent of the variable cost per unit of the leader who is further along on the learning curve as well as being in a position to employ techniques of fabrication more suitable to his higher volume. If the sales margin before taxes for the number two supplier is 2 percent, what is the sales margin of the leader? What is the leader's fixed cost as a fraction of sales and what is the ratio of variable to fixed expenses for the number two company?

9–8. A company announces that its revenue dollar has been spent during the year as follows:

R&D-new products—2 percent
Manufacturing technology advances—1 percent
Market research—2 percent
Employee wages, and fringe benefits—30 percent
Plants, facilities and equipment, maintenance and depreciation, including new facilities expansion—25 percent
Purchased parts and materials—30 percent
Dividends to stockholders—2 percent
Interest on debt—2 percent
Taxes—6 percent

Assuming that the company is in a 50 percent tax bracket, how much would the earnings of the corporation after taxes be improved, if the company had spent a quarter of one percent more of the sales dollar on productivity improvement and if, as a result, labor costs would have been reduced by two percent.

9–9. Since the market leader has so many cost advantages, why would it not be the best strategy for him to keep his prices no higher than the prices set by his lesser volume competitor?

9–10. A new product is lagging badly in sales against plan. Careful study shows that, as expected when the product was launched, it is unique and no competitor is active or in sight. Furthermore, at the offered price the product is extremely cost-effective for the customer. Up to the present time 15 percent of the customers believed to be in position to benefit from buying the product have been solicited and only one-fifth of them have made purchases. At the present sales level the product activity is in a loss position. At least twice the sales rate is needed to break even. State which of these proposed strategies you would recommend: (1) Drop the line and accept the liquidation losses; (2) cut costs to seek break-even at present sales volume; (3) cut price to increase sales, perhaps planning to raise the price later; (4) increase and improve the marketing effort.

9-11. A company is considering entering the market with a highly technological product for which there are already three competent suppliers. In view of the competition, some favorable factor beyond ordinary capabilities is needed to justify the late entry. Suggest four such factors which, if they existed, might justify the company's going ahead.

9-12. If you are Number Two in market position in a product endeavor, explain why tabulated experience discloses that increasing the R & D budget often will not help you attain a higher market share. But if you are Number One in market position, increasing the R & D effort will most often yield an increase in your share of the market.

10

GROWTH AND RETRENCHMENT

Rationale for Growth Objectives

Ours is a technological society. Every year the fraction of all the goods and services we produce that properly can be labeled technological increases. If scientific discoveries and technological developments are applied wisely and to the fullest, then we should expect to discover regularly lower cost methods of providing for the requirements of society, substitutes for materials in short supply, and ways of processing materials and manufacturing for our needs with less harm to the environment. We should be able to perceive new products so economical and socially attractive and beneficial that they merit risk and investment to develop them because of the value of anticipated returns.

All this means that well run technological industries should expect to grow. A technological corporation that does not is presumably not operating efficiently, has not chosen the proper mix of products that will match its potential and resources to the needs of the market, or has not plowed back enough of its earnings or arranged for proper financing to take advantage of its opportunities. This does not say that growth must take place every single year in sales, earnings, earnings per share and the returns on assets employed and equity. Recessions, mistakes, technological breakthroughs by competitors, unusual government actions—these and many other factors can enter to disturb what might otherwise be a steady growth pattern. However, the general trend is bound to be one of growth if on the average all goes well with a technological corporation.

Diversification and technology as they mature follow a similar list of factors that militate for growth. But diversification itself is a source

275

of growth, if the diversification is properly managed. As more applications are worked out for a new technological development, the sales volume should grow. As complementary apparatus is required to make an initial product work in still another application, that additional equipment is a source of product line growth. The market also grows geographically, as more and more nations enter the picture, playing catch-up as technological societies needing the technological products.

Of course, any individual product line defined narrowly follows an "S" curve of growth for a while. Its market rises slowly at first and then steeply. As the product reaches full application or some applications are better served by still newer developments, the market rise flattens out (and eventually disappears). However, the corporation that produces that product presumably will develop many others. Because of the existing product, it will have come to know the market and have the product design and manufacturing capability to lead in providing successor products. The net result of the integration of a large number of successful individual products rising and falling should be a growth curve.

Worship of growth of itself does not equate to good management. But growth is essential to success of a technological corporation. If growth does not take place, it may mean that the competitor is doing a better job and is dominating the market, reaping the advantages of volume and of being farther along on the learning curve. If a corporation finds that in certain fields of endeavor it is not growing, it should consider dropping out of those areas and putting the investment instead in other fields where it can register growth—only consider, because a diminishing sales period for a product may still be a very profitable and useful phase.

Aside from the competitive situation, growth is basic to attaining size and realizing the advantages of a large operation in providing R & D funds, start-up costs for further market penetration, and motivation for management and employees generally. Career opportunities, advancement, and security of employment require a growth objective and actual growth performance. Because these points are held to be true be those who judge corporations (such as present shareholders, potential shareholders, bankers, security analysts and management) growth is seen by the marketplace as an indication of success and lack of growth for a technological corporation as a symptom of failure to manage well. Thus, growth is also associated with the cost of capital and ease and flexibility with which capital can be attracted when needed. Growth, particularly of earnings and positive cash flow accompanying growth of sales, virtually assures the availability of capital for further growth.

Granted the advantages of, and imperative requirement for, growth for long range success in managing a technological corporation, arranging for growth is not a simple task. Adding to the unpredictability of technological products is the constantly changing science and technology base. As the totality of product efforts by a technological corporation grows, individual products must be constantly introduced, withdrawn, modified, or extended. They must be applied, marketed and distributed in different ways and places as time passes. Success in managing growth requires parallel success in managing retrenchment and divestment. At the right time some projects should not be allowed to grow. Some product lines should be harvested or milked as cash cows. Other activities should be liquidated, sold off or cut down in volume. Assets frequently must be reallocated. Shiftable assets include, in addition to facilities and working capital, the engineers, marketeers and manufacturing experts. One might say that growth (defined both positively and negatively) is at the heart of the process of management of technological corporations. In this chapter we shall take some of these important interactive problems of growth management and subject them to further scrutiny.

Internal Growth

We recall the formula

$$g = \frac{1 - R_V}{1 - R_{DA}} (R_A - iR_{DA}) \qquad [1]$$

(Recall also that in deriving this formula it was assumed the depreciation expense exactly equaled replacement outlays, an assumption we shall retain in this chapter.)

Transposing Equation 1,

$$R_v = 1 - g \frac{1 - R_{DA}}{R_A - iR_{DA}} \qquad [2]$$

Thus, if it is regarded as necessary to finance a particular g to hold market position against competitors in a growth field, then with given R_A, R_{DA}, and i, we can determine from Equation 2 how much we can pay out to the shareholders as dividends and still have enough left over to reinvest for growth. Given R_A, we can also investigate doing some adjusting of R_{DA} so that, within reason, we can arrange the divident ratio we would like while maintaining the growth needed.

To illustrate, for a growth rate of 10 percent per year, $R_A = .15$, $R_{DA} = .30$ and $i = .05$, then

$$R_V = 1 - \frac{.10 \times .7}{.15 - .05 \times .30} = .48$$

In this instance the dividend apparently can be generous and the required growth totally financed internally while maintaining a good debt-equity ratio.

On the other hand, consider a company whose return on assets employed is only $R_A = .10$ but nevertheless requires the financing of a growth rate, g of .14, or it will lose out in market share to its competitors. Here even with no dividend whatsoever paid out, the growth rate can only be internally financed with a heavy debt. Specifically, from Equation 1, when $R_v = 0$,

$$g = (R_A - iR_{DA})/(1 - R_{DA}) \qquad [3]$$

and

$$g - gR_{DA} = R_A - iR_{DA}$$
$$R_{DA}(i - g) = R_A - g$$

or

$$R_{DA} = (g - R_A)/(g - i) \qquad [4]$$

Substituting $R_A = .1$ and $g = .14$

$$R_{DA} = .04/.09 = .444 \qquad [5]$$

If a corporation has an unusual opportunity to build a position in a new product area believed to possess high profit potential as high volume is reached, then most evaluators of the company will consider it good strategy, albeit one to be tolerated only for a few years, to hold down dividends and reinvest earnings in growth. The company also might be expected to carry more debt than would be considered prudent in the long run. It would be considered inexcusable for management to lose the opportunity to dominate the field. The typical investor would argue that, if holding back dividends and adding debt are not sufficient to finance the desired growth, more equity stock should be issued. Keeping up growth to hold market share would be the prime, starting condition. Recalling the formula for a steady-growth company

$$C_Q = R_V/M + g \qquad [6]$$

at a given expected return C_Q, the investor would tolerate a low R_V, if he believed a high growth rate, g, would result. He would pay a high multiple, given by rewriting Equation 6, to

$$M = \frac{R_V}{C_Q - g} \qquad [7]$$

The low R_V would not deter him from purchasing the shares, and it would not make M low in Equation 7, if g is close to C_Q. (Recall that this formula only holds when $g < C_Q$.).

So far we have commented only on the matter of adjusting the debt and dividend parameters or considering further equity stock sale in order to finance growth. Suppose financing is available and thus is not the problem. The other side of the coin is to so manage the company and the product selection that growth opportunities will always be present. A growth opportunity is not alone a product line whose sales can be made to grow, but one which while growing will meet the company's return criteria. We perhaps have implied in the preceding paragraphs that the highest growth rate that a product opportunity can engender always should be financed. This is an exaggeration, of course. Often a healthy product line should not be allowed to grow faster than a certain rate. Such a limitation goes to the details of the market for that product line and the situation vis-a-vis competitors.

Suppose, for instance, that your corporation already dominates a growing market. You might make the market grow at an even faster rate by lowering the price because doing so might increase the economic value of the product to more customers. The higher volume might cut unit costs so that the unit profit might be preserved despite the lower unit sales price. However, it might be that, although the previous growth rate of sales was totally financed from within (by plow back of earnings after dividends), the new higher growth rate might require either more debt or the issuing of more equity stock. The proper decision might in this instance be not to increase the rate of growth. Of course, if the earnings were to rise sufficiently with the higher growth rate to continue the practicality of internal financing, or if a competitor were in a position to challenge the corporation for first place market position, then the higher growth strategy might be chosen.

The ability to finance growth from within is so dependent on the basic overall performance in generating earnings, as judged by the ratio, R_A, that a good deal of attention must be given by management to ensuring a high steady value for this parameter. But R_A for the typical corporation is the result of earnings performance in the use of assets in many profit centers operating in parallel. At any given time, some products are more important than others in their effect. Sometimes a disappointing performance, say, a sudden large operating loss in a small part of the company's business, can adversely affect the overall R_A very severely. If the corporation can avoid making serious mistakes on product selections, it will avoid having very low or negative R_A in such product categories.

Consider, for example, a corporation containing two categories of products, those with high and those with low R_A. The total earnings of the corporation result from the separate earnings of each of these categories of products. That is

$$E = A(R_A - iR_{DA}) = E_1 + E_2 \qquad [8]$$

where

$$A = A_1 + A_2$$

so that

$$E_1 = A_1(R_{A1} - iR_{DA})$$
$$E_2 = A_2(R_{A2} - iR_{DA})$$

where the debt has been allocated to the two categories in the same ratio as assets employed. Combining, we obtain

$$AR_A = A_1R_{A1} + A_2R_{A2}$$

or

$$R_A = \frac{A_1R_{A1} + A_2R_{A2}}{A} \qquad [9]$$

Thus, if

$$R_{A2} = .1R_{A1} \text{ and } A = 2A_1 = 2A_2$$

then the overall return on assets employed is

$$R_A = 1.1/2 = .55R_{A1}$$

If $R_{A1} = .20$, $R_{A2} = .02$, and $R_A = .11$. $R_A = .20$ is very satisfactory, but $R_A = .11$ probably hovers near the average cost of capital, C_A, for the company and may not be acceptable over the long term.

If a substantial fraction of the assets of a corporation are in very low return activities, it is incumbent upon the management of the corporation to evaluate removing itself from these activities. It may be necessary to lose some of the assets in the process of trying to extricate them out of low-return product lines and inject them into high-return ones. Once the loss is taken, however, a much improved earnings situation for the future will be set up. This raises an interesting question of optimization to be taken up later as we discuss divestment and liquidation.

Growth by Acquisitions

Mergers and acquisitions continually take place in the coporate world. This happens for many different reasons, some of which are special to technological corporations. The route to growth of a corporation by taking over others has both a stock market promotion aspect and a substantive one. These two aspects are not necessarily independent. We shall discuss the stock market aspects first.

Mergers have been at times the result of efforts by promoters to create a bigger operation for the promoters to run or for them to exploit on the stock market. Some investors will rush to purchase the shares of a corporation they observe to be growing by acquiring other companies. Apparently they rate the management as outstanding if it is active in making acquisitions, bigger looking better, the rest of the data about the company constituting relatively uninteresting detail. This especially can be true if the stock of the acquiring corporation catches on, that is, if enough investors share a sense of success about the corporation engaged in such acquisition activity. This may also mean that the stock of the acquisition prone company is at the time overvalued, although obviously not widely recognized as such. With the stock overpriced, it is possible for the corporation to issue more shares and trade with shareholders of other corporations having poor recent records and whose managements are regarded as not overly competent. The shares of such available companies might be selling at an especially low price on the stock market compared, say, with their potential if newly perceived as well managed. The market value of such shares may be well below book, and the merger-minded survivor corporation may obtain valuable assets that are underpriced in trade for shares of stock that are overpriced.

Earnings Per Share Manipulation

If an acquirer corporation can make a series of mergers with corporations whose mutiples are lower, then every time a merger takes place that surviving corporation will end up with a higher earnings per share. Consider a survivor corporation whose shares are selling at a price P_S, with earnings per share E_{S1}, and hence, a multiple $M_1 = P_S/E_{S1}$. This company issues shares to acquire a second company whose price per share is also P_S, but whose earnings per share are E_{S2}, meaning it has a multiple $M_2 = P_S/E_{S2}$. M_1, we shall suppose, is greater than M_2. We assume the corporation to be acquired has N_2 shares outstanding.

Suppose the survivor corporation can persuade the shareholders of the acquired company to accept one of its common shares for each common share they now hold. This is not unreasonable, since the market price for each share is the same. That is the market's way of saying that one share is equal in value to the other. The total earnings of the two corporations after the merger, now reported in the name of the surviving corporation, are

$$E = N_1 E_{S1} + N_2 E_{S2} \qquad [10]$$

which is just as before the merger, of course, since no time has elapsed and no changes have taken place except in this newly stated reporting of the same period's earnings. If we divide these total earnings by the total number of shares, we shall have a new reported earnings per share for the surviving corporation as follows:

$$E_S = \frac{N_1 E_{S1} + N_2 E_{S2}}{N_1 + N_2} \qquad [11]$$

But, because $P_{S1} = P_{S2}$, the original per share earnings of the two companies are related by

$$E_{S2} = E_{S1} M_1 / M_2 \qquad [12]$$

and we can rewrite Equation 11 as

$$E_S = \frac{N_1 E_{S1} + N_2 (M_1/M_2) E_{S1}}{N_1 + N_2}$$

or

$$E_S = E_{S1} \frac{N_1 + (M_1/M_2) N_2}{N_1 + N_2} \qquad [13]$$

The multiple M_1 is greater than the multiple M_2, as stated. Hence E_S is greater than E_{S1}.

The investors of whom we have spoken might look superficially at the increased reported earnings per share for the survivor corporation and regard this as evidence their original hunch was right: the corporation engaged in the acquisitions is doing an outstanding job of management. They are likely to build in their minds a scenario for future events that includes a high growth for the corporation. Its stock may be driven up still higher as purchasers are willing to offer an even higher multiple for its shares. This makes it possible for the acquisition minded corporation to find even more companies with whom to trade shares, continuing to drive up its earnings per share with each acquisition.

Of course, unless the corporations assembled in this manner have inherent profitable growth as a result of their product activities, or the combination of the various operations in one well managed company creates a superior future for all of its activities, the bubble will burst. A lion cannot be produced by merging a bunch of dogs.

Merging for Added Strength

We shall say no more about the corporate merger activities that stem from this kind of stock market promotion, although this has been a factor in the stock market and probably will continue to be forever. We are more interested in the substantive reasons for mergers and acquisitions. In this regard it must be recognized that it may very well be true that combining companies A, B, C, and D will make a strong corporation. This means the individual activities of A, B, C, and D, when in the same corporate entity as the others, may be greatly enhanced. The management now is able to optimize, cut costs of common services, exploit important synergistic effects, because the activities complement one another and provide career outlets and motivations for the management employees of all four entities that were not available to them before. The result may be a corporation with a higher average R_A and a higher growth rate because of the possibilities of putting more assets behind those activities that deserve backing for growth. The market position of the corporation in the various products of the separate elements, A, B, C and D, may be greatly advanced and the corporation may be in a much better position to finance new products, divest unsatisfactory activities or terminate them, operate in more countries, and generally have more overall available competence in management than any one of the companies had before.

Often a merger is justified because what one company needs badly the other enjoys plentifully. A company with high growth potential but inadequate funds can be an excellent merger partner for another company with mature product lines, high earnings and no place but dividends to put the excess cash flow. Mergers can sometimes be advantageous because they constitute a way to create a critical mass of capital, technological competence, ideas, management skill and other resources sufficient to attack an area that cannot be well handled by either company acting alone.

Sometimes in a good merger the product lines are highly synergistic. Perhaps the typical customer needs both lines and one marketing organization is all that is needed to supply the customer and furnish good application engineering and efficient distribution. Again, one corporation may be very strong in ideas, research and development and product engineering but weak in manufacturing technology and accordingly handicapped in the market place. Another corporation may be especially strong in manufacturing, its management skilled in the efficient operation of factories, in working with labor and labor unions, in suggesting how to redesign for minimum use of critical and expensive materials and for efficient high quantity production. If the second company, although strong in manufacturing, lacks an R & D organization that can provide it with new products for future growth, the combination of the two corporations might then be extremely beneficial.

Some companies have found it a practical approach to growth to minimize expenditures for R & D on new products. Instead, they maximize short-term earnings and cash flow. Then, periodically, they use available cash to purchase a small company engaged in a new product area of interest to the company. In this way a good deal of the gamble has been eliminated and the sorting of the good ideas from the large number of possibilities has been accomplished. Of course, the price of the acquisition, assuming they limit themselves to proven potentials, will be relatively high. However, the company may feel it is still cheaper in the long run for it to pay the higher price for the established articles than to engage in the game of playing the odds by carrying out exploratory R & D and new product entries in-house. This route has proven successful on a limited basis for some technological corporations. Most often, an optimum combination of in-house development and acquisitions leads to superior long-term growth results.

To the survivor corporation, the wisdom of an acquisition depends not only on the potential advantages just cited but also on the price to be paid to realize these advantages. Most often the survivor corporation has to pay a premium in stock or cash to make possible the bringing into the fold of another corporation. That is, it pays more than the market price of the shares of the corporation it is acquiring. The shareholders who hold the acquiree corporation may be reluctant to take the risk of exchanging shares, or simply elect not to part with their shares, unless they receive more than the market price for them. Had they not held the opinion that the shares were worth more they might have sold them yesterday.

If two companies are merged one should not look for miracles. Changes, either adverse or beneficial to the shareholders, will result from the conbining. It should not be expected that the two original pieces of the newly merged corporation will continue to go about their business, making decisions independently and operating their product lines precisely as before. If they did, the annual performance results of the combined company would then simply constitute a total of the two pre-merged operations, the figures turning out exactly as they would have had anyone been interested in summing the numbers of the two, previously separate, corporations. Something always happens in a merger, if only the elimination of some key people and the assumption of leadership by others out of the total cast of managers available to run the combined operation. The pattern of activities of one is bound to influence the other. Perhaps, of the two companies, one is accustomed to ubiquitous organizational bureaucracy, and it spreads that bureaucracy into the other corporation which previously had less of such handicaps. Maybe the better marketing strategy of one company will elevate that of the other one. Both good and bad will result from a merger.

In the absence of other information the two companies together should be regarded as worth on the market about the same as the sum of what they were worth separately—perhaps a bit more or less, but the sum of the two is a starting point. The burden of proof is on those who believe a major boost of market value is justified. Sometimes the people so convinced are those running the survivor corporation. Equally often, however, those who are acquired, who in effect allow their corporation to be run henceforth by the surviving corporation, feel they are gaining. They are placing their company in the hands of a superior management, one that will do more with the assets being acquired than was being achieved before the merger.

Sometimes a technological corporation may go completely outside of its area of competence and experience and acquire a company in a distinctly different business. An electronics equipment corporation, for example, may acquire a car rental agency. Obviously, dangers exist in such an acquisition because the management of the surviving corporation might lack competence in the added product area. The combination nevertheless may work out in special circumstances. An example is where the company acquired happens to be a bargain, can be left to its own competent management, and produces a strong cash flow for years which the technological corporation advantageously employs for investments in its own fields. Most often, however, technological corporations should stick to expansion by highly selective diversification in which the areas of endeavor of acquired companies are highly related to that of the corporation doing the acquiring.

Even related diversification by acquisition is not always safe. The degree of relation sometimes is exaggerated and the merger may simply put together two relatively weak technological corporations that can do very little to add to the probability of success of either but can add up to a big set of problems for the surviving management. If the company being acquired has weak management, then the surviving corporation must make up for it. It must be in a position to contribute the added management competence and effort required or the merger will prove a failure. This is worth emphasizing, because very often the reason that a company is available for acquisition is that it is not doing well, and the reason that it is not succeeding is because it has incompetent management. When this occurs, it may be that the acquiring company sees an unusual opportunity, if it does indeed have management capability to spare. This is because it buys resources at a low price and is able to inject what is needed to increase the value of the acquired assets.

Potential Negatives of Mergers

We need to discuss further such subjects as evaluating acquisitions and deciding on whether in making an acquisition it is better to purchase the assets of the acquired company by use of cash, or to trade shares to effect the merger. First, however, we should pause to mention some of the reasons against acquisitions. To begin with, the happy blending of two business entities is not the easiest accomplishment in the world, because people are involved. The managements and staffs of the two companies may not be compatible. Even if they turn out to be, considerable reorganization and changes of responsibilities usually have to take place and this can take much time for adjustment. Also, it must be assumed some mistakes in organization and executive assignments will be made and will have to be rectified as it is seen how people relate to one another. Although some poor performers may be ejected, good performers may choose to leave because of their disappointment with the new allocation of roles and missions.

As with the human components, the product lines may not be adequately compatible. Consider the merger of a corporation that has been making the highest priced, highest quality items in a product area with one that has been making the economy models. Each product line may be hurt by the presence of the other in the same corporation. The customers of the high quality line may now look upon the source of those products as having compromised its quality by being willing to take into their company the low quality products in which those customers have no interest. They may fear that the previous emphasis is bound to be diluted since attention has to be given by management to making a success of the cheap line. On the other hand, those interested in the economy products will be concerned that the "Cadillac" background of the new owners will creep into all product lines causing prices to be raised in an effort to improve a product they think fine just as is.

Many mergers turn out to be unsuccessful for the rather simple reason that the survivor corporation, through a misjudgement and too great a desire to build size, has acquired the other entity at too high a price. The problem of making the return on the acquired unit high enough to justify the purchase price may be insurmountable. Trying to do so by cutting costs may impair the health and vitality of the acquired operation. Also, when one corporation acquires another, it is usually discovered that the acquired corporation has serious negatives that were not seen ahead of time (it is not usually a high priority for the acquiree to make its shortcomings crystal clear). The management of the survivor corporation often finds itself very busy trying to solve an array of bothersome problems it did not realize the acquired corporation had to the neglect of the mainline activities in the survivor corporation.

Two corporations usually have differences in their methods of evaluations and reviews of investment decisions, means for selection of product lines, pensions, public relations, accounting, relationships with unions, philanthropic contributions, retirement practices, promotion policies, and many other patterns of management. Also, when two corporations are put together, a translation problem immediately arises in most communications, oral and written. A cultural adjustment problem displays itself, probably for both parties. ("We don't do things that way.") A small corporation being acquired by a large one is often expected to change its approaches to conform to the overall pattern of the large corporation. When two large corporations merge, especially if each is geographically widespread and substantially diversified, the result for years may be a hodgepodge of different patterns of control and a Babel in communicating the information needed for control and evaluation of operations.

Further negatives of the acquisition route are simply relative. Acquisition may be not as good as an alternative: to build up from within an activity similar to that of the acquiree, or one just as useful to the broad objectives of the corporation. We shall give this matter more discussion later.

Mergers' Impact on Reported Results

Given that one company is intent on absorbing another, let us take up the two basic ways in which this can be accomplished. One is by the acquirer's purchasing the assets of the acquiree for cash. The other is by merging the two corporations, the survivor issuing its stock to the shareholders of the acquired corporation in return for their shares. If common shares are exchanged, then we have already discussed what happens to the earnings per share of the surviving corporation. Let us now examine some other impacts on the reported results of the survivor.

If the returns on assets employed of the two companies are R_{A1} and R_{A2}, the assets A_1 and A_2, and the earnings E_1 and E_2, what will be the return on the combined assets? Using the subscript 3 for the new, merged corporation and assuming we have performed no alteration whatever in the two entities, then

$$E_3 = E_1 + E_2$$

or

$$E_3 = R_{A1}A_1 - iR_{DA1}A_1 + R_{A2}A_2 - iR_{DA2}A_2 \qquad [14]$$

$$= R_{A1}A_1 + R_{A2}A_2 - i(R_{DA1}A_1 + R_{DA2}A_2)$$

$$= \frac{R_{A1}A_1 + R_{A2}A_2}{A_3} A_3 - i\frac{R_{DA1}A_1 + R_{DA2}A_2}{A_3} A_3$$

and

$$E_3 = R_{A3}A_3 - iR_{DA3}A_3 \qquad [15]$$

where we have set

$$A_3 = A_1 + A_2 \qquad [16]$$

$$R_{A3} = \frac{R_{A1}A_1 + R_{A2}A_2}{A_3} \qquad [17]$$

$$R_{DA3} = \frac{R_{DA1}A_1 + R_{DA2}A_2}{A_3} \qquad [18]$$

We should note that the new R_{A3} of the combined company is a weighted average of the R_A's of the two original companies and the same thing applies to the new R_{DA3} in relation to the two companies' R_{DA}'s. Neither is at all influenced by the stock market multiple differences. Of course, the management of the combined new company may decide on a different R_{DA} for the future than R_{DA3} from Equation 18, or it may take internal steps to cause the R_A to differ from R_{A3} of Equation 17. All we have done is assume that on the night of Dec. 31 the two companies are merged and, starting the next morning, Jan. 1, they are looked at as a new company. Then that merged company will have a reported last year's performance as described in part by R_{A3} and R_{DA3}.

Suppose the two companies had dividend policies, as described by R_{V1} and R_{V2}, that were properly tailored to provide for each company its individual optimum growth as shown by g_1 and g_2 through reinvestment of some of the earnings. If, on merger, we allow the two entities to continue on the optimum path for each, what will R_{V3} and g_3 turn out to be?

Since each entity will have the same net cash flow as it had before the merger, will need the same plowback to maintain the same growth, then the generated cash available after plowback to pay dividends will be the same for each. Thus, assuming the same R_{DA} for both,

$$R_{V3}E_3 = R_{V1}E_1 + R_{V2}E_2$$

or

$$R_{V3} = \frac{R_{V1}R_{A1}A_1 + R_{V2}R_{A2}A_2}{R_{A3}(A_1 + A_2)} \qquad [19]$$

Also, recall the familiar formula for growth rate,

$$g_3 = \frac{(1 - R_{V3})(R_{A3} - iR_{DA3})}{1 - R_{DA3}} \qquad [20]$$

If, to take one example, $R_{A1} = R_{A2}$, then from Equation 17, $R_{A3} = R_{A2}$. If also, $R_{DA1} = R_{DA2}$, then from Equation 18, $R_{DA3} = R_{DA2}$. Calling these two quantities R_A and R_{DA}, and, finally, assuming that $R_{V1} = R_{V2}$, we see from Equations 19 and 20 that $g_3 = g_1 = g_2 = g$.

Suppose, however, that a mature company paying regular dividends merges with a younger one that has been paying none and, instead, investing all its available funds in growth. Specifically, if $R_{V1} = 0$, $R_{V2} \neq 0$, $A_1 = A_2$, $R_{A1} = R_{A2} = R_A$ and $R_{DA1} = R_{DA2} = R_{DA}$, then from

Equation 19,

$$R_{V3} = \frac{R_{V2}R_A}{2R_A} = \frac{R_{V2}}{2} \qquad [21]$$

as we might expect, and, from Equation 20

$$g_3 = \frac{1 - R_{V2}/2}{1 - R_{DA}}(R_A - iR_{DA}) \qquad [22]$$

This can be rewritten in terms of g_1 and g_2. Thus

$$g_1 = (R_A - iR_{DA})/(1 - R_{DA}) \qquad [23]$$

and

$$g_2 = (1 - R_{V2})(R_A - iR_{DA})/(1 - R_{DA})$$

or

$$g_2 = g_1(1 - R_{V2}) \qquad [24]$$

Rewriting Equation 22 as

$$g_3 = g_1(1 - R_{V2}/2) \qquad [25]$$

we see that g_3 of this corporation, obtained by merging two companies of the same A, R_A, and R_{DA}, falls half way between the higher growth, g_1, of one company and the lower growth, g_2, of the other.

Cash Acquisitions

Now let us shift to analysis of the cash acquisition approach. Company No. 1 buys the assets of Company No. 2 at book value using available cash. Company No. 2, let us assume, has assets employed of A_2, and $(1-R_{DA2})A_2$ is the book value of its shareholders' equity. Company No. 1 will pay $(1-R_{DA2})A_2$ in cash to the shareholders and maintain the debt, $R_{DA2}A_2$. The companies' balance sheets before and after the transaction (constructed to emphasize the pertinent points) are as shown in Table 10–A.

Only Company No. 1 survives. It is be instructive to see how its basic parameters are suddenly changed by the transaction. The new R_{DA}, shown in the table, is given by

$$R_{DA} = \frac{R_{DA1}A_1 + R_{DA2}A_2}{A_1 + R_{DA2}A_2} \qquad [26]$$

For an illustrative example assume $R_{DA1} = R_{DA2} = .33$, and $A_1 = 3A_2$.

Table 10–A

Company No. 1 (Before)			
Assets		Liabilities	
Cash used for the acquisition	$(1 - R_{DA2})A_2$	Debt	$R_{DA1}A_1$
Other assets	$A_1 - (1 - R_{DA2})A_2$	Equity	$(1 - R_{DA1})A_1$
Total	A_1	Total	A_1

Company No. 2 (Before)			
Assets		Liabilities	
		Debt	$R_{DA2}A_2$
		Equity	$(1 - R_{DA2})A_2$
Total	A_2	Total	A_2

Company No. 1 (After)			
Assets		Liabilities	
Remaining assets from Company No. 1	$A_1 - (1 - R_{DA2})A_2$	Debt	$R_{DA1}A_1 + R_{DA2}A_2$
Assets acquired from Company No. 2	A_2	Equity	$(1 - R_{DA1})A_1$
Total	$A_1 + R_{DA2}A_2$	Total	$A_1 + R_{DA2}A_2$

Then

$$R_{DA} = (A_2 + .33A_2)/(3A_2 + .33A_2) = .4 \qquad [27]$$

In addition to Company No. 1's debt-to-equity ratio rise, its cash position has been substantially impaired. Instead of the acquisition, the company could have chosen to pay off debt, in which case it would have had a greatly improved balance sheet situation for debt. Before we jump to the conclusion that the acquisition was a mistake, we need to ask what happens to earnings.

Before the acquisition the earnings of Company No. 1 could be written as

$$E_1 = R_{A1}A_1 - iR_{DA1}A_1 \qquad [28]$$

However, it will be convenient to break this up a bit more to show the part of the earnings that was interest income on the cash that was used to purchase Company No. 2, That income, at rate i' on cash of amount $(1 - R_{DA2})A_2$ will no longer be received after the transaction. Thus, introducing R_A' as the return on the other assets, we can write

$$E_1 = i'(1 - R_{DA2})A_2 + R'_A[A_1 - (1 - R_{DA2})A_2] - iR_{DA1}A_1 \qquad [29]$$

After the acquisition, the new earnings, E, will be higher because of adding Company No. 2's earnings and lower by loss of the special interest income. Specifically,

$$E = R'_A[A_1 - (1 - R_{DA2})A_2] - i(R_{DA1}A_1 + R_{DA2}A_2) + R_{A2}A_2 \quad [30]$$

To illustrate, assume again $A_1 = 3A_2$, $R_{DA1} = R_{DA2} = .33$, $i = .05$, $i' = .04$, $R'_A = R_{A2} = .15$. Then from Equation 29, the stated earnings of Company No. 1 before the merger are

$$E_1 = .11A_1 \quad [31]$$

and, from Equation 30, the earnings after the merger would be stated as

$$E = .145A_1 \quad [32]$$

This is a very substantial increase in earnings, and also in earnings per share since the number of shares are unchanged. The acquisition might be between a large company (No. 1) with excess cash with no good place to invest it internally and a smaller company (No. 2) with high growth potential but insufficient cash flow to finance its growth. The higher earnings suggest that Company No. 1 will be able to choose to finance growth, or perhaps increase dividends or pay off debt, or a combination of the three.

Let us consider another case. Company No. 1 borrows the additional cash needed to acquire the assets of Company No. 2. Table 10–B shows the pertinent before and after balance sheet figures. Again we assume that in making the purchase, Company No. 1 pays book value for the equity shares of Company No. 2 and assumes the debt of that company. The new debt-assets ratio, R_{DA}, is now

$$R_{DA} = \frac{R_{DA1}A_1 + A_2}{A_1 + A_2} \quad [33]$$

If $R_{DA1} = .3$ and $A_1 = 3A_2$

$$R_{DA} = (.3 + 1/3)/(1 + 1/3) = .4725 \quad [34]$$

As to the new earnings, E, compared with E_1, assume $R_{A1} = R_{A2} = .15$, and $i = .05$. Then

$$E_1 = R_{A1}A_1 - iR_{DA1}A_1$$
$$= .135A_1 \quad [35]$$

while

$$E = R_{A1}A_1 + R_{A2}A_2 - i(R_{DA1}A_1 - A_2) \quad [36]$$

Table 10–B

Company No. 1 (Before)		
Assets	Liabilities	
	Debt	$R_{DA1}A_1$
	Equity	$(1 - R_{DA1})A_1$
Total A_1	Total	A_1

Company No. 2 (Before)		
Assets	Liabilities	
	Debt	$R_{DA2}A_2$
	Equity	$(1 - R_{DA2})A_2$
Total A_2	Total	A_2

Company No. 1 (After)		
Assets	Liabilities	
	Debt	$R_{DA1}A_1$
		$R_{DA2}A_2$
		$(1 - R_{DA2})A_2$
	Total Debt	$R_{DA1}A_1 + A_2$
	Equity	$(1 - R_{DA1})A_1$
Total $A_1 + A_2$	Total	$A_1 + A_2$

which, with the specific numbers of the example, becomes

$$E = .15A_1 + (.15/3)A_1 - .05(.3A_1 + A_1/3)$$

$$= .1633A_1 \qquad [37]$$

Again, as in the previous example, a substantial reported earnings increase takes place for Company No. 1. This can be used in part to finance growth from within. Suppose that Company No. 2 has growth potential and Company No. 1 has none, and that, consistent with this, Company No. 1 previously paid out all its earnings in dividends. Thus for the year just being reported we would have, from Equation 35

$$V_1 = E_1 = .135A_1 \qquad [38]$$

If Company No. 2's growth rate potential was g_2, this means that for that entity, employing assets A_2, the increment in assets required in a year to support the growth would be

$$\Delta A_2 = g_2 A_2 \qquad [39]$$

The new combined company must now supply this increment in

assets. As seen against the new larger asset base, the growth will be only

$$g = \Delta A_2/(A_1 + A_2) = g_2 A_2/(A_1 + A_2) \qquad [40]$$

Let us continue with the use of numerical illustrations and assume g_2 = .20. Then

$$g = \frac{.20 \times A_1/3}{A_1 + A_1/3} = .05 \qquad [41]$$

With this growth accommodated out of available earnings, how much will be available for dividends and how will the new dividend, V, compare with V_1, a matter of some real interest to the shareholders of Company No. 1? We can get at this in a number of ways. Using either g_2 = .20 or g = .05, the asset increment needed to support this growth is, from Equation 39,

$$\Delta A = .05(A_1 + A_2) \text{ or } .20 \times A_1/3 = .067 A_1 \qquad [42]$$

Of this, a fraction ΔQ must come out of earnings and the rest (if R_{DA} is constant) will be borrowed according to the relation

$$\Delta Q = (1 - R_{DA})\Delta A$$

which, using Equations 34 and 42 yields

$$\Delta Q = .035 A_1 \qquad [43]$$

Finally, using Equation 37, and remembering that

$$V = E - \Delta Q$$

we have

$$V = .13 A_1 \qquad [44]$$

Company No. 1 can finance the growth and continue with almost the same dividend. However, the debt is too high. The management should either issue more common or cut the dividend. Probably the first course will work out best unless the stock multiple appears to the management to be unjustifiably low at the moment.

Stock versus Cash for Acquisitions

If combining two corporations is seen to be sound for general business reasons, should it best be done by trading stock or buying assets with cash? Whether a corporation can and should acquire another by stock or cash involves two different sets of shareholders' considerations. One involves the circumstances and desires of the corporation to be acquired. And the other goes to the options available to the survivor corporation. Very often a corporation being acquired is insistent on stock because principal owners of the shares may have obtained them at a very low value compared with today's market price. If they receive cash, then a very large part of it would go to the government through a capital gains tax. The Internal Revenue Service allows a tax-free deal if the shares are tendered for shares in the surviving corporation. (It is possible to satisfy the IRS with a combination, some cash and mostly stock, but we shall not go into the details in this text.) Stock may be preferred in addition by the shareholders of the acquired company, because of the good dividend of the survivor corporation. The merger might be of a company not yet paying a dividend with a mature company with a well established dividend record.

Sometimes the owners of the corporation to be acquired want cash. If such owners receive shares in a trade, then they will want the privilege of selling the shares immediately to realize the end result they seek, which is cash. It may be that if a corporation's shareholders are to receive cash they will bargain hard to receive an amount of cash greater than the market value they would accept in stock. This is because they will want enough additional funds to be able to pay some or all of the tax on the capital gains and still net the after-tax cash figure they have in mind.

From the viewpoint of the management and shareholders of the survivor corporation the situation involves many more options and details. First of all, the debt-equity ratio of the survivor is an issue. If the survivor corporation already has a great deal of debt and does not wish to see it increased then it will have to prefer the route of issuing more shares. Or, it could be the other way around. The surviving corporation might have surplus cash or a very conservative debt-to-equity ratio. It could use its excess cash, or borrow to obtain cash, to purchase the new corporation's assets. It may be reluctant to issue more shares if it thinks they would be undervalued on the market at that time. The management may feel it knows more about the growth promise and general future performance of the corporation than the market appreciates. It does not want to see its earnings per share diluted, as it might have to be, if more shares were issued to make possible the merger.

In an exchange of shares the accounting is relatively straightforward. The two balance sheets are simply put together, and the survivor corporation has the integrated total of assets and liabilities of each.

The relationship between the price paid for the acquisition and the book value of the acquired company is not a factor so far as the balance sheet is concerned, although it is pertinent to the total number of shares that will be outstanding. Just as the survivor corporation's pre-merger market value is not usually the same as its book value, so after the merger an inequality may exist, although probably a different one. On the other hand, if the acquired corporation is purchased for cash, then any difference between the purchase price and the net worth of the acquired company will show on the new balance sheet. It is most often true that in an acquisition the price paid for a company is greater than the book value. This means the asset side of the balance sheet of the survivor corporation will display an intangible equal to that difference.

The intangible represents a crude valuation on the stream of earnings of the acquired corporation over and above what should be expected from the book value alone. The acquiring corporation is willing to pay a price higher than book value because the acquired corporation is worth it. What makes it worth it? Either the intangible really is an asset approximately equal to what was paid, over book, to obtain that asset or else the buyer made an error in judgment. Nevertheless, balance sheets with large intangibles resulting from acquisitions are regarded by some analysts as weaker than if all the assets were tangible. This is neutralized in time by writing off the intangibles, usually a few percent per year. The rationale for depreciating or amortizing the intangible item in this way is that the stream of anticipated added earnings represented by it will diminish with time and eventually will come to an end. The amortizing portrays this reduction.

Acquisitions versus Internal Growth

For the survivor corporation, we have already listed many qualitative considerations that might cause it to desire a specific acquisition at a suitable price. Quantitatively we need only return to some of our earlier discussions about the evaluation of investments in general to add some pertinent comments on the evaluation of acquisitions. Presumably, the survivor corporation has many options for the investment of funds, whether the funds are in the form of cash or shares of stock which give the new shareholders the privilege of dividends from the corporation into the future. To compare an investment in an acquisition with other investment alternatives on a quantitative basis we can use again the present value and internal rate of return approaches. For every acquisition candidate, as with every other kind of investment, a merger-minded corporation should construct a scenario of the best estimate it can make of flow of funds in and out of the investment project. Then it should use this scenario to figure the net present value of the investment and the discount rate that would cause the net P_V to be zero.

For instance, if a corporation is being acquired for cash, then it is necessary to draw up a forecast for the future of cash benefit flows back to the survivor corporation and to compare the internal rate of return represented by the investment with other alternatives. Let us illustrate this with the case of Analog Corp., which is considering acquiring Digital Corp. for $3,600,000, or alternatively, to create a line of similar digital products through internal development. Table 10–C shows some key figures for the two corporations. (For simplicity, to avoid complicating the figures soon to be calculated with relatively nonimportant interest charges, we have chosen to assume neither corporation has debt.) The market for the product of Digital Corp. is estimated in Table 10–D.

The Digital Corp. product is quite unique, but Analog Corp. believes its experts can design one just as good in every way. The development costs are estimated to be $500,000 before taxes for each of two years. Analog will offer its product for sale in the third year and believes it will capture 25 percent of the market listed in year three of Table 10–D. During years four to ten it expects to have 50 percent of the market. At the start of the third year, $800,000 of operating equipment will

Table 10–C   (Thousands of dollars)

Analog Corp.	
Sales	$40,000
Earnings, pretax	4,000
Taxes	2,000
Earnings, after tax	2,000
Total assets	$13,300
Digital Corp.	
Sales	$ 5,000
Earnings, pretax	500
Tax	250
Earnings, after tax	250
Total assets	$ 1,800

Table 10–D   (Millions of dollars)

Year	0	1	2	3	4	5	6–10
Sales	5	6	7.5	10	12	15	16

be purchased and will be depreciated fully over eight years (straight line). (We assume incremental working capital requirements to be negligible.)

Table 10–E portrays this internal development alternative with the incremental investment integrated with the P & L and balance sheet items for Analog as previously listed in Table 10–C. In Table 10–E a return on the incremental new sales of 10 percent before tax is assumed. Hence, in year three, with 25 percent of a $10 million market (Table 10–D) or sales of $2.5 million, the incremental earnings are listed as $250,000. The return on assets employed figures shown, R_A, indicate that this annual measure is first hurt by the startup costs of the new product and then enhanced over the original 15 percent R_A with which the scenario starts.

Table 10–F has been constructed to divulge the cash flows, both benefits and outlays, resulting from adding the new products. *This table is solely concerned with incremental figures.* Note that a tax credit is taken during the two years when the net annual incremental earnings are negative. This justifies including only $250,000 (rather than the before-tax figure of $500,000, the actual expenditure) for the R & D expenses in each of the first two years under cash outlays.

In the last row are listed the figures for the P_V's of the cash benefits and outlays using Analog's C_A, average cost of capital, of 10 percent as the discount rate. The net P_V is $937,000, positive, so the scenario indicates the project passes this hurdle. The ratio of $2,031,000 to $1,094.000 is 1.86, which shows an attractive potential. The internal rate of return (which calculation is called for in one of the problems at the end of the chapter) will be substantially above C_A.

Tables 10–G and 10–H repeat this scenario exercise on the assumption that Analog acquires Digital.

The $3,600,000 purchase price exceeds the assets of $1,800,000 by $1,800,000. This means that Analog will start out with an intangible asset on its balance sheet of $1,800,000. This it plans to amortize in 10 years arguing that, by that time, the special head start advantage it is realizing in requiring Digital's position in digital products will have been reduced by succeeding developments. Also, the tangible purchased assets of Digital will be depreciated fully straight-line, over

Table 10-E Alternative No. 1—Internal Development (Thousands of dollars)

Year	0	1	2	3	4	5
E, orig., pretax	4,000	4,000	4,000	4,000	4,000	4,000
R & D	0	(500)	(500)	0	0	0
E, inc., pretax & dep.	0	(500)	(500)	350	700	850
Incremental dep.	0	0	0	(100)	(100)	(100)
E, inc., pretax	0	(500)	(500)	250	600	750
E, total, pretax	4,000	3,500	3,500	4,250	4,600	4,750
Tax, @ 50%	2,000	1,750	1,750	2,125	2,300	2,375
E, net	2,000	1,750	1,750	2,125	2,300	2,375
A, orig.	13,300	13,300	13,300	13,300	13,300	13,300
A, inc., cum.	0	0	800	800	800	800
A, inc., dep., cum.	0	0	0	100	200	300
A, total	13,300	13,300	14,100	14,000	13,900	13,800
$R_A = E$, net/A, total	15%	13.2%	12.4%	15.2%	16.6%	17.2%

Year	6	7	8	9	10
E, orig., pretax	4,000	4,000	4,000	4,000	4,000
R & D	0	0	0	0	0
E, inc., pretax & dep.	900	900	900	900	900
Incremental dep.	(100)	(100)	(100)	(100)	(100)
E, inc., pretax	800	800	800	800	800
E, total, pretax	4,800	4,800	4,800	4,800	4,800
Tax, @ 50%	2,400	2,400	2,400	2,400	2,400
E, net	2,400	2,400	2,400	2,400	2,400
A, orig.	13,300	13,300	13,300	13,300	13,300
A, inc., cum.	800	800	800	800	800
A, inc., dep., cum.	400	500	600	700	800
A, total	13,700	13,600	13,500	13,400	13,300
$R_A = E$, net/A, total	17.5%	17.7%	17.8%	17.9%	18.0%

Table 10-F   Alternative No. 1—Internal Development (Thousands of dollars)

Year	0	1	2	3	4	5
Incremental sales	0	0	0	2,500	6,000	7,500
R & D expense	0	500	500	0	0	0
E, inc., pretax & dep.	0	(500)	(500)	350	700	850
Depreciation	0	0	0	100	100	100
E, inc., pretax	0	(500)	(500)	250	600	750
Taxes	0	(250)	(250)	125	300	375
E, inc., net	0	(250)	(250)	125	300	375
Cash benefit, actual	0	—*	—*	225	400	475
Cash benefit, P_V	0	—	—	169	273	295
Cash outlays						
R & D		250	250			
Equipment			800			
Total, P_V		227	867			

Year	6	7	8	9	10
Incremental sales	8,000	8,000	8,000	8,000	8,000
R & D expense	0	0	0	0	0
E, inc., pretax & dep.	900	900	900	900	900
Depreciation	100	100	100	100	100
E, inc., pretax	800	800	800	800	800
Taxes	400	400	400	400	400
E, inc., net	400	400	400	400	400
Cash benefit, actual	500	500	500	500	500
Cash benefit, P_V	310	282	257	233	212

1–10 yrs P_V: Cash Benefit 2,031 – Outlay 1,094 = Net P_V = 937. Profitability Index = 2,031/1,094 = 1.86

* The loss is written off against cash outlays for R & D.

Table 10-G Alternative No. 2—Acquisition (Thousands of dollars)

Year	0	1	2	3	4	5
E, orig., pretax	4,000	4,000	4,000	4,000	4,000	4,000
E, inc., pretax & dep.	0	780	930	1,180	1,380	1,680
Incremental dep.	0	180	180	180	180	180
E, pretax & amort.	4,000	4,600	4,750	5,000	5,200	5,500
Tax, @ 50%	2,000	2,300	2,375	2,500	2,600	2,750
Amortization	0	180	180	180	180	180
E, net	2,000	2,120	2,195	2,320	2,420	2,570
A, orig.	13,300	13,300	13,300	13,300	13,300	13,300
A, from Dig. Corp.	0	3,600	3,600	3,600	3,600	3,600
A, dep., cum.	0	180	360	540	720	900
A, amort., cum.	0	180	360	540	720	900
A, total	13,300	16,540	16,180	15,820	15,460	15,100
$R_A = E$, net/A, total	15%	12.8%	13.6%	14.7%	15.7%	17.0%

Year	6	7	8	9	10
E, orig., pretax	4,000	4,000	4,000	4,000	4,000
E, inc., pretax & dep.	1,780	1,780	1,780	1,780	1,780
Incremental dep.	180	180	180	180	180
E, pretax & amort.	5,600	5,600	5,600	5,600	5,600
Tax, @ 50%	2,800	2,800	2,800	2,800	2,800
Amortization	180	180	180	180	180
E, net	2,620	2,620	2,620	2,620	2,620
A, orig.	13,300	13,300	13,300	13,300	13,300
A, from Dig. Corp.	3,600	3,600	3,600	3,600	3,600
A, dep., cum.	1,080	1,260	1,440	1,620	1,800
A, amort., cum.	1,080	1,260	1,440	1,620	1,800
A, total	14,740	14,380	14,020	13,660	13,300
$R_A = E$, net/A, total	17.8%	18.2%	18.7%	19.2%	19.7%

Table 10-H Alternative No. 2—Acquisition (Thousands of dollars)

Year	0	1	2	3	4	5
Incremental sales	0	6,000	7,500	10,000	12,000	15,000
E, pretax, dep. & amort.	0	780	930	1,180	1,380	1,680
Depreciation	0	180	180	180	180	180
E, pretax & amort.	0	600	750	1,000	1,200	1,500
Taxes	0	300	375	500	600	750
Amortization	0	180	180	180	180	180
E, inc., net	0	120	195	320	420	570
Dep. & amort.	0	360	360	360	360	360
Cash benefit, actual	0	480	555	680	780	930
Cash benefit, P_v		436	458	510	532	578
Cash outlays, P_v	3,600					

Year	6	7	8	9	10
Incremental sales	16,000	16,000	16,000	16,000	16,000
E, pretax, dep. & amort.	1,780	1,780	1,780	1,780	1,780
Depreciation	180	180	180	180	180
E, pretax & amort.	1,600	1,600	1,600	1,600	1,600
Taxes	800	800	800	800	800
Amortization	180	180	180	180	180
E, inc., net	620	620	620	620	620
Dep. & amort.	360	360	360	360	360
Cash benefit, actual	980	980	980	980	980
Cash benefit, P_v	553	503	457	416	378

1-10 yrs P_v: Cash Benefit 4,821 − Outlay 3,600 = Net P_v = 1,221. Profitability Index = 4,821/3,600 = 1.34

the same 10 years. Each of these items, depreciation and amortization, causes an annual $180,000 expense figure to appear on the P & L table. However, we should note that while the depreciation expense is tax deductible as an ordinary expense, the annual amortization is not.

We recall from Table 10–C that in the year before the acquisition the earnings of Digital before taxes (but after depreciation) were $500,000. This figure was 10 percent of the sales that year of $5,000,000. In the first year after the merger this earnings figure (assuming Digital holds on to the whole market for its product) will be $600,000, according to Table 10–D. With the depreciation expense of $180,000, the earnings before depreciation will thus have been $780,000, which accounts for this figure's appearing in Table 10–G. Again, we see that the annual figure for R_A is first lowered then increased by the impact of the acquisition.

Table 10–H describes the cash flow. The cash benefit row is obtained by adding the sum of annual depreciation and amortization ($360,000) to the net incremental earnings. Again the P_V's of cash outlays and benefits are calculated using the hurdle discount rate of 10 percent. The net P_V is $1,221,000, positive, showing that the acquisition meets the hurdle rate condition, if the scenario is to be believed. The ratio of P_V's, benefits to outlays, of 1.34 suggests the internal rate of return will substantially exceed the 10 percent figure.

It will be instructive now to shift from the quantitative to the qualitative for discussing how Analog should proceed to compare the two alternatives under consideration. Many issues would figure into Analog's decision that cannot be garnered from the figures we have been through. What does the length of time to get into the digital field mean about competitors? We assumed in the acquisition alternative that no competitor will enter to share the market. Is this realistic? What is the impact of the time delay in making entry through the internal development route, and, for that matter, the impact in general of entering this new field on all other product lines of Analog Corp.?

How would the important constituencies see the acquisition in the absolute sense and as compared with the internal development? How might the choice of alternatives affect the stock? If the acquisition route is selected, what of the compatibility of the two organizations— the reaction of management in Digital to being absorbed by another and larger company, the differing habits, patterns and goals of the management acquired, the systems used for accounting and management control? Is there a special high value that should be attached to the acquisition of some of the management personnel of Digital?

How will the customers view the acquisition, both those of Analog and Digital? What economies might a merger bring not shown by simply adding up expected financial performances of the product lines themselves? What new opportunities are opened up by combining the total resources of the two corporations? Finally, how will the government's antitrust division view the merger? Even if they approve it in the end, will that be only after a long court fight and an enormous legal bill?

Obviously our discussion cannot settle all of these questions, because this would mean going further into the description of the makeup of these two corporations and their markets than we can do in this text. However, these are the kinds of questions that Analog and Digital management will ask themselves before going ahead with the merger. The best judgments available to answer such questions must be applied and the answers used to construct the most realistic quantitative scenarios. Then the numbers from the scenarios can be useful. Otherwise they are just numbers that can be switched up and down with arbitrary changes in assumptions.

Price Models for Acquisitions

The price it is worth paying for an acquisition, be it in cash or stock, depends on many qualitative and quantitative considerations. Some of the more important quantitative aspects can be approximated by the same kind of models used previously in this book for investment decisions. To illustrate, let us consider several cases.

First assume the acquisition yields to the acquiring company an annual cash flow benefit, F, of constant value forever. Then, if the hurdle rate for return on investment for the acquiring corporation is R_I

$$P = F/R_I \qquad [45]$$

where P is the proper price to pay for the acquisition.

If the company being acquired has earnings E of which a fraction R_F are paid out as cash flow benefits so that

$$F = R_F E \qquad [46]$$

then with the price-earnings multiplier being

$$M = P/E \qquad [47]$$

by definition, the appropriate M for purchase of the company is given by

$$M = R_F/R_I \tag{48}$$

A second and common situation is one in which the acquirer expects a steady cash flow benefit F but delayed in starting by N years. Then obviously the two relationships above for price and multiple need to be altered to

$$P = \frac{F}{R_I(1 + R_I)^N} \tag{49}$$

and

$$M = \frac{R_F}{R_I(1 + R_I)^N} \tag{50}$$

Another useful model is one in which the cash flow stream starts with a first payment F at the end of the first year and grows at a constant rate g with $g < R_I$. Then the familiar relation

$$R_I = F/P + g \tag{51}$$

applies, or

$$P = F/(R_I - g) \tag{52}$$

$$M = R_F(R_I - g) \tag{53}$$

Again, if a cash flow stream growing forever is the appropriate model provided only that the start of the flow is delayed by N years, the above relations become

$$P = \frac{F}{(R_I - g)(1 + R_I)^N} \tag{54}$$

and

$$M = \frac{R_F}{(R_I - g)(1 + R_I)^N} \tag{55}$$

Often an acquisition will require a cash injection or further investment before it gives back a cash flow benefit. The present value of such investments should be subtracted, of course, from the price to be paid for the acquisition.

Most often the price paid for the acquisition is greater than book value resulting, for a cash purchase, in an intangible L, which is amortized over Y years. An annual amortization expense, L/Y, which is not tax deductible, is subtracted directly from the earnings after taxes. This means that when a corporation becomes interested in acquiring by cash the assets of a second corporation and asks what price it should pay as a multiple of earnings, the reported earnings figure must be adjusted for the added amortization expense. More particularly, if the company being acquired has after tax earnings E before the acquisition then its reported earnings to be integrated into the acquirer corporation's P & L is given by

$$E' = E - L/Y \qquad [56]$$

If the purchase price is related to the book value of assets purchased by

$$P/Q = a \qquad [57]$$

then

$$L = P - Q = P(1 - 1/a) = P(a - 1)/a \qquad [58]$$

and the proper multiple for the purchasing corporation to have in mind is not $M = P/E$ but rather

$$M' = \frac{P}{E'} = \frac{ME}{E - L/Y} = \frac{M}{1 - M(a - 1)/a} \qquad [59]$$

Of course the amortization expense, while it is subtracted from earnings, is added back to calculate the cash flow. In other words, the cash flow, F, to be used in the models just described is not altered by the need to amortize the intangible.

Divestments, Spinoffs, and Liquidations

We have already discussed some reasons why a corporation might be wise upon occasion to abandon a product line. We shall now add some more comments on this subject. The basic reason why a corporation should remove from its activities some endeavor in which it presently engages is that it can do better with the assets. In practice, the study of whether this is truly the case in an individual instance may be very complicated, and we need to separate a number of quite different factors from one another.

Financially the product area under consideration for termination may not meet the hurdle rate set by the corporation for return on assets employed. But this usually is not the whole story. Suppose the corporation as a whole is enjoying an average of 20 percent return on assets employed and the product line on the spot only provides a 10 percent return. It may also be true, however, that no way exists, whether by divestment to another company, spinoff to the shareholders as a separate corporation, or quick or gradual liquidation, to drop this problem line without incurring a big loss. For instance, most of the assets involved may be a large factory so disadvantageously located it cannot be sold to anyone. If the product activity is stopped and this plant made idle, the book value of the assets will not be recovered and shiftable to something else. The incremental R_A will merely go from 10 percent to zero.

Sometimes obligations exist to complete deliveries to customers and maintain previously delivered items. A large inventory that is not moving might be sold off gradually over the years. If all marketing activity is suddenly halted, it might instead have to be junked and its total value written off as a loss.

A product line may be off from the company R_A criteria by two to one, that is, 10 percent instead of 20 percent, but if the loss to be taken in terminating is greater in final, after-tax dollars than this 10 percent difference will amount to cumulatively in present value for a period of 10 years, it may be just as well to keep the activity going. The comparative evaluations have to be based on the real, practical alternatives.

In some companies R_A may range, say, from 10–20 percent, with an average of 15 percent. Those items contributing only 10 percent are therefore going to be constantly scrutinized to see if they should be continued. However, even if the activity can be discontinued and the book value of the assets recovered with no negative continuing consequences or liabilities, the next question is then: What will the corporation do with the assets now made available? Does it have other product areas, that will bring more than 10 percent, into which it can place the funds? We have already said the company activities include some with up to 20 percent R_A, but perhaps those activities do not involve a growing market and do not need additional assets. Of course, the corporation could pay a higher dividend. It could even pay a one-time special dividend returning unneeded cash to the shareholders. It could pay off debt and have an improved debt-equity ratio. It could consider buying its own stock on the stock market. It could invest the new cash made available in long- and short-term securities of various kinds. But it might be true that none of these alternatives are any better than simply accepting the 10 percent return after taxes that the below-average endeavors yield, all factors being taken into account.

Sometimes an area of activity no longer fits in the company. It takes up the time and energy of management and hurts the clarity of the image of a corporation whose management wants the world to view it as engaged in primarily different activities. Perhaps the operation is in a country where the political-social-economic climate is such that the corporate management no longer wants to engage in business there. The activity may not be in financial difficulty and may fully meet the corporation's minimum requirements for return on assets employed, yet it no longer is compatible with the company. Then some form of divestment is worth studying.

One way to divest an operation is to sell it to some company where the fit is better. A handsome gain might result from the sale, the unit being worth more to some other corporation than it is to the seller. Or, the operation may be quite able to stand well on its own. Then it could simply be set up as a separate corporation, spun off, its stock delivered as a dividend to the shareholders of the parent corporation.

Even when logical and advantageous mergers and acquisitions are implemented, it very often happens that certain units of either the surviving corporation or the acquired corporation do not belong in the final package. Perhaps pieces must be separated to satisfy antitrust law requirements. Thus Corporation A that competes with Corporation B in one small phase of Corporation B's activities might nevertheless be allowed by the government to acquire Corporation B, if the merged company then divests itself of one of the two competing units.

If a corporation manages to divest itself of its lower return product lines, it will face the future with a higher average return on assets employed. But it is not certain that it will necessarily be in a better overall position. For one thing, since it is no longer as large, it may suffer from many of the disadvantages of being too small. A low or medium return on assets employed area of activity may be a cash generator. It may be an area that has no growth but yields a steady return on the constant investment. As long as it provides a return greater than the average cost of capital to the company, it makes a contribution to the capacity of the company to fund new developments that may produce negative cash flows for substantial startup periods. It is often characteristic of technological endeavors with high return on assets employed that they are growing rapidly and are cash users even though the annual reported earnings may be outstanding. Every technological corporation is faced with a constant need to fund new technology. If the corporation can incorporate a combination of cash generators and cash users a healthy continued existence is fostered.

Special Situations for Growth

In a technological corporation growth opportunities may occur from time to time which require special handling. They are not described well by any formula for routine management decision making about growth.

One such example is the technological breakthrough. Should that occur within a corporation, or outside it but in matters that very materially affect the corporation's situation, the opportunity must be grasped or the problem dealt with. For example, it may be that exploitation of the breakthrough requires a sudden infusion of capital, a major expansion of the organization, a large scale risk, perhaps, which could suggest a joint venture with others, or a merger of the company with some other corporation that for some reason is in a much stronger position to exploit the advance. New shares may have to be issued in a substantial refinancing of the corporation. For a sufficiently radical breakthrough an appropriate response may require creating a wholly separate corporation devoted to the new field, with the original corporation owning only a part.

In technological efforts the government, as we shall point out in the next chapter, is a very powerful participant. A new military, space, energy or environmental program of the government may create an opportunity for some corporation to participate advantageously. Sometimes such projects arise fairly quickly, and they can expand the size of a small- or medium-sized technological corporation in record time.

Other special situations for technological corporations result from the fact that the corporation's product activities constitute only segments, albeit on occasion very vital ones, of a more complex, broader system that makes use of those products. This means a whole chain of interrelated products are tied in with the success of the corporation's endeavors. On occasion it may be realized that one of those other members of the chain constitutes a weak link that threatens the system and, more specifically, the health of the corporation supplying its specific products. It is not uncommon, particularly in new complex technological product endeavors, that suppliers will let a corporation down. Very often there is only one supplier of a critical unit. Sometimes this risk, this shortcoming in security of the corporation's product line, may be overcome by an acquisition to provide control of the supply of that component.

The idea of being one's own supplier and going into the manufacture of a larger fraction of the (presently purchased) parts that make up a corporation's products is always around. From time to time it will happen, perhaps without warning, that the decision has to be made to mount precisely such an effort. Even if this starts out as a defensive measure to provide for continuity on existing product lines, it may constitute a very important special situation for the growth of the corporation. This is because seldom will the component previously purchased have been made for the corporation's exclusive use. If the corporation starts producing it for its own use economically, then, in essence, a new product line that can be sold to others is being established. Once in the market selling such components, the corporation had better manage the product line properly, setting up goals and strategies and a chain of investments which, if successful, might constitute a significant growth dimension for the corporation.

In almost every area of high technology some corporation of substantial size, and many more small ones, will be in serious trouble at any given time. As crises occur in such corporations, some may need to be rescued, as seen by their shareholders, if not their managements. These companies offer an opportunity for takeover by other more stable corporations. This kind of event cannot be planned ahead of time. To the corporation in difficulty, the occurrence is like an automobile accident happening to someone who has scheduled a safe ride instead. Those corporations that pick up the pieces simply have to examine the opportunity when it arises and be prepared to act quickly. Enough of this goes on, and will continue to, that it is worth noting here as another example of special growth opportunities for technological corporations.

Problems

10-1. A company that has opportunities for faster growth in its product lines than it is fully exploiting is considering selling more shares to provide additional capital for such growth. Top management is agreed on not increasing the debt but is thinking of cutting the dividend as an alternative to selling more shares. Announcing a program of greater growth might increase the stock price multiple. On the other hand, lowering the dividend rate would displease some shareholders, which might cause a reduction in the multiple. Can you suggest what kind of studies and analyses to make to resolve this question of the best way to increase investment funds? Is the model of a steady growth company of any value for such analyses?

10-2. In the example presented in the chapter of acquisition versus internal development for Analog Corp., assume all specified conditions and figures remain unchanged except as follows: The original equipment line of Analog (which produced earnings before tax of $4 million with total assets of $13,300,000) will fall off during the 10 years in a straight line fashion to half of these initial values. Reconsider the two courses of action, acquisition and internal development, and give reasons why you think the company should now prefer one route over the other.

10-3. Marketing suggests adding a product that it is expected will be cost-effective for 10 years. Two routes are available: A company can be acquired, or, losing one year, the equivalent product can be developed in-house. Assume sales, assets employed, and earnings will be steady and the same for either the acquisition approach or the in-house development, except that the stream of earnings will be 10 years in one instance and 9 in the other. Assume depreciation expense will equal replacement capital costs each year and that in each instance the assets can be removed without loss at the end of 10 years and assigned elsewhere. The acquired company has no debt and can be purchased for $2 million. Its assets employed are $1 million. If the acquisition takes place, the intangible will be amortized 5 percent per year for 10 years, with the remainder written off at the end of the 10-year period. Also assume annual sales constant at $3 million and earnings contribution from the product after taxes (but before amortization of intangible) $400,000. Using as a discount rate the cost of capital (11 percent), calculate the amount of funds the company could expense before taxes during the first year on product development and start-up costs and still cause the 10-year program to provide the same financial performance (net present value) whether the internal development or the acquisition route is selected.

10-4. A large company with constant earnings, no debt, no growth, and all earnings paid out as dividends acquires another company that has been paying no dividends and has been reinvesting its earnings to finance steady growth. The assets employed by the no-growth company are twice those of the growth company, and the R_{DA} for the growth company is .5. The companies are merged with an exchange of stock. After the merger, assume the total of dividends paid is maintained the same as before the merger. What is the growth rate for the new, merged company, its R_{DA} and R_V? Assume the R_A of each company is 15 percent and i = 5 percent.

10–5. Company No. 1 borrows the $2 million necessary to buy Company No. 2 for cash. Company No. 1 (before the acquisition) has a book value of $7 million and a debt of $3 million, while Company No. 2 has no debt and a book value of $1 million. The R_A of each company is .15. (Assume, for simplicity, that the intangible will not be amortized by Company No. 1 after the acquisition.) Company No. 1 is a no-growth company which pays out all its earnings in dividends, while Company No. 2 has a 20 percent growth rate. What is the new R_{DA}, growth rate, and dividend ratio of the augmented survivor company, and how has its earnings per share been altered by the acquisition? Assume all earnings beyond that reinvested for needed growth are paid out in dividends.

10–6. Two companies are merged by an exchange of common stock. Key figures expected for the two companies in the year ahead are respectively: Sales $300 million and $150 million; earnings after taxes $30 million and $8 million; net worth $75 million and $10 million; debt $25 million and $40 million; dividends $30 million and zero; common stock price multiple 4 and 10. The first company is regarded as not having prospects for growth, the second company as having a high probability of growth. Assume the total dividend payout is maintained and i is 5 percent. Calculate the above operating figures for the combined company. Also, calculate the R_{ES} of the two companies separately and combined, and the R_A for the three. Assuming the new common stock is shared by the owners of the two companies in the same ratios as the market values of their total common stock before the merger, state how the total dividends received by the two shareholder groups will be divided.

10–7. A corporation decides to sell off, liquidate, spinoff or otherwise divest itself of its low return products to place available assets behind its higher return product lines. Carrying out this process involves taking some losses and hurting earnings per share. However, company management believes the divestment is wise, because the company will achieve superior financial performance in the future unhandicapped by the low return lines. How do you think this company action would be reviewed by sophisticated judges as shown by the market value of its stock, all other conditions affecting stock market prices neglected for the moment?

10–8. A division of your company is expected for the following 10 years to show a steady R_A of only five percent. It is planned to sell the division and invest the realized cash in a new product which over 10 years will produce an internal rate of return of 15 percent. The sale can only be made at a price less than book value of the assets and a loss will be incurred immediately. You want to be at least even at the end of 10 years, if you make the sale. Assume that at the end of 10 years the market value of the assets in the existing division will be worth nothing, while the market value of the assets employed behind the new product will remain at its then full book value. At how small a fraction of book value could you justify selling the existing division today? Assume a 50 percent tax applies to gains and losses.

10–9. Another company makes a very high offer to purchase one of the high return divisions of your company, a division with assets of $25 million producing new products with a steady high growth rate of 20 percent, a strong market position, and a very high R_A (30 percent) compared with the average of the company's products. The company had never thought to sell this strong division, but at the right price, why not? What is the right price? Express it in relationship to the value to the company of the earnings stream of the division. Also discuss some of the qualitative factors involved in the decision to sell such a high R_A line.

10–10. Calculate the internal rate of return for the internal development project depicted by the numbers of Table 10–F.

10–11. Repeat the preceding problem for the acquisition project of Table 10–H.

10–12. You can buy a company for cash at 20 times its anticipated reported earnings which happens to be twice its book value. You think it will grow steadily in earnings at 18 percent per year for five years (if all its earnings are plowed back) and have a market value of 20 times its then earnings at the end of the five years. If your hurdle rate for investments is 15 percent, will the purchase meet your investment criterion?

10–13. An analysis of the last five years indicates that the top twelve computer companies averaged a growth rate of sales and earnings per share of around 15 percent, a debt to total assets ratio of approximately 20 percent, and a return on assets of about 10 percent. Explain from these figures why, on the average, these companies could not pay dividends and also finance their growth entirely from earnings. Show why IBM, with a 20 percent return on equity during this period and a growth rate of about 13 percent, was both able to pay dividends and finance growth from within.

10–14. A company must have a growth rate of 10 percent to hold market share in its product field on a steady, long-term basis. The company can expect a steady R_A of 12 percent. It plans a steady dividend of 25 percent of earnings. Assume the growth is to be financed from within, and all the main operating parameters remain constant. If i is 5 percent, what debt to total assets ratio should the company plan on? What return on equity will it attain? If the cost of equity capital is 15 percent, approximately what ratio should the company expect for the market to book value of its common shares?

10–15. Company A is a survivor in a merger with Company B in which additional common shares in Company A are issued and traded to the shareholders of Company B for all of their common shares in Company B. The shares are traded at market value, but Company A has a market value to book value ratio for its common stock of 1.5 while this ratio for Company B is .75. The significant figures for Company A for the year ahead are: Sales $100M; total net earnings $7 million; shares outstanding 10 million; total dividends $3 million; stockholders' equity $25 million. The figures for Company B for the year ahead are: Sales $80 million; total net earnings $3 million; shares outstanding 8 million; total dividends $1 million; stockholders' equity $30 million. Assume that in the first year after the merger, the operations of the two units will be precisely as they would have been if not combined, so that the new merged corporation will have total earnings equal to the sum of what the two units would have earned separately. Also assume the total dividends paid to all the shareholders will be precisely the sum of the dividends that would have been paid by the two units if separate. Calculate the effect of the merger on the earnings per share and the dividends per share of the original owners of shares of Company A. Also, calculate the effect of the acquisition on the total dividends received by the owners of Company B.

11

GOVERNMENT—INFLUENCES AND INVOLVEMENTS

Government as a Sponsor of Technological Advance

Of all impacts by organized groups on the advance of science and technology, the national government is the most powerful in every nation. In the United States the federal government is the chief sponsor and funder of research and development, most influential judge of progress, prime setter of priorities, most demanding regulator and leading customer.

Basic research is mainly performed in the universities and almost all of it is funded by the federal government in the United States and other countries. In fiscal 1979, the United States government allocated about $28 billion for R & D. The Department of Defense providing about 45 percent of this figure, almost $13 billion. The Department of Energy was next at over $4 billion, with NASA and HEW each almost equal to that. Of this $28 billion, the government described $3.6 billion of it as basic R & D, a category covering not only the pure research (tied to no specific final mission objective and typically spent in the universities), but also the more advanced aspects of the R & D of the mission-oriented agencies just named.

The reason why basic research has become almost totally dependent upon the government is that the nation sees basic research as a general aid to all citizens, to their health, security and welfare, and hence a service that should be paid for by all. Efforts to understand better the laws of nature, of man and beast, the earth and the universe, cannot be readily related to some specific application, Hence someone

315

who sets out to do such research, if it is truly fundamental in scientific thought and experiment, is not dominated by the objective of seeking a stream of patents or proprietary products that he can design, build, and market and on which, if he invests in them, he will obtain a good financial return. Basic research is perceived as paying off for the society, but in the long term and not through a perceivable and controllable path.

Although basic research in the universities does not have a guaranteed, predictable connection to the short-term goals of technological corporations, this does not mean the effort fails to have an impact on those corporations. Technological corporations find it desirable, in fact necessary in the long run, to maintain adequate contact with basic research sources to be aware of what is happening and to start contemplating the possibilities of those corporations' developing marketable applications based on the new scientific advances. Since the government is the sponsor of basic research and makes the rules, in essence it sets the detailed patterns that cause the results of basic research to be made available to the public at large.

One way for a technological corporation to maintain the proper kind of liaison with government sponsored basic research is to be involved with government sponsored R & D that is not so pure but is rather mission oriented. When it comes to such focused R & D, again the government is the largest single source of backing. The government's budget for R & D (in defense, energy, biomedicine, space, agriculture, environment and other areas) is the equal of the expenditures on all privately financed R & D. Only when one adds all the product engineering design work, product redesigns and extensions to meet specific market opportunities and the development of new manufacturing means does the total of technological effort in private inddustry exceed government expenditures on science and technology based projects. However, the work that is done under government leadership and with government funds is heavily concentrated on frontier areas. Most of the advanced technology funded by the government in specific mission areas, is carried out not by government laboratories and universities and other nonprofit institutions, but rather by privately owned industry under government contracts. In other words, the government is also the largest single force in advanced technological developments as well as in basic research.

Military research and development offers a pertinent example. The jet airplanes that are purchased and operated by the commercial airlines all over the noncommunist world have come from aircraft companies whose engineering effort leading to the know-how to design and produce such vehicles was paid for in substantial part by government contracts. These contracts provided detailed engineering advances and experiences on military projects that taught aerodynamics, structures, control, propulsion and other techniques also applicable to solving design problems of commercial planes. In addition, parallel military projects helped to provide volume and coverage for the fixed expenses of those companies. Without such assists many of the commercial planes would have cost too much to justify their use by the airlines and would have involved too great a risk for the aircraft manufacturers. Fortunately, projects for the Defense Department provided United States manufacturers with the opportunity to design jet planes, jet engines, and advanced electronic devices for communications and navigation.

Quite apart from aircraft, a substantial fraction of other advanced technological projects today are characterized by start-up costs in the billions of dollars, a very long time (on the order of a decade) from the beginning of the project to a period of stable profitable growth, and a risk-to-return ratio that does not lend itself well to free enterprise investment. Moreover, present interpretation of the antitrust laws virtually precludes large corporations' pooling resources and know-how in order to spread the risk. As we shall now illustrate, these huge projects tend to involve the government in such a way that independent corporate decision-making is not the dominant parameter.

Large scale military weapons systems, such as the intercontinental ballistic missile, constitute obvious examples. It would have made absolutely no sense for even the largest of corporations to develop an ICBM, undertaking start-up costs and an investment risk on the order of $10 billion, with the idea that the company would end up in a strong position to market these missiles at a profit to the United States military. This would have supposed that at some later time the government would see it needs the missiles and would buy them at a price yielding a good return on the investment. Of course, the judgment whether the product was a required one would have been entirely the government's. The military weapon system represented by the intercontinental ballistic missile (and the myriad test and production facilities, launching bases, command and control centers, warheads, spares, maintenance and training programs, etc.,) involves political-military-security strategies and decisions that only the United States government could handle. Thus, this was not a case of a free market that pits the perceived need or desirability of the product against the cost.

Even the United States military could not have made the decision on the ICBM alone. The civilian parts of the government, including the Congress as well as the Executive Branch, had to join with the military to decide whether this military weapon system was justified by broad considerations of security and economics and assessment of the actions of potential enemies. The government had to define the nation's security risks and the cost-effectiveness of dealing with the risks in whatever way, that is, by technology, diplomacy, or political actions. The government's attitude on such issues would have been too unpredictable for a multi-billion dollar, private enterprise commitment to be predicated on it ten years ahead.

Similarly, sending a man to the moon and back would hardly fit into the pattern of intelligent decision-making as an entrepreneurial business project for a private corporation seeking an eventual favorable return on investment. Even if permitted by the Justice Department, a collection of very large companies would not have taken on manned lunar rockets as a product line for private investment at risk, at least not in the past, and the same would apply to the near future.

Still holding to space technology examples for the moment, communications satellites might appear to offer a free enterprise opportunity. It is practical for large technological corporations to invest in design, launch and operation of communications satellites as far as money and time periods are concerned as investment parameters. For most commercially interesting applications it is quite practical to analyze the cost effectiveness of satellites. Those in the business of moving signals from one part of the world to another can compare the approach of sending them up to communications satellites and back down against using ocean cables or microwave links or reflections of short waves from the ionosphere. However, we must note that the capability to put complex apparatus into space orbits with reliability and adequate precision has stemmed from a government program to provide the intercontinental ballistic missile system and to send research spacecraft aloft. The boosters, launch facilities, flight controls and satellite monitoring equipment were developed and put in place by the government on its military and space programs. Even today if a corporation wishes to launch a satellite for any purpose—domestic or intercontinental telephony or television, movement of computer-based data for business, logistic and transportation scheduling, airline navigation and traffic control, weather observations, examination of earth resources from space—it is still necessary to work out with the government the availability and ututilization of boosters and other equipment that make possible putting the satellite into space and the use of government facilities from which the launchings and all of the other monitoring and control aspects will take place.

For some of the applications mentioned—airline navigation and traffic control, to focus on one—the project makes no sense as a private venture unless it is in very close cooperation with the government. Airline navigation and traffic control are not successfully accomplished without the approval and cooperation of many nations of the world and numerous civilian and military government agencies within the United States alone.

The energy field offers another example of very high risk-to-return ratios and the existence of important, inevitable, and seemingly permanent roles for the government, even though private enterprise also has a role to play. As this book is being written, the United States government is budgeting over $4 billion of expenditures per year for the Department of Energy to covver technology-based development programs. This figure compares favorably with the total of all expenditures for technological advance carried on by private industry in energy related products and services. Through these numbers alone, we see that what will happen in energy R & D, development of alternatives to petroleum, conservation, and setting of priorities among various competing technologies will be considerably influenced by government. A free market does not exist in the field of substitutes for petroleum-based fuels. Any technological corporation engaged in product activities relating directly to energy will need to give careful consideration to government policies and trends before making an investment and in managing a project once an investment decision has been made.

A good example is in the development of synthetic gaseous and liquid fuels from coal. Technology already exists to produce such fuels and further technological development could improve the processes. Those who are expert in these matters tell us that through research and development we can learn better how to desulphurize coal, produce high quality gas and liquid fuel from it, limit environmental degradation in its burning and mining, mine it with greater safety, and even obtain gas and liquid from coal while it is still in the ground. The price of the fuel resulting from a broad effort to use coal as a source probably would be substantially higher than the present price of petroleum, but because the funds would remain in the United States the effect on the domestic economy might net out as advantageous compared with the present large negative impact on the United States balance of payments of large scale purchase of petroleum from overseas. The United States has enough coal to last a century or more.

The questions about greater dependence on coal, and there are many, pertain mostly to nontechnological factors with which the government is involved and is the most important influence. If a syndicate of several technological corporations containing all of the necessary know-how and financial resources were to embark upon a program to provide a generous 100-year supply of gas and liquid fuel from coal, they would be hard pressed to guess at what price the government would allow them to sell it. They also could not be certain what regulations they would have to meet as to environmental protection and safety nor could they have confidence in being able to predict the availability of land, transportation, water, and other requirements that go to bringing off the entire project with success.

What they would know is that they are dealing with investments of the order of tens of billions of dollars and time frames, from the beginning to the attainment of full scale, steady, clearly debugged operations, on the order of a decade and more. The return-to-risk ratio would not look good. Since the nation appears to require the development of coal-based fuels as an alternative to petroleum and natural gas, and the free enterprise system cannot operate well in this area, then government sponsorship becomes the only way to make it happen. Nevertheless, the technological industry has much to contribute here. Indeed, no satisfactory development could be contemplated without using the know-how in technological industry. However, from the standpoint of private industry, its contribution had best be planned as some form of cooperative effort with government. This could be through direct government contracting or government guarantee of purchase of output or of loans. An alternative would be cost sharing projects with the government.

Shifting now to the important example of food and nutrition, the Department of Agriculture is the most important source of funding for research and development. This is done in part through a chain of land-grant colleges engaged in agricultural experimentation. The nation also has a network of small and large private organizations involved in agriculture. This includes individual farms and companies engaged in fishing, planting, growing, harvesting, processing, packaging, storing, distributing, canning, freezing, and otherwise dealing with food. Many companies are involved in pesticides, fertilizers, preservatives, additives, and other aspects of the food field. In addition to R & D funding, the government's actions have a strong influence on land use, market price of agricultural products, sales to foreign countries, and water supplies. The government is involved also through control of quality, this through the Food and Drug Administration, in licensing and testing and through numerous subsidies and controls on what is grown and what is shipped and stored.

Clearly a systems problem must be handled if the United States is to realize maximum benefits from its natural and technological agricultural resources. Much is involved in the overall process from seed to mouth. No group, not even the government, is actually engaged in working this systems problem with the goal of optimum food and nutrition supply by integrating the many interacting parameters. But the government is the party closest to the center. It is hard to imagine a technological corporation allowing itself to be engaged seriously in fields related to agriculture and food without considering the many policies and activities of government in these fields that affect the success of any investment project.

To take a final example, in health matters, from basic biomedical research through to the treatment of patients, the government is the largest source of funds. It is the principal operator of hospitals and the most active builder and richest possessor of facilities. It is the largest employer of physicians. Through funding of medical research and educational grants to universities, hospitals, nurses' and technicians' training centers and the providing of health care to the military, the government exerts an enormous influence on practitioners and medical education as well as R & D.

The Government as a Regulator

As this text is being written some 90 agencies of the United States government have been created to regulate one or another aspect of the nation's business operations. They regulate products for safety, labeling, and advertising. They regulate conditions of hiring, firing, promoting, compensating, pensioning, and providing for the environment of employees. To handle these and many other regulation areas, government and industry together require that forms be filled out, processed, and reviewed in detail to a total cost of some $30 billion dollars, with overall compliance costs to meet government regulations of more than $100 billion.

Government regulations affect the activities of technological corporations in numerous ways. To begin with, the product design is affected by government safety and environmental laws and administrative regulations. For some products the extent of government control is pervasive and dominant. The government often sets prices on either the end product or on the materials used. The government sets minimum wage scales and safety and environmental standards applying to the operations within a technological corporation, apart from those affecting the utilization of the product. The government controls rates on supplied services and allocations of markets for some technological corporations. In some instances, the government must officially approve before a product can be put on the market.

Excessive government regulation can be penalizing to a small technological firm. For example, compliance with requirements of OSHA (the Occupational Health and Safety Act) involves much more than being certain within the firm that the operations are adequately respectful of the health and safety of both the employees and the users of the product. The government requires a steady flow of information concerning the company's activities and, in order that the company know what is or is not required, it must employ experts in the government regulatory apparatus itself as well as in the technical requirements. The result is that the small corporation must have an effort of such size and with such a degree of expertise that it is difficult to fund. Also required are measurements and testing facilities and specialists to operate them, both, constituting severe cost handicaps. It is one thing to comply with what is right, but it is another to have to satisfy an overly complex, overstuffed government bureaucracy that itself lacks competence but is so set up to require a high level of communication, interaction and negotiation.

Through patents the government has an effect on whether a specific corporation can enjoy a partial monopoly of the product or must desist from manufacturing and marketing a product or using a process. Through antitrust law enforcements, the government determines which corporations are allowed to merge, sets a limit on the degree of cooperation among corporations, and keeps some corporations entirely out of some fields of endeavor.

Generally all of these regulatory activities of government simply result from the democratic process. The regulation is intended to help the general public. Whether the action of government is to remove a drug or a food product from the market, force a lower degree of pollution from industrial activities or increase the safety of a product when used or in the factory when manufactured, the objective is meritorious. The reason for the government regulation activity is to make products safer, the system of manufacturing and distributing them fairer, to increase competition and provide the public with the benefits of that competition, to stop monopoly and to shield the public from deceptive practices of unscrupulous manufacturers and marketeers.

Regulation is also a part of, and the result of, a political process. Much government regulation is created because politicians believe the proposed practice to be popular with the voters. Sometimes the voters do not understand the problem. They can be taken advantage of by politicians who provide to the public simplistic, though erroneous, explanations that sound so reasonable they not only provide support at the polls when the proposed actions are promised, but they also ensure public support after the actions are taken. Thus, it is not necessarily true that all regulatory activities of the government are in the best interests of the people. The system is too complicated to imagine that such a happy situation will exist. However, for those managging a technological corporation, it is safe to assume that the regulatory process will expand through more regulations whether all are wise and beneficial or not.

The management must understand the nature of the regulations with which the corporation will have to deal. The corporation presumably wants to be law abiding and will only occasionally challenge a regulation as unconstitutional, say, or as being misinterpreted by an administrative unit of the government. This is because it is usually much too expensive to make the challenge. That is, the return on investment in funding such a contest will be low. It is better to use the funds in some other endeavor where there is a greater chance of a high return.

Not every technological corporation deals with product endeavors that are at a high political level with resulting concentrated attention by the media and great interest to the public. For those corporations that do, the need for attention to government policies and actions is greatly heightened. At the moment this paragraph is being written, polls show that petroleum companies are held in disfavor by the public, because it is believed they are making unconscionable profits. This is so despite the refutation of the claim by the facts on returns on investment. The return on investment figures of the large petroleum companies are public knowledge, available for all to see. They are often quoted in objective articles to prove that, on the whole over the recent past and as estimated for the period ahead, the return on investment is in the same ballpark for large oil companies as for other industrial corporations. However, petroleum companies must be realistic about, and deal with, this negative image as an important parameter in their planning as they go about comparing various alternatives for investment of funds.

Many analysts of government regulation believe that the United States government over-regulates in many areas, and that this is harmful to our nation. This textbook is not a place to put forth the arguments on both sides of such a question. It is worth noting, however, that the attention we recommend management must give to the subject of regulation has to include the potential of change in the regulatory process and in specific regulatory patterns and actions. It is conceivable that government regulation has become too severe, and that this will be noted, with the Congress and the Executive Branch taking steps to cut back on the harmful parts of regulation and improving the competence and efficiency with which the remaining necessary and desirable regulation is carried out.

As an example, consider the fact that new pharmaceutical developments in recent years require a very much longer period for testing and approval of a new drug than was true a decade or two ago. When pharmaceutical drug companies make an investment in a new product line, they must consider the timing of all the steps (from conception to development to testing and approval and then through start-up, dissemination and acceptance) before the drug reaches a profitable stage. If the whole program is stretched out much too long, it becomes far less inviting and wise to invest in the R & D. The way the laws are now written, the Food and Drug Administration has little choice but to keep a drug off the market until there has been a very broad and thorough investigation to see that, for all practical purposes, no noticeable side effects exist. The FDA is not empowered by law to make an objective tradeoff comparison in which the net benefit of the drug to the society is estimated by pitting the value of the benefit against the harm owing to side effects. Thus, for example, a drug which cures cancer, let us say, in 90 percent of the cases and fails in 10 percent should not be kept off the market, if the only side effects noticed may be far from fatal.

If the regulation of the entry of new drugs is not done with a proper balancing of potential benefits against harms, the net result is that the regulatory process will curb R & D in pharmaceutical drugs in the United States and will deny us the benefits. Although it protects us from certain hazards, it leaves us with the disadvantage of lack of progress in drugs. If other countries have different policies, including those that call for a proper comparison of positives and negatives, then funds available for R & D in pharmaceuticals will move to other countries where the new drugs will be introduced. The drugs will be marketed in the United States years later and the expertise in new drug development gradually will move to other countries.

As another example, if the government agencies concerned with the regulation of airline and railroad travel are overly intent on ensuring that high profits are not realized, they may fix it so that losses are common. This will satisfy critics hypersensitive to profiteering, but it also will guarantee little private investment to improve these transportation systems. Adequate earnings are necessary to provide the plowback for research and development.

A vicious circle formed long ago with United States railroads. The threat is that this also could happen to the aiirlines. They can be held back on rates enough to register a poor return on investment even as the growth of the movement of people and things by air continues at a high rate. If this happens, the airlines will be in no position to make long-term commitments for superior, more economical and safer craft. The technological corporations that invent, design and produce the aircraft will find it difficult to acquire the funds and take on the risk of developing the aircraft for the future. In the end the government may come to the rescue, because of the necessity for air travel on the part of the public and for security reasons. The government will provide R & D contracts (probably by way of the military) to advance aircraft technologyy, an advance which government regulation inadvertently will have prevented from occuring adequately through nonmilitary, commercial channels.

In some technological activities the government is a necessary regulator to allocate roles to technological corporations. One example is in telephony. It would be an absurd, chaotic and ridiculously expensive situation for two telephone companies to share a geographical area, competing to put telephones of their separate systems in homes and businesses. We would all need duplicate equipments in order to be able to reach other businesses, friends, families, the physician and the market (stock or super). An allocation is, in effect, a monopoly for that city or area. With this monopoly comes the reasonable requirement that the government control rates and examine periodically the return on investment to see that two things happen at once: the telephone company has a reasonable return on investment, so it can raise the capital needed to expand and improve the system as required in that area; the public is not taken advantage of and is charged only a proper rate for the services which it gets. This kind of governmental control is high in leverage. With over-zealousness in holding down rates, investment in improvements can be halted.

Another example is in the assignment of radio and television channels. Here it is necessary the public not receive a hodgepodge of competing signals, which would add up to noise with no communication of information or entertainment at all. The limited space in the radio spectrum must be assigned to minimize interference and maximize service to the public. When an individual or company is given a license to operate a radio or TV station and benefits from that privilege, then it is reasonable that certain standards of ethics and values must be adhered to in the public interest. A government agency must exist to deal with these matters.

It is inevitable that part of the time of management of technological corporations must go to understanding these interrelationships of government regulation with technological advance and with the attainment of reasonable returns on investment in the technological industry. It becomes incumbent on the managers of technological corporations that they engage in continual dialogue with politicians and the media to add their input to the attainment of the balance of views.

The Impact on Technological Corporations of Overall Government Policy

In the last few years United States corporations have experienced the most severe recession and inflation in decades, a massive increase in the price of energy, shortages in a number of basic raw material resources, a ten-fold step-up in the level of government regulations (involving environmental protection, safety, minority employment, etc.), double swings in the stock market, politically unacceptable high unemployment rates, a collapse of productivity increases, a greater than two-to-one increase in interest rates and a serious devaluation of the dollar against other important world currencies. These conditions are all components of the exterior milieu in which the corporation must operate. The government is the single most influential causative agent setting this environment.

Technological corporations are affected, as is all business and every activity of the citizenry, by numerous actions of government. Quite aside from the sponsorship and regulation of technological effort already discussed, governments are engaged in influencing the overall social-political- economic environment in every part of the world. In the noncommunist nations, such as the United States, Western Europe and Japan, the Executive and Legislative Branches of the government and the decisions by the Judicial, set a pattern and create trends and intentions which, among many other influenced aspects of life, go directly to the return on investment, growth potential, timing, market characteristics and other fundamental aspects of the operation of a technological corporation.

A key example of general governmental influence on the economic state of the nation is the fiscal and monetary policy of the government. How big a deficit (or surplus, theoretically conceivable) the government runs between the funds it collects from business and individuals and the money it spends is as important to corporations of the country as government regulation of imports, prices, or the environment. These policies and the actions that go with them have a great deal to do with the extent of inflation, the currency exchange ratios between countries, consumer spending, patterns of investment by individuals and corporations, and a a host of other detailed economic parameters. The tax policies of the government create their own set of biases and priorities in corporate investment and risk-taking, since they influence available funds for investment, including rather pointedly the funds available for financing growth.

A substantial part of all government spending in all of the noncommunist countries constitutes a wealth redistribution process in which moneys collected by taxation froindividuals and corporations are apportioned to individuals and to some extent to organized groups to achieve various objectives considered by the government as socially advantageous. Thus the provision of government sponsored health services, social security income for the retired, subsidies to various industries, unemployment relief, education expenses, and aid to the poor, handicapped, aged and infirm are all in this category. To provide for administration and distribution of this money transfer, the government employs a substantial fraction of the white collar workers of the country. Accordingly the purchasing power of the nation is determined in substantial part by government policies that set the degree of money transfer and the extent to which those administering the transfer of wealth receive funds by working for the government.

Every corporation has to assess trends in purchasing power and relate unemployment and employment trends to consumption-investment ratios as well as to other pertinent economic parameters. In setting goals for the near or long term a corporation has to make some assumptions about the state of the economy and the specific ways in which the various parameters that make up a description of the economy may vary. The government is the biggest influence on these economic parameters, in substantial part through spending and wealth redistribution policies.

A powerful impact on costs and pricing results from bargaining between labor and management to determine wage levels and fringe benefit levels. Government policies are much in the act in this negotiation process. What happens on this front affects inflation and the extent to which a corporation can invest in its future and maintain its present position.

The attitudes and actions of government set the climate in which the idea of achieving a profit is or is not acceptable to the public. In recent years, the government, presumably responding to majority voter preferences, has become increasingly less sympathetic to the idea of profit. The concept that capital has a cost and that it will not be made available if the return is unsatisfactory is not well understood by the general public. Again and again in recent years, polls have shown that the public's impression of the margin on sales is off by a factor of 5 to 10. For almost all corporations listed in the stock exchanges, R_{ES} runs around 5–10 percent, but the public thinks it is around 40 percent.* Inconsistent as it may be, some folks whose personal pensions and immediate annual income are dependent on the nation's enjoyment of a healthy economy, which means adequate returns on investment to encourage that investment, tend to be sympathetic to government actions that discourage investment. Perhaps this is a temporary condition that will pass when there is better understanding of the free enterprise concepts which, vaguely, the majority of the citizens of America probably still believe are important to preserve. Meanwhile, however, it is easier to be elected by being against profit than to go about presenting long explanations of fundamental economics, including the concept of return on investment.

The economies of the noncommunist nations are not correctly characterized as capitalist economies. Neither are they usually totalitarian, government controlled, socialist, or communist economies. They are a hybrid combination, in part a free market economy with private investment seeking a return on that investment, on one hand, and government control of the economy through control of prices, allocation of goods and materials, setting of priorities, providing of subsidies and preferential taxes and even government ownership of some of the production resources, on the other. The balance between these two aspects varies from country to country. In the United States, for example, about half of the market phenomena of interest to a technological corporation might be characterized as free market, the other half government controlled through one or another of many actions, policies and administrative patterns of government. In Italy and the U.K., to take other examples, very important segments of technological industry have been taken over by the government.

Government's Influence on Markets

When a technological corporation makes decisions about entering a market, continuing in an existing one, or adding or cutting back on

* See Appendix B.

an investment, we have already emphasized how important it is to understand the need for the products, the competition and other market basics. To this we must now add the need to understand how the government figures into every market dimension. The extent to which the market is determined by open and free actions by the customers versus the degree the government sets, controls or greatly influences the market must be studied and compared.

For example, if a corporation is interested in airplanes or parts of airplanes, it must have in mind that the government is the biggest customer and that the commercial airlines have their rates, routes and many other parameters of operation set by the government. This means the interests of the airlines in new equipment or in maintenance of existing equipment are based to a very considerable extent upon government control. In many countries the airlines are completely government owned. The interest of the public and industry in the use of airlines for passenger and freight transport is a factor, of course, and a substantial fraction of this interest may be interpreted as a free enterprise phenomenon. The whole is a mixture of government control and private enterprise and the separate impacts must be documented, analyzed and evaluated.

Similarly, if the field of a technological corporation is equipment for telephonic communications, then it is fundamental to recognize that the market, nominally set by the telephone utilities who supply service, is also importantly determined by government actions that set rates and returns on investment and, with these settings, the motivation and promise for sound investment. Again, in many countries, the telephone system is a department of the government.

The Example of Electronic Funds Transfer

One of the highest growth industries is the general field of electronic information handling, including accounting and scientific computers, intelligent terminals, digital communications systems, micro-processors, and process control. When information technology reaches maturity as a development, virtually all information that is involved in the control and operation of business, industry, banks, government, professional activities, and even educational operations, will involve networks of electronic devices and human brains and sensors. The combination of man and machine here will constitute informational and intellectual capacity that can gather data, store, process and categorize it, change its form, transmit, receive, utilize and ponder it automatically—all with a speed, economy, capacity and accuracy well beyond human capabilities alone. We called attention to the potential of this area of advancing technology for large improvements in productivity in Chapter 8. This field of technology is also one in whose development the government will play a big role.

As a specific example, electronic signals to keep track of money, its storage, flow, transmission between people, between people and businesses, and between either of those categories and government constitute a far superior way to handle money transactions than pieces of paper, checks or cash. Keeping track of who owns what, what has changed hands and at what price, and providing the shift of funds from one pocket or source to another will probably eventually be done almost entirely electronically. But for this to happen it is necessary that there be standardization of the ways in which the information is expressed electronically. Specifications must be set for the equipments that have to work with other equipments, otherwise we would have a chaotic condition precluding the interconnections required to make the whole network fully advantageous to the society. Providing for this kind of integration, and refereeing it all, is a government function.

But there is much more. The government must protect against monopoly. There should be many sources for the providing and installation of the equipment and its maintenance so that lively competition will cut costs and advance the art. There must be rules to decide what is the role for the regulated utilities that provide communications, the telephone companies, on one hand, and, on the other, the computer companies, who provide the apparatus that processes information and make it available to the communications lines for transmission. Public privacy must be protected, and there must be security against easy access to the information to prevent fraud.

Even more fundamental is that the government must redefine banking, another regulated industry. Who owns the funds in process when they are in the form of electrical signals and not cash in hand in the conventional sense? Who is allowed to charge, or expected to pay, interest on the funds that are presumably owned by someone or some company or the government and are continually being shifted about? Present banking patterns will have to be modified as new technology moves into the picture.

Technological corporations that are participating in providing the equipment, systems and services in the field of information technology cannot make intelligent plans as they study the market without appropriate recognition of the powerful effect that government actions and policies will have on this market. The government's actions will be key to setting the environment in which technology will be applied.

Government's Influence on Risk

Perhaps no concept is more valuable in decision-making in the corporation than the idea of comparison of return with risk. It is necessary to examine each decision about the return on the incremental investment, and it is also necessary to attempt to assess the degree of risk inherent in, the solidity of, the assumed scenario for the project's future. Government policies and actions directly affect both the return potential and the risk magnitude. If the government changes the rate of taxation and the various exemptions, deferments or credits allowed on taxes, then the return to be expected on any given investment is greatly altered. Typical is the government's attempt to encourage investment by industry, and in this way to create more jobs through the expansion of industry, by allowing a tax credit for added investment. Or the government may decide that it is important to encourage more export. It then allows a corporation to separate its export business into another unit whose income taxes may be deferred until the money earned abroad is actually returned to the United States. On some facilities the corporation may be allowed accelerated depreciation, which cuts taxes and increases cash flow in the near term.

Government policies and actions are important to the assessment of risk, because there is always a chance that during the period when the investment is being developed, and the eventual returns are being generated the government may step in to alter all of the rules and limit the return. As examples: the government may increase taxes; it may cut out the inducements on which the investment was predicated; it may stand in the way of the transfer of technology to another country which had been assumed as totally proper in making the investment in a foreign nation; it may stop deferral of taxes on export earnings; it may slap on price controls at so low a range that it hurts the return, or it might pass a new minimum wage law which, as it escalates upward to all employees, causes labor costs to go up.

One of the most important influences of government on technological industry is in setting the environment for risk-taking in the private funding of innovation. The most often cited handicap to be surmounted if technological innovation is to be accelerated is excessive government regulation. The United States does not yet have a realistic understanding of the limits to which social change can be brought about through legal compulsion. Laws and regulations may be beneficial to the society where properly applied, but today government is regulating more than it can and more than it needs to. This over-regulation usurps funds that might otherwise go to innovative effort.

Innovation requires financial investment; and adverse tax legislation, along with inflation, has created a bad stock market and dried up venture funds. The whole economic environment is loaded with uncertainty. This further diminishes investment in innovative technology, which is already inherently risky.

Although the support for R & D by the United States government is large, it is not focused on meeting the civilian needs or the market requirements of the economy. It is for defense, or to raise health standards, or to find technological solutions to energy needs—all situations where it is thought the free enterprise system alone can not provide the answers. The situation is different in certain other developed countries. Japan, Germany, Sweden and France spend their government funds on technological developments intended primarily to further the economic strengths of those countries. They provide tax incentives to encourage, or underwrite the early costs of, speculative developments. Government funds in those countries are used to lower the risks of private investment in new technology.

What a powerful government does about policy and implementation actions either can increase or decrease the risk of investment in technological advance.

Technology Transfer

One broad question of government policy particularly important to technological corporations is that which affects technology transfer. The United States government has rules and procedures intended to monitor and restrict the transfer of equipment and technological know-how to other nations when that equipment and know-how may relate to military preparedness and may affect the security of the United States. To improve United States economic competitiveness the U.S. government is also considering broad and detailed control of the flow of advanced technology out of the United States to other countries, quite aside from security requirements. The reasoning here by those who believe that there should be such controls is that the transfer affects the economic strength of the United States adversely. The opposing view is that without such transfer American industry would cut itself off from export markets and would be unable to make investments in foreign countries to produce technological products there based upon American technology, thus leaving those fields open entirely to foreign corporations who presumably would soon duplicate American technology. The debate will probably go on for years, but meanwhile there are substantial restrictions.

Technology transfer is an issue in all countries and the actions of the various governments are important to any American corporation operating overseas. We shall discuss this subject more thoroughly in Chapter 13.

The Government as a Partner

We have already noted that in the noncommunist countries of the world the economic systems in which technological corporations operate might be described as a hybrid of capitalism and government control of the economy. The market for technological products and services is set partially by a free market and partially by government edicts and actions. We have also indicated this is specifically important for technological corporations, because government has so great an influence on budgets for research and development, on the areas of investment either by government or private sources in new technology and in expansion of technological products and services production.

Let us now look at this from the position of the technological corporation finding itself a partner of government. A partner may share with another partner in various ways when they join together to attain some mutual ends. One partner may be a financial backer only, perhaps even a silent partner, while the other partner manages the resources available to generate returns for both partners. The partners may divide up the functions of operating the business or decision making. They may have a pattern of operation in which everything important is decided by a concensus between the partners.

Unlike United States based companies, foreign corporations are more at ease in setting up joint ventures with governments as partners. For that matter, the foreign-based corporations seem to be more adept at making joint ventures with each other. In the early 1970s studies showed more than half of the foreign ventures of continental European companies were joint ventures, while more than half of United States operations in other countries were wholly American. Some 15 percent of all joint ventures of European corporations were with a government. Less than 1 percent of United States corporations' joint ventures involved a government as the partner.

On certain very large technological projects—those for which (1) the return/risk ratio is bad for free enterprise investment alone, (2) the market is dominated by government decision-making, (3) the required funds at risk are greater than the net worth of almost any private corporation, and (4) the time from inception of the project to its maturity is exceedingly long—it may be assumed that the government will be involved in the activity. If a private corporation is also involved, then in some respects it often might be thought of as a partner when there is any kind of agreement, that is actual legal contractual relationships between the government and the private corporation, transfers of funds between them, or delivery of products or services in accordance with a contract to which both are parties.

It is obvious that such partnership arrangements are here to stay for project areas like: militarrry weapon systems, the larger space projects, a program lasting decades for development of controlled thermonuclear fusion, and the depolluting of a major waterway serving highly populated, industrial areas. Technological corporations that choose to participate in projects such as these as partners with the government must become expert in understanding how the government operates and what its requirements, budgets, imposed rules and allowed rewards will be. Corporations that have chosen to operate independently in those areas of technology where the government is heavily involved will also find it extremely important to follow, understand and make use of what the government is doing.

Let us consider the example of digital communications. It is turning out that if information of almost any form (speech, video, data, music, facsimile) is put into the form of digital electronic signals, then greater channel capacity, and improved signal-to-noise ratio, economy, growth potential, reliability and flexibility can be the result. The Defense Department has a program to exploit digital techniques on behalf of military communications and other aspects of military information handling, such as intelligence, reconnaissance, command and control. A corporation that elects for itself some aspect of the field of digital communications equipment, intending to supply only the commercial telephone market, let us say, and not at all interested in seeking business from the American military can avoid the equivalent of partnership with the government. The company will nevertheless find it extremely important to follow what the military is doing. It might find it highly desirable to bid on and occasionally do some work for the military in order to be in the fraternity of partners. Part of the work is of course classified. It is not open to nonparticipants until a substantially later time. Because the American government is spending a great deal of money to develop these techniques, it is not wise to overlook the resulting advanced technology. What will happen later in the commercial world, which competitors are likely to be in a good position, what the timing will be for various steps of additional stages of development—all this will be substantially influenced by the activity sponsored by the government.

In some of the countries where technological corporations operate, their effort in digital communications needs to relate to government because the government owns the communications company. In almost every foreign country, telephonic and other communications are under tighter government control than in the United States. Less free market participation exists in those countries in determining what will happen in the development of new communications technology and in the speed and spread of the applications. In those countries any company aspiring to a position in digital communications will have to climb into bed with the government.

Similarly, a technological corporation wishing to participate in environmental control—in improving production processes, energy generation and transportation methods to minimize pollution of the air, land and water—will find it sensible often to look upon the government as a partner in advancing the field. In numerous areas of environmental control, progress involves the cooperative effort of many diverse and semiautonomous entities, both private and governmental. The government is the closest thing we have to an overall systems integrator. It alone sets the rules and regulations that are binding on the market for products and services.

If government regulations describe the allowable pollutant effluence from certain chemical production operations then the industrial corporations engaged in such activities need to buy services and apparatus to meet these regulations. Technological industry can be expected to step up to provide the equipment and services for this new market, which the government has been a major factor in establishing. Proper study of the market by a technological corporation anxious to fill it requires more than dealing with the customers, the other private technological corporations to whom it expects to sell its products. A company producing products for sale in the environmental improvement market, even when it sells to private corporations and not to the government, will not be adequately competent in predicting market trends without careful scrutiny of the motivations, pattern of behavior and specific actions of government.

Let us move now to what might be called defensive actions in partnering up with government. If for any reason (right or wrong, justified or not, as a technological corporation might see it) the government sets up a substantial R & D budget to be spent in a particular field, then a company interested in that field must consider becoming a partner with government to share some of that government funding. To remain independent may be dangerous in the competitive sense. The corporation then will be limited to what it can allot to the area, while competitive corporations might have government money to develop teams of experts with broader technological capabilities, new facilities and other resources.

A good example is found in the development of methods to extract liquid and gaseous fuels from shale. A number of corporations have spent their own funds in the past to explore this field. They presumably had hoped to gain an edge on potential competitors. In view of the overall energy situation confronting the nation, however, the government is now arranging to spend 10 times more in such shale oil development as has previously been invested by all private corporations combined. Virtually every corporation with a past or present interest in shale is now competing for the privilege of a partnership with government. Government cooperation to make available appropriate land areas, water supply and needed facilities comes with the bargain, along with the R & D backing.

Of course, getting in bed with the government does not necessarily make for comfortable, blissful sleep and an awakening to a sunny, highly profitable day. The government is a bureaucracy. It is big and powerful and sometimes its bureaucratic action is arbitrary, incompetent and even downright illegal. Under the worst circumstances it is necessary for a technological corporation to complain by going to court to reverse penalizing actions government may take. At best, accepting government funding, even if only on a cost-sharing basis and not as a total source of backing, involves giving up some or all of the patent rights to the proprietary products and processes that may come from the project. It also means making the results available to others, something not in keeping with an optimum strategy of the corporation, but rather in accordance with government policy that says when R & D is paid for by the government, then the results are to be made public.

If the government is a partner to a private corporation in any way, it may often be a busybody, buttinsky partner. It may insist on delving into administrative details and participating in selecting methods of budgeting and record-keeping, and the personnel, overhead, inventory, and depreciation policies of the corporation. The corporation will find the government has many heads and arms, not all of them working together. One part of the government may make one insistent demand on the corporation, while another part may issue directions inconsistent with the first request. Both benefits and penalties may be expected in working with the government as a partner in technological projects.

The Government as a Competitor

It is not only in communist countries that the government operates industry; in all noncommunist nations of the w world the government owns and runs some of it. Many of the government owned businesses are directly competitive with existing private corporations with similar missions. In some nations whole industries have been nationalized, that is, taken over by the government. In others the government owns a share in corporations operating in specific areas, while leaving untouched in terms of direct takeover other corporations in those same countries that operate in the same fields. For example, the aircraft industry in Britain is now virtually totally government controlled. Some of the computer and automotive companies, but not all, are government owned in France, where roughly one-fourth of the top twenty industrial companies are owned wholly or partially by the government. Italy has ownership of some of the chemical and petroleum industries. In the United States some electric power utilities are owned by government and others are private. Also in the United States some railroad activities are government owned and controlled, while others are private although highly regulated by the government. The government in almost all countries, including the United States, owns the post office operations, although in most countries some messages or articles can be transported between parties using private corporations.

The Comsat Corporation in the United States furnishes communications services by satellite. As a corporation, it is essentially a hybrid of public ownership and government control. Its stock is owned by public investors and communication companies. The corporation itself was set up, and its board of directors chosen in part, by the government. This corporation is not, however, the only one providing communications services by satellite. Other corporations, including publicly held ones, like Western Union and IBM, are involved in providing such communications services.

The government is an important competitor to technological corporations in various ways. It is obviously dangerous to be operating in a field where the government is your competitor but there are advantages too. It is usually claimed—the claimers also claiming they are making objective studies—that government-run corporations and government-owned corporations (which most often means the same thing) are badly run corporations. Comparisons of return on investment and output per employee usually show that private corporations, when competing with government corporations, achieve better results. However, government-operated corporations may have poor records because governments often get into the business of owning and running corporations when those are in serious trouble. The whole relationship between what such a corporation does and the real market need may be unsound. The company may be going (or may have gone) bankrupt. Usually if there is not a viable set of goals, the product choice is wrong, and the management is weak, the government, in taking over, will not cure the situation but will make it worse instead.

It is little consolation to a well-run technological corporation that its government owned competitor is not being operated efficiently. The market is not a competitive, free one when the government is a competitor. The government may even allocate to itself certain parts of the market. All in all it is tough to compete in any nation against the government, even when the government permits it.

Problems

11-1. A corporation, using an investment hurdle rate of 14 percent, is considering a government project allowing a before tax profit of seven percent of costs. After disallowables and taxes, the company believes an after-tax return of three percent on sales will result. The government will furnish half the facilities and the other half will cost the company roughly 1/10th of the total sales expected over the five years of the program. Assume that these facilities are written off in five years, straight line, and that the interest expense on short term government guaranteed loans (used to furnish working capital in the interim before progress payments) are included in the disallowables already referred to. If internal return on investment alone were to dominate in the decision, should the company contract for this project? State some qualitative considerations that might cause the company to accept or decline the opportunity.

11-2. Suggest how you think a competent, sound United States government should go about deciding the proper level of government expenditures for basic research in the universities.

11–3. Concern is often expressed that American industry does not do enough research and development to create new products and improve manufacturing technology and that the government should create incentives for a larger R & D effort in private industry. Suggest some government actions that you believe would stimulate higher levels of such expenditures.

11–4. Some industries previously strong in the United States are being displaced by foreign based industries with lower labor rates. It has been suggested that the United States government should mount a government funded program to develop new automation techniques that will lower United States costs and make those industries competitive again. As an example, it is proposed that government sponsored R & D to develop superior shoe machinery might cause American shoe manufacturers to compete successfully against foreign shoe imports. What do you think of this proposal?

11–5. Technological transfer from the United States to foreign countries is controversial and it has been suggested that often the interests of an individual corporation and its shareholders are in conflict with the interests of the U.S. as a whole. Choose an example where you believe the United States government should exert substantial control in technology transfer because such a conflict does indeed exist and only by U.S. government control of the transfer process can the national interest be safeguarded.

11–6. If, everything else being equal, it is very advantageous to a company to be the overwhelming market leader, why does not the number one company use its position to drive its competitors out of business? Specifically, the leader, using all the advantages of higher volume, more advanced position along the learning curve, lower costs and broader marketing might simply lower its prices to the point where none of its competitors could operate in the black and would eventually have to quit the business.

11–7. List the pros and cons of government funding, participation, regulation or control versus free market and free enterprise in the field of energy, specifically for: (1) R & D in fundamentally new techniques for energy generation; (2) development of alternatives to petroleum-based fuel; (3) setting prices; (4) conservation of energy; (5) rationing; (6) tariffs on foreign imports of oil; (7) nuclear reactor development; (8) nuclear waste disposal; (9) development of electric automobiles.

11–8. It has been suggested in the Congress and elsewhere that the executive branch of the federal government should set up a new Department of Science and Technology headed by a cabinet member and including at least the following: (1) the National Science Foundation (which mainly funds basic research in the universities); (2) the National Aeronautics and Space Administration; (3) the present Department of Energy; (4) the National Bureau of Standards (now in the Department of Commerce); (5) all biomedical R & D now largely funded by HEW; (6) the R & D of new weapon systems and advanced military technology, leaving the procurement of specific hardware to the Department of Defense. Comment on this proposal. Include in your comments the question of the impact of this kind of government reorganization on technological corporations.

11–9. It is often suggested that over regulation by the government harms the health and growth of certain industry segments. However, when the cutting down of government regulation is proposed, only a portion of the companies being regulated approve of the reduction. For example, if the federal government allows more free competition for air transportation industry routes and fares, certain of the large airline companies will be enthusiastic, but other (usually smaller) companies will be concerned. Explain why this should be expected and state how the government should go about objectively deciding on the level and nature of regulation of business in the interests of the nation at large.

11–10. In this chapter a number of important areas of technological advance were cited, where large scale, private technological corporation investment and participation to realize the benefits of such advance appears to involve too low a "return-to-risk" ratio. Consider various ways, such as total government funding, joint ventures or partnerships with government, government guaranteed loans, by which the government might set out to decrease the risk or improve the potential for return on investment, thus causing these important technological areas to develop more rapidly in the national interest.

11–11. The government for some years has been active in seeking to break up AT&T, which furnishes so large a part of the telephone service in the United States. Specifically, the government has proposed that the Bell Laboratories (a portion of AT&T which carries out R & D), the Western Electric unit (which manufactures telephone equipment for AT&T) and the operating telephone companies should be separate—this separation consistent with the intent of the antitrust laws to maximize competition and avoid harmful monopolies. List and discuss some of the pros and cons of leaving AT&T as, is versus splitting it. Consider both the national interests and the shareholders' interests.

11–12. IBM has a very large part of all computer business. The Department of Justice's antitrust division has been pressing a suit to force fragmentation of IBM. List the pros and cons to the nation and to the IBM shareholders of the two alternatives, namely leaving IBM as is or segmenting IBM's activities into several independent corporations.

11–13. The corporation you manage has a lead in a certain important area of technology and is building a strong patent position. The government decides to sponsor R & D in precisely this field at a funding level roughly 10 times your R & D budget with the requirement that any company accepting government funds must make its patents in the field available at no royalty to the government and at a reasonable license fee to others. List a potential pro and a potential con associated with each of the following alternative strategies you might adopt: (1) Disregard the availability of government funding and accept no government R & D sponsorship for your continued efforts. (2) Try to win as many government contracts as possible to augment your R & D budget with government funding. (3) Try to convince the government that you deserve special handling because of your previous R & D and patent position (attained by use of your own private funds with no government support whatever) and accept government R & D funding only if the government requirements for sharing technology with others will apply solely to results of the R & D the government specifically funds with you.

12

MANAGING DURING INFLATION

Inflation's Effects on a Corporation

If Calvin Coolidge were alive today and asked about inflation he might remark that "an inflationary period is when costs and prices are generally rising." It is equally a decrease in the purchasing power of money.

How simple to state and how difficult to deal with!

The difficulty, moreover, is hardly an occasional and short-lived one. It is realistic in managing a corporation in present times to do long range planning and make day-to-day management decisions on the assumption that inflation is chronic. The variable is only how high the inflation rates will be for the various costs and prices pertinent to the product lines and activities of the corporation in the countries in which it operates.

Inflation seems to have become institutionalized in our culture and is a worldwide phenomenon. During the decade of the 1970s, only Germany, Japan and Switzerland held their inflation to an average of a few percent. The United States has averaged over eight percent, sometimes reaching 12 percent. Typically, if a United States technological company's sales have grown at a given rate, say, 10 percent, over the last decade, then the real growth has been much less than that, or about two to three percent. The U.K. inflation has averaged over 12 percent, France 8 percent, Canada 10 percent, Brazil 40 percent and Italy 20 percent. Opinion samples in recent years have indicated that most leaders in business expect a United States inflation of 6-10 percent well into the 1980s. Such expectations can be self fulfilling, because, if the public expects a specific rate, then government policy makers tend to consider that rate of inflation acceptable,

342

unions press for annual raises at least equal to the expected inflation, and pricing and investment planning by industry are built around these figures. A well established expectancy of substantial inflation is usually paralleled by a low rate of capital formation and investment, high interest rates and a depressed stock market.

Inflation is a distorter of the economic balance around which a corporation must be managed. With the best possible understanding of inflation factors, an uncanny ability to anticipate inflation rates and a determined effort to take actions to counter the negative effects of inflation, management will still be frustrated and will find that the inflation will impair results and plans. It is not always practical to raise prices, and adjust to rising wages, on a timely basis. When management attempts to predict the declining value of money, it can overshoot and price the company out of the market. The instability of the value of money interferes with the workings of the market place. It complicates competition, at least healthy competition, and it can produce windfall profits and accidental losses.

Cost Increases Precede Price Increases

A good starting point in discussing the numerous effects of inflation on the managing of a corporation is to focus first on the costs of doing business. For reasons we shall discuss in a moment, in a period of rising inflation rates costs usually go up before the sales price of the final product does. This means the sales margin, R_{ES}, drops. Everyone expects prices to rise in the period ahead and a corporation must plan to have to adjust its labor costs upward. It probably will have contractual commitments with the labor unions representing its employees to increase wages periodically. The government regularly has passed new minimum wage bills that require the corporation either to increase the wages of those at the minimum or to dismiss them as no longer cost effective at the new wage rates. A rise in the minimum wage, of course, means that the wage scales for those more skilled and highly paid will also have to rise. In an inflationary period, where frequent increases in wages and prices become the expected trend, a stable employee situation usually requires an increase in wages annually in response to the higher prices of everything that the employees must purchase. Without attempting to delve into the causes of inflation and the possibilities of its control, we can nevertheless put down as a fundamental factor, in a period of accepted, lasting inflation, that labor costs will rise from year to year.

Materials and purchased parts will also rise. Of course, in detail, each such rise is related to the rising costs of acquiring, transporting and delivering those materials, but also it responds to supply and demand factors as various materials become less readily accessible and available. The rise of prices for certain materials needed in business and industry may involve some complex social-political parameters as well. An example is the sudden quadrupling of the price of imported crude oil in the 1973–74 period.

For most products of technological corporations, substantial competition exists with no one company in dominant control of the market. Each of the competitors, for reasons that have been elaborated upon earlier in this text, is immensely interested in market share. Increasing it is thought to be importantly advantageous and a loss of market share is considered bad. The result, when costs increase, is great reluctance on the part of all competitors to increase prices unless competitors do so first. This stalemate takes time to break. The producer who increases his prices first will lose some sales to those others who have not increased their prices. Those who grab more of the market share this way are tempted to believe that the advantage to them, if they can hold on to the gained market increment, is great enough to justify a temporary decrease in profit margin.

With highly technological products the customer may postpone a decision to acquire the new product, if its price rises. The customer has his own internal problems with increasing costs and is trying to cut costs in every way possible. Buying the new technological product may still be a good idea, even at its higher price, if it brings the customer enough economic advantage that he clearly hurts himself in postponing that advantage. Nevertheless, he may put an even greater priority on conserving his cash, may be fearful of the future in view of the negative impacts of inflation on his profitability and growth, and may find it desirable to reassess whether going to the new technology will really be as valuable to him as he had thought when he had expected a more secure and prosperous period ahead. Thus, sales volume may go down with rising inflation, and unit costs increase.

Of course, it can sometimes work the other way. With everyone assuming a permanent inflation, the demand for cost reduction, which may result from new technology, should get an uplift. On the whole though, as we shall develop in the next several pages, inflation hurts a business's earnings, decreases cash flow and impairs the capital investment program. New applications of advances in science and technology to business and industry get the best reception in an era of expansion. Inflation has the effect of curbing real expansion. The indirect but very pronounced effect of all this is that inflation in the sales prices of technological products tend to lag the inflation in costs of developing and producing them.

Inflation of Working Capital Requirements

As costs increase, so does the requirement for working capital in a typical technological corporation. Inventories rise as the prices of purchased materials rise and the costs of producing the work in process and the finished products not yet sold go up with wage increases. A sudden spurt in the inflation rate may indeed result in a proportionately far larger sudden rise in inventories. The purchasing agents, in anticipation of still higher prices of purchased materials and components usually become aggressive in trying to stockpile ahead of the rise. The greater demand itself tends to raise prices of materials even more. Whatever it is that a corporation has in inventory in pre-inflation times, it is very likely to find itself with a higher inventory value in relation to the annual sales rate.

Receivables go up with inflated invoices, and those who owe payments become slower in making them. There is a tendency for everyone to try to hold on to and make use of cash as long as possible instead of getting the checks out in a hurry. Of course, the company's cash account would be expected to rise with inflation in proportion to other balance sheet items that rise with sales and costs.

As materials and purchased parts inventory is used and sold off, a higher inflated price has to be paid for replacement. Items purchased earlier, at less than today's replacement cost, can be incorporated in products sold today for a new inflated price. This gives a spurt to the earnings if the historical costs of the materials and components are used in the accounting for profit. Since any inventory item sold has to be replaced at a new higher price, if replacement cost had been used to figure the cost of the item sold, then the earnings calculation would have produced a lower figure. We shall go into this question of inventory accounting and its impact on the earnings, cash flow and general financial performance of a corporation later in the chapter. For the moment let us merely note that inflation offers an opportunity for a corporation to report higher earnings. The boost comes merely from cashing in on the sale at a new higher price of something purchased earlier at a lower price. The company would then show incremental profit, not from improvement in its normal, substantive activities, but rather from having inadvertently invested its capital in some goods that went up in price.

Inflation's Effect on the Balance Sheet

The accompanying working capital increase when the inflation rate turns up can create a serious cash flow problem. If the selling prices of the products do not rise as rapidly as costs, and the real cash flow is lower as a result of inflation, then the corporation may have difficulty generating the increased working capital its continuing operations require. The corporation may have to increase its debt substantially because of the inflation. But more short-term debt, and any new long-term debt, can only be obtained at a higher interest rate. Thus, at just the time when the working capital requirements rise, and there is an earnings and cash flow generation squeeze, an increase in the cost of debt capital will occur.

We have had occasion earlier to note that the figures listed on a company's balance sheet are book values and that these values are not necessarily the same as market values. Thus, the net worth, or shareholders' equity, has both a book value and a market value. In an inflationary period, it is important to recognize that almost every number on the books of the corporation, asset or liability, will usually not depict market or replacement values. For example, much of the fixed assets of buildings, equipment and real estate were probably acquired when the purchasing power of the dollar was higher. A plant that may have cost $10 million ten years ago might bring $15 in a sale today and not be replaceable for less than $20 million.

Even though an asset of a corporation during inflation will usually have an average worth substantially more than that listed on the balance sheet (historical prices paid, less cumulative depreciation generally shown) the long-term debt on the liability side of the balance sheet usually will be replaceable at a lower figure. Thus, if a corporation shows $100 million of debt in debentures sold 10 years ago with another 10 years to maturity at an interest rate of 5 percent, it is certain those debentures are being traded on the market at a price substantially below the $100 million. This is because similar debentures are being offered now with a yield of 10 percent or higher. In effect, the corporation can repay the old debt wih inflated dollars that are worth less than when the funds were first received.

If a corporation were to adjust the values on the balance sheet to true market or replacement values, the assets figure thus would be higher and the debt figure would be lower. These two substantial increments, if applied, would require an equal upper adjustment in the shareholders' equity, that is, the net worth of the corporation. Adjusting the book figures would recognize, in effect, that the corporation has earned money for its shareholders as a result of inflation. By buying assets and committing to debt years earlier, the corporation has gained in the value of its investments and borrowings expressed in today's dollars.

Generally accepted accounting practices do not permit this adjustment, at least not in the broad way we have just described. Of course, if a piece of real estate or equipment is sold at an inflated price then the gain is acknowledged—in fact, it must be and a capital gains tax is owed. If it were the accepted practice to adjust balance sheet items and register earnings due to inflation, then the IRS would demand its cut of those earnings and this would worsen the cash flow problem for the corporation. The re-doing of the book values would enable the corporation to report higher earnings, but it would not add to cash flow even if no additional taxes had to be paid.

It is interesting to ask how an investor should look at this idea of reinterpretation of balance sheet figures and values in an inflationary period. With the balance sheet not amended for inflation, the corporation could be viewed as stronger in certain respects than the balance sheet shows. Its assets are worth more than stated, and its debt is less. Thus, the debt-equity ratio should appear as better than calculated from stated figures. Furthermore, a higher, hidden increment of value could be thought of as backing up the book value of the shares. This suggests then that the market value of the shares should be higher when these inflation effects are considered.

On the other hand, imagine both the assets and the equity seen as deserving upward adjustments to allow for these benefits of inflation. Then, with no change in either the operating earnings or the cash flow, the important ratios of earnings and cash flow to assets and to equity would appear to suffer. During inflation, when a corporation reports a return on equity or a return on assets employed, the investor who appreciates the understatement of both assets and equity, can be justified in arguing that the real performance ratios are actually poorer than being reported. On this basis, the investor might be inclined to downgrade the market price of the shares.

Some of the cash flow of a corporation must go toward replacing the depreciating plant and equipment. For a technological corporation that must grow and advance in technology, it is necessary that enough cash be generated each year to provide for investment in new machinery, instruments and facilities to improve the product, lower production costs, and maintain the market share, not to mention the requirements for investment in entirely new products. The Internal Revenue Service, however, requires that depreciation expenses be based on historical costs. (This is also the Generally Accepted Accounting Practices, or GAAP, rule.) Thus a million dollar machine depreciated straightline for 10 years leads to an allowable depreciation cost, or charge against gross revenues, for tax purposes of $100,000 per year. The fact that, after a number of years of inflation, replacing the new machine requires two million dollars rather than one million is of little interest to the IRS. It is of great interest to the management of a technological corporation that has to acquire the funds for replacement.

By understating depreciation costs as compared to the real life cash requirements for replacing depreciating facilities a corporation's earnings are overstated. At least it is accurate to say that the stated earnings are inflated. This means the income taxes paid are higher than they would be if a higher depreciation expense were allowed. If the depreciation, judged by replacement cost in the example just cited, would have been $200,000 rather than $100,000 per year, then the required two million dollars of cash would have been built up in the 10 years to cover the replacing of the machine. As it is, the corporation's stated earnings are inflated by $100,000, and the IRS takes $50,000 of cash from the corporation as the government's cut. The corporation is thus not only behind by $100,000 in the cash it needs to generate from depreciation charges to provide for replacement, it has lost another $50,000 in cash to boot.

To illustrate further the way inflation's negative effects for a corporation are compounded by government rules, consider the following: the electric utility industry, highly government regulated, has had a very difficult time raising adequate capital in recent inflationary years. Depreciation rates of the utilities are controlled by government agencies and are usually based on original cost of equipment. Because of inflation, replacement costs have turned out to be approximately twice the allowed and recorded book depreciation. The government also controls the rates charged by the utilities to their customers and bases these rates on the inflated reported earnings stemming from using the low historical depreciation costs. The Securities and Exchange Commission is requiring the utilities to estimate and report the effect of current replacement costs on their stated earnings—in effect, telling the utilities to disclose the truth to their shareholders about how they are overstating earnings—this, while the rate-making units of the government, including the Federal Power Commission, and the IRS in combination require both these very overstatements about earnings and a depreciation schedule that prevents the electric power companies from accumulating the cash needed for replacement investment.

The use of the most conservative accounting would increase cash flow and make funds available for reinvestment, and a change to replacement accounting for depreciation would help here. Some government leadership is opposed because, at least initially, business would pay less in taxes to the government and its revenues would fall. Some unions also would be against the change because they would lose some of their best arguments for large wage increases, namely, the relatively large reported earnings. Finally, some business executives would be against the changeover because, with reported earnings reduced, even though cash flow would be increased, the companies under their management might appear to many superficial observers in the short term to be poorly managed.

As this book is being written, the SEC is plugging replacement cost accounting hard, because it believes that present methods of accounting overstate the profitability of many corporations and therefore mislead investors. Why, the SEC chairman asks, should business pretend to make more money than it really does? *Forbes Magazine*, in 1978, performed statistical analyses on 100 large manufacturing companies and found that for most companies the stated earnings, if replacement accounting were used, would fall very substantially below the dividend actually paid. For a substantial number, the earnings would be in the red. The requirement by the IRS that corporations figure depreciation based on historical cost caused corporate depreciation in the United States in 1977 to be understated by more than $30 billion. This led corporations to overpay taxes by about $15 billion. That $15 billion would have been available for investments to create additional product expansion or to carry on R & D projects that might have reduced costs. It has been estimated that in the year 1974, when inflation reached double digits, American corporations paid a real tax on their true earnings of something close to 80 percent. This was the extent to which earniings had been overstated by inclusion of inventory profits and failure to use real replacement inflation. Of course, by the same token, the balance sheets of those corporations understated the assets. To replace those listed assets would have required substantially more funds than the balance sheet showed.

There is, however, another side to this question. Granted that given an inflationary environment, the replacement of facilities and equipment costs more than the original purchase price. However, with advances in technology that have meanwhile occurred, the new items purchased are sometimes more productive per dollar of cost than the old models being replaced. A company may have paid $10 million for a facility which is being depreciated at historical, not replacement, rates and the replacement cost would be $20 million. However, the new facility may be much more productive than the old. Also, perhaps the company has no intention of continuing in the product endeavor made at that facility and would not plan under any circumstances to replace this depreciating asset. Would it be proper to report poor earnings based upon a very high replacement cost for such temporary assets?

In a period of inflation, and particularly one of rising inflation, a corporation may find itself with a serious cash flow deficiency, the result of all of the factors indicated in the foregoing. Another way to say it is that the corporation may be caused by inflation to have a liquidity problem. It may have a good balance sheet and a basically sound business which is profitable and yields a satisfactory return on investment in noninflationary times. It may have entered the inflationary years with a safe debt-to-equity ratio and have enjoyed a reasonable growth rate financed by internal reinvestment of generated cash left after paying a suitable dividend. Yet when inflation sets in strongly, that same corporation may find itself with lower cash flow and a dangerously high debt-to-equity ratio. It may have to take some drastic steps. For example, it may have to decide to drop out of certain fields in which it is competitive, but not as strong as others, and dump the inventory in that product area at a low price as it liquidates to generate cash. This kind of action by some companies is another factor in keeping prices from rising as rapidly as costs. The weaker companies unload their inventories as they liquidate. The companies that stay in those fields will experience a temporary, highly price competitive environment during which they cannot readily increase sales prices.

Earlier, reference was made to the fact that the long-term debt of a corporation in an inflationary period could generally be replaced at a lower figure. If the balance sheet shows $100 million of long-term debt, most of which has many years still to run at an interest rate substantially below present rates, then the corporate debt is lower, for replacement value, just as the assets and equity are higher, than stated. The balance sheet, if appropriate numbers are substituted for listed items to account for the effect of inflation, would appear stronger than the unadjusted figures indicate. This would suggest that banks and other sources of funds should be more willing to lend funds to the corporation that has added to its financial strength as a result of inflation.

Furthermore, from the standpoint of the real cost to the corporation of borrowing, there would appear often to be a greater inducement to carry debt in an inflationary period than in a noninflationary one. To be specific, suppose that in a period of very low, say, 2 percent inflation, the interest charge (before taxes) on debt is 6 percent. This means that the basic cost of borrowed money is the difference, or 4 percent, during that noninflationary period. Let us next assume a high inflation of 10 percent and a higher interest now charged by the banks of 12 percent. The difference, the real interest charge, is now only 2 percent, half of the previous figure. If, as has happened as inflation increases, the interest rate rise on debt lags behind the inflation rise, then at times the two rates can be almost identical. For all practical purposes, if the inflation continues, the interest charges, while being nominally high, may actually amount to nothing; the loan can be repaid with inflated dollars. This would say a company should not be reluctant to borrow during high inflation—everything else being equal.

However, the commercial banks that do short-term lending and the longer term bond market may show great disinterest in those companies most in need of added loans to get them through their cash bind. As interest rates rise and there is an increased demand for short-term borrowing by corporations, the suppliers of credit can be choosier. They will be less than anxious to lend to the company that already has a high interest charge and whose cash flow does not provide an adequate margin of coverage over the fixed requirements for interest payments and dividends.

The Stock Market During Inflation

At such times corporations cannot readily or advantageously turn to the stock market for more equity to raise capital. The market is already down during an inflationary period for a number of reasons. For one thing, reported earnings may be lower. The real earnings of corporations and real return on equity are perceived as lower still. (That the replacement costs of fixed assets and debt are changed by inflation and imply hidden profits appears to interest stock buyers less than the poorer cash flows.) Confidence is decreased in the ability of business to recover from the negatives, if inflation continues and shows no sign of relenting. With interest rates high, the cost of equity capital is also high. Typically a corporation is judged to have a lower real growth rate potential than without inflation and the dividends now represent a relatively poor yield compared with alternatives for investment of funds. This means the multiple relating the price of a share to the earnings per share will drop greatly. Just when a corporation may need equity funds to balance its new higher debt, the practical availability of such funds by way of sales of common shares goes down.

To get a quick quantitative impression of the effect of inflation on the stock market, recall first from Chapter 2 that, for a company whose cost of equity capital is equal to its return on equity, the market price of the common stock should be expected to be around book value. Also, the multiple of the stock should roughly equal the reciprocal of the cost of equity capital. Next assume, as is often done, that the interest rate for secure, gilt-edged bonds in a situation of zero inflation is, say, three–four percent. Let us next add to this another two–three percent for the risk of owning common stocks in place of the more secure bonds to arrive at a figure of around six–seven percent for C_Q with no inflation. This translates to a multiple of 16 times. If we now add an inflation of 10 percent, then the cost of equity capital should jump to 16–17 percent, if the investor wishes to be even, and the average stock market multiple for a company envisaged as healthy and steady should drop to six–seven. (Assuming a small inflation of, say, three percent instead, the multiple would be about 10.)

Stated earnings of the corporation may tend to rise with high inflation owing to such factors as inflated inventory profits or inadequate charging of depreciation, but they may sustain a net decrease because of the severity of other factors brought in by inflation (such as the lag of price rises against cost rises, the higher cost of interest, the higher debt-equity ratio required to provide working capital, and increased costs of responding to various government involvements with business). Recall also that for a steady-growth company with R_{EQ} less than C_Q the market price may be expected to be below book value. All in all, it is not surprising if the stock market averages for many companies collapse to one-half as we go from negligible to double digit inflation.

We might add that less funds are available during inflation to invest in the market in the first place. This is in part because inflation increases everyone's taxes. Even if real income stays even, the nominal income in inflated dollars is higher and this puts the income tax payer in a higher bracket. The government thus takes a higher fraction of earnings and cash flow from everyone. Considering both the capital

gains tax and inflation, it has been estimated that the typical purchaser of stocks and bonds in 1968 had left in 1978 around 50 cents
of an original dollar of investment. In Japan, France and Germany,
where the capital gains tax is zero, the annual business investment,
as a fraction of the GNP, has averaged 25–30 percent in recent years,
while in the United States the figure is 17.5 percent. Not surprisingly,
these countries have enjoyed real GNP and productivity increases, at
least some of which would be expected to result from higher capital
investments, 150–200 percent of the United States figures in each
instance.

Special Inflation Problems for a Technological Corporation

Most of these considerations are pertinent to a technological corporation. The general impression of the stock-buying public is that the
success of technological corporations is caused by their ability to invest
continually in new technology. Lower cash flows are thus regarded as
very penalizing. Furthermore, it is thought that the acceptance of new
technological products hinges on the health of the economy. Inflation
is thought in general to equate to lack of such health.

A startling invention that can cut costs radically or provide other
great economic advantages to the purchasers will still make for an
attractive investment, with or without inflation. And particular kinds
of technological advances can be the answer, in part, to some sources
of inflation. Thus, if today some corporation really had a way to
produce plentiful and cheap energy, it would probably be able to sell
its shares on the market with ease despite the generally high cost of
equity capital. But investors, including the professional managers of
large pension funds and trust officers of banks, are less inclined to
speculate in an inflationary environment. Thus, that corporation
would have to present very strong evidence of economic success for its
new energy source or it might have trouble attracting the funds to
complete development and provide adequate full scale demonstrations.
These steps might take a rather large amount of capital which it
might be very difficult to raise in an inflationary time with its attendant poor stock market.

The factors so far discussed all combine to limit the real growth of
technological corporations during an inflationary period. With high
inflation it is harder to finance growth either from the inside or the
outside. Without growth a technological corporation's vigor is in doubt.

In the following chapter we shall discuss the management of a technological corporation operating on an international basis. As we discuss inflation further in this chapter, it is well to have in mind that inflation makes international operations much more complex and adds greatly to the risk of engaging in foreign activities. Inflation rates in various countries are generally different from one another, because the rates revolve around the semi-independent government actions based on the social, political and economic situations of each nation. The word semi-independent was used because, of course, in today's world of motion of funds and products between countries, more than a loose interconnection exists among the economic conditions of the countries. In particular, inflation is exported from one country to another and adjustments in the separate economies result in part from the way in which the inflationary factors of the countries interact.

If there is a great deal of inflation and expectancy of even higher future rates, say, in the United States compared with Japan, then those who hold Japanese yens will be willing to convert that currency to the American dollar only if, as the inflationary gap grows, they receive more in dollars for yen as time passes. As inflation continues and varies from country to country, the world's currencies are daily revalued one against the other and the exchange rates shift about. When United States consumers and industry buy goods from overseas, paying for these with dollars, more dollars may be sent out of the country than come back to buy United States products or to invest in the United States. The balance of trade and the balance of payments in currency, and even the varying investments made in each country by other countries' nationals, are all related to the relative rates of inflation.

We have pointed out that a technological corporation, as it matures, will find itself having to operate internationally in order to exploit its resources adequately on behalf of its shareholders. Its annual earnings, cash flow, taxes, balance sheets and growth rates will be affected then by inflation on an international, and not merely a national scale. A corporation may appear to do well in a foreign country when the local operations are expressed in the local currency. When, however, those operations are re-expressed in dollars and interpreted on the balance sheet of the parent corporation in America, the results may be quite different. We shall discuss these factors further in the next chapter.

The Apparent Permanence of Inflation

Before we take up some specific examples to illustrate the various effects of inflation just described, it will be well for us to consider whether the inflationary environment in which the world finds itself is only a temporary condition. A number of the more decisive aspects of inflation suggest otherwise. It is because substantial inflation is likely to confront the manager of a corporation for many years to come that it is important to consider the effects of inflation on management approaches with seriousness and depth.

Although those who devote their full time to study of inflation—its sources, consequences and potential cures—are in disagreement over many aspects, general consensus exists about a number of important fundamental points. The social-political pattern of the noncommunist world leads the citizens of each nation to place heavy demands on their governments to provide for programs and services whose annual costs exceed government revenues. The governments operate with substantial deficits, have done so for years, and appear inclined to have to continue to do so for many years to come. Under some circumstances of economic lag and recession, some economic analysts recommend that the government should stimulate the economy, put more money in circulation, by deficit spending. This appears particularly true in a situation where there has been substantial deflation and the money supply appears to be too low to make possible economic growth. Most often, however, deficit spending is coupled, as a result of social-political forces, with increased money supply and higher prices.

Little disagreement exists among professional economists who have studied inflation phenomena that the United States government's fiscal and monetary policies have provided the basic fuel for the inflation of the past decade. National goals, manifested by congressional action in response to voter insistence, have resulted in large budget deficits that have been financed in major part by expansive monetary policy. In contrast, efforts to contain inflation have treated symptoms rather than causes. Attempting to control price and wage increases that are largely the result of government policies has not worked whether the controls are voluntary or mandatory. Specifically, in the first seven years of the 1970s the expenditures of the federal government have more than doubled, from under $200 billion to over $400 billion a year. Between the actual 1977 and the proposed 1979 budget, the projected rise is an additional $100 billion. In the most recent five years, the deficit has been averaging about $60 billion as compared with $15 billion for the five years preceding.

The value of money rests on a balance between supply of and demand for it. The demand is a function of the strength of the whole economy, which is influenced first of all by government practices. The government directly controls the supply of money through regulation of the banking system and government deficit financing. The government also diverts resources, both material and personnel, from activities that might add to supply of goods and services into nonproductive ones under direct government employ. The government also regulates the private sector to an extent requiring the assignment of a substantial fraction of the talent of the private sector. The Federal Reserve Board is supposed to provide for an orderly growth of the money supply, but the large federal deficits stand in the way as public deficit financing competes wih private demands for money and puts pressure on interest rates. Thus, unfortunately, during the 1970s the money supply (currency and demand deposits) has grown at a compound annual rate of six–seven percent, more than twice the rate of growth of real output of goods and services

During this same time, government regulatory activities have increased by leaps and bounds. This has increased the price of all manufactured items. Even though the objectives of the regulation has been to improve the basic quality of life, it has not always been clear that the cost of regulation in terms of inflation and its negatives for the society has been pitted against the positive values expected to result from the added regulation. The accumulated expenditures for pollution abatement alone over the decade of the mid-1970s to the mid-1980s has been estimated recently by the Council on Environmental Quality between $500 and $600 billion.

In summary, inflation and higher regulation costs hurt real earnings and increase taxes through the inflating of reported earnings. With the lower expected return on investment, capital investment drops, as does R & D. With these two factors reduced, productivity gains slacken. That productivity growth is low adds force to inflationary pressure. The whole appears to be a solidly closed circle with no end.

There are many theories about what could or should happen to curb inflation. But present fears and patterns are well established. If an effort is made to stop inflation by severely cutting government spending or greatly increasing taxes or tightening up drastically on the money supply through actions of the Federal Reserve, many politician's fear that a severe recession would be brought on, accompanied by high unemployment. This would be so socially and politically unacceptable that it could hardly get started before it would be reversed and the government would be expected to increase government spending, lower taxes and increase the money supply by making easy credit available, all so as to combat unemployment. Closer government control over the increase of the money supply could lessen inflation, but it would bring higher interest rates in the short term. Political forces would then act to curb high interest rates.

In summary, it is not wise for a corporation's management to bet on the government's stopping deficit spending and controlling the money supply to constrain inflation.

There is also a pattern which relates wages to prices. Having accepted inflation as an incurable and ever-present phenomenon, organized labor has adequate political support for an approach in labor negotiations that makes automatic wage increases a certainty by tying the new period's wage increases to the previous period's average consumer price increases. Of course, this virtually guarantees that there will be price increases for the period ahead, since labor costs are a substantial part of the total costs and productivity increases are not as large as the wage increases and the inflation rate.

As long as the public demands effort by the government to try to guarantee a rising, or at least a nonfalling, standard of living and an opportunity for those below standard to rise to higher levels of enjoyment of the nation's output, powerful inflationary pressure will exist. High government spending and taxing means less funds available for investment by private industry to provide expansion and growth of the economy. If the economy does not grow in real terms, then the higher wages do not buy more for the purchaser. In fact, his taxes increase more in proportion to wages, because his tax bracket rises. Higher wages thus have not meant higher purchasing power in the years of maximum inflation. Generally the lower the ratio of investment to consumption, the less likely we are to improve efficiency and increase supply. We can count on the demand increasing and on government actions to please the public that exerts that demand with either a nonincreasing or an actual decreasing supply of what is demanded. The combination spells inflation.

Meanwhile, certain critical materials are in decreasing supply as time goes on, such as readily extractable crude oil from the ground. As the world's supply of crude oil diminishes on land, the more expensively extractable oil from beneath the seas or from shale, or synthetic liquid and gaseous fuel from coal, will have to be tapped to provide the total supply. The average cost to provide the crude oil will rise and all products and services based on petroleum will rise in price. Technological advance, if the society were able to invest in it adequately, might buck this trend. However, another effect of inflation is that a lower fraction of the nation's GNP is going into R & D.

Certain social trends are accepted, are inflationary and show no signs of abating. For example, the minimum wage laws that are passed periodically exert inflationary effects in more than one way. Those who make minimum wages are employed in the least skillful of jobs.

The elevator operator we mentioned in an earlier chapter may earn his $80.00 at $2.00 per hour for a 40-hour week, make a contribution to the GNP and avoid being on relief. When his wage is changed by law to $3.00 he is likely to be fired, because it becomes good economics for the corporation that employs him to junk the elevator he operates and put in an automatic one. Instead of the $80.00 per week of earned wages, the elevator operator is now on relief at $40.00 per week. The government must spend more than the $40.00 to cover the bureaucracy costs of the unemployment program. Both the higher costs of running the elevators and the higher government expenditures are inflationary.

While the basic reasons for the inflationary environment are constantly being debated in detail by the experts, some of the trends just described are regarded by most observers as fundamental and here to stay for quite a while.

Now, accepting all this, still, to a technological corporation the inflationary environment may not be totally negative. Scientific discovery and advancing technology are tools which, if used fully and avidly, can counter some of the negatives of inflationary trends. This offers opportunities for technological corporations. Properly employed, R & D investments in the right technological products and services have at least a chance of leading us to: more economical substitutes for materials in short supply; new ways of producing for our needs at lower costs and with less harm to the environment; novel products that justify the investment and lead to new jobs to produce them; ways to move people and things about the world with less use of energy; new ways to provide resources of all kinds; higher productivity in the expenditure of human effort and in relationship to capital investment.

Inflation's Impact on Operating Performance Measures

To adapt policy to an inflationary environment, management must increase the hurdle rate for investments and use a higher goal for return on assets employed. It becomes incumbent on management to get rid of operations that are not profitable or where the return is below the desired level, and it is possible to get all or much of the asset value back by liquidation or sale. To provide available cash to handle all emergencies, the company's management should favor a lower debt-equity ratio. The company's estimated costs of materials and labor should be increased and contracts should include anticipated inflation. The dividend should not be allowed to grow as rapidly as before, because it may be difficult later to meet the expectancy of the shareholders. In noninflationary periods, it may be satisfactory to have a return on assets employed of 10 percent and to pay out half the earnings to the shareholders. In inflationary times, it may be necessary to earn 15 percent on assets employed and pay out only a third to the shareholders.

To illustrate further the impact of inflation on operating performance, consider a highly simplified examination of inventory evaluation. We shall assume that a company's total operation consists of the resale of purchased parts that go up in price from year to year, because of inflation. The only other costs in the corporation in this example will be sales and general and administrative (G & A) expenses which we shall assume will increase directly with the inflation rate. The inflation for this example will be 20 percent per year.

The P & L Statement and the Balance Sheet will be examined for a two-year period, with gradually more complex conditions introduced. At first income taxes will be ignored. Then those taxes will be included at a 50 percent of profit rate. Finally, we shall add a 30 percent dividend payout. For all of these situations the inventory accounting will be done by two alternative methods, LIFO and FIFO (last-in-first-out and first-in-first-out).

Table 12–A shows the income statement for Year 1 issued at the culmination of that year. The difference between the two income statements, LIFO and FIFO, is in the ending inventory. With LIFO we started the year with 1,000 units valued at $2,500. The same is true for FIFO. In both instances we purchased 5,000 units for a total of $15,000. Should we figure that included in the 5,000 units sold were

Table 12–A   P & L—Year 1

	LIFO	FIFO
Sales 5,000 units @ $5.00	$25,000	$25,000
Inventory		
Beginning 1000 @ $2.50	2,500	2,500
Purchases 5000 @ $3.00	15,000	15,000
Ending 1000	2,500 (@ $2.50)	3,000 (@ $3.00)
Cost of items sold	15,000	14,500
Gross earnings	10,000	10,500
Sales + G&A expense	3,000	3,000
Net earnings	7,000	7,500

the original 1,000 units that were the first in? With FIFO we do just that. The FIFO column shows the company ending the year with an inventory of the higher priced units. In the LIFO case it was assumed that the last in units were sold first. Hence it is the original units that are left in inventory.

Since LIFO and FIFO assume some of the units sold were purchased at different prices, the cost of items sold reported by the accounting department will be different between the two cases by the amount of this difference in the purchased cost of the 1,000 units at the beginning unit price versus the end unit price, namely $500. With the cost of items sold different, the gross profits are also different between the two cases. After subtracting the identical sales and G & A expenses, the two net earnings differ between the two cases to the tune of $500.

Table 12–B shows the same situation for Year 2. The price of the units to the corporation's customers has now gone up by 20 percent and sales are higher, and, of course, equal for LIFO and FIFO. Again, for the same reasons as before, the ending inventories differ between the two cases, as do the earnings. It is obvious that the FIFO method results in greater book profit and that the gap becomes larger each successive year. Our common sense tells us to be wary of this booked result because we know we have bought and sold the same items at the same price and incurred the same in-house expense. The difference in the earnings can only be in the way we choose to do the bookkeeping for the value of inventory. However, let us continue, looking now at the balance sheets.

Table 12–C shows the balance sheet at the beginning and end of year 1 and at the end of year 2. We see that with FIFO accounting for inventory the total assets listed on the balance sheet build up from

Table 12–B P & L—Year 2

	LIFO	FIFO
Sales 5,000 units @ $6.00	$30,000	$30,000
Inventory		
Beginning 1000	2,500 (@ $2.50)	3,000 (@ $3.00)
Purchases 5000 @ $3.60	18,000	18,000
Ending 1000	2,500 (@ $2.50)	3,600 (@ $3.60)
Cost of items sold	18,000	17,400
Gross earnings	12,000	12,600
Sales + G&A expense	3,600	3,600
Net earnings	8,400	9,000

Table 12–C   Beginning Balance Sheet

Cash		0	Common stock	$2,500
Inventory		$2,500	Retained earnings	0
Total assets		$2,500	Shareholders equity	$2,500

End of Year 1

	LIFO				FIFO		
Cash	7,000	Common	2,500	Cash	7,000	Common	2,500
Inventory	2,500	RE	7,000	Inventory	3,000	RE	7,500
Assets	9,500	Equity	9,500	Assets	10,000	Equity	10,000

End of Year 2

	LIFO				FIFO		
Cash	15,400	Common	2,500	Cash	15,400	Common	2,500
Inventory	2,500	RE	15,400	Inventory	3,600	RE	16,500
Assets	17,900	Equity	17,900	Assets	19,000	Equity	19,000

year to year as do the retained earnings. As shown in Table 12–D, the FIFO approach, which books higher earnings and shows higher total assets, also gives a slightly higher ratio of earnings to assets, R_{EA}.

Let us now add a touch of realism by injecting a 50 percent income tax on the stated or book earnings. Table 12–E compares the earnings after tax for LIFO and FIFO for the two years. Again we see that FIFO leads the company to report higher earnings than it does using LIFO. Let us now look at the balance sheets with tax included, Table 12–F. It still remains true that with the FIFO method the total assets and the retained earnings are greater. However, we observe now a very important respect in which LIFO exceeds FIFO, namely in the cash generated.

The FIFO approach has utilized inflation to inflate the egos of management, that is, if management prides itself on the book value

Table 12–D R_{EA}

	LIFO
Year 1	7000/9500 = 73.7%
Year 2	8400/17,900 = 46.9%

	FIFO
Year 1	7500/10,000 = 75%
Year 2	9000/19,000 = 47.4%

Table 12–E

	Income—Year 1	
	LIFO	FIFO
Earnings before taxes	$7,000	$7,500
Taxes	3,500	3,750
Earnings after taxes	3,500	3,750
	Income—Year 2	
	LIFO	FIFO
Earnings before taxes	$8,400	$9,000
Taxes	4,200	4,500
Earnings after taxes	4,200	4,500

of its inventory and the stated value of its retained earnings and total assets. A management somewhat less impressed with the size of those numbers and with concentration instead on the cash generated would favor LIFO. How is it that LIFO manages to accumulate more actual hard dollars when, as before, the prices paid for inventory during the year and the prices charged for the product are the same in the two cases? The answer is that FIFO, by showing higher income, had to pay Uncle Sam more money in income taxes. Management will never see again and have the privilege of using that tax money paid to the government.

Next let us investigate the effect of dividend policy. Regardless of how the accounting is done for inventory, suppose the company pays

Table 12–F

			Balance Sheet—End of Year 1				
	LIFO				**FIFO**		
Cash	3,500	Common	2,500	Cash	3,250	Common	2,500
Inventory	2,500	RE	3,500	Inventory	3,000	RE	3,750
Assets	6,000	Equity	6,000	Assets	6,250	Equity	6,250
			Balance Sheet—End of Year 2				
	LIFO				**FIFO**		
Cash	7,700	Common	2,500	Cash	7,150	Common	2,500
Inventory	2,500	RE	7,700	Inventory	3,600	RE	8,250
Assets	10,200	Equity	10,200	Assets	10,750	Equity	10,750

a dividend of 30 percent of the stated earnings after taxes. What now will be the impact on the availability of funds for reinvestment, that is, on net cash flow? Table 12–G shows these figures. As by now we might expect, the dividend policy results in paying out more dividends in the FIFO case than in the LIFO case and the cumulative net cash flow available for reinvestment is superior in the LIFO case by an even greater factor as a result of the 30 percent dividend policy. The investors during the two years would receive $165 more in dividends under FIFO, but the same company owned by the same investors generates an additional cash flow of $665 with LIFO. Unless the stock market as a whole is paying an extremely high premium on current dividend yield, it would appear that the investors are considerably better off if the company adopts a conservative approach to inventories by the use of LIFO.

This example illustrates how with the coming and staying of inflation, company earnings are often overstated because of the inclusion of inventory profits. At the same time the companies are adversely affected as to cash flow because they also are overpaying taxes.

Table 12–G

Cash Flow—Year 1	LIFO	FIFO
Sales	$25,000	$25,000
Purchases	15,000	15,000
Sales + G&A expense	3,000	3,000
Gross cash flow	7,000	7,000
Taxes	3,500	3,750
Dividends, 30% of earn	1,050	1,125
Net cash flow (RE)	$ 2,450	$ 2,125

Cash Flow—Year 2	LIFO	FIFO
Sales	$30,000	$30,000
Purchases	18,000	18,000
Sales + G&A expense	3,600	3,600
Gross cash flow	8,400	8,400
Taxes	4,200	4,500
Dividends, 30% of earn	1,260	1,350
Net cash flow (RE)	$ 2,940	$ 2,550
2 years cumulative RE	$ 5,390	$ 4,675

Inflationary Effects on Operating Parameters

The interest rate i will rise with inflation, of course. Typically, if the price indices measuring inflation increase by several percentage points (say, from a modest inflation of 3 percent to a double digit value of 10 percent), the prime rate for bank loans will also rise, though not as much (say, from 6 percent to 11 percent).

The cost of equity capital, C_Q, will rise with inflation. However, the new cost will not be as large as the sum of the noninflationary cost plus the inflation rate. The augmented return an investor is able to get under inflation is still determined by supply and demand trade-offs on the investment market. Competitive rates of return set the size of the return for the investor in common stock and, in the end, the investor will be able to obtain only a part, not all, of the inflation's effect. If, under no or modest inflation, the value of C_Q is, say, 10–12 percent, it may rise with an inflation of 10 percent up to 15 or 16 percent.

We have already explained that it is common to expect that as inflation rises, the debt-equity ratio of most corporations will also rise. The return on assets employed is more difficult to generalize about. We have pointed out that the fixed and depreciating assets tend to be understated on the books, and the working capital assets tend to rise with inflation. Costs and prices also rise but generally at different rates, and, with the depreciation expense understated, it can happen that the overall effect as to computed and reported return on assets employed can range from a rise with inflation to a fall. A rise would mean that the extent of understating costs and the ability to realize price increases outweigh the negative factors.

With increased debt leverage measured by a rising R_{DA} and the possibility of R_A rising more rapidly than the interest charges, the return on equity may also rise. We are speaking here, of course, of the reported results on these two important margins, R_A and R_{EQ}, and we must be mindful that while the reported figures may indicate a rise (suggesting to the unsophisticated judge a superior corporate performance), it may be only a bookkeeping increase. Thus we must particularly examine cash flow and increasing debt to make a proper evaluation of how things are going with any company reporting higher margins during inflation.

For the reasons just discussed about the margins, the earnings may sometimes increase—the reported earnings, that is—with understating of inventory replacement and true depreciation influencing the result. If, as often happens, the dividend ratio, R_V, is maintained by the corporation as inflation sets in, the dividends will rise as the reported earnings rise. However, the increased dividends generally are not enough to fully compensate for the inflation to a shareholder. Thus his return, measured by the value of the stream of dividends, usually will not keep pace with inflation.

The growth rate potential of a corporation seeking to do its growing by internal financing may actually appear to rise with inflation. A company that has the basic potential and a record of real growth of, let us say, seven or eight percent before inflation may exhibit a growth rate of sales and earnings somewhat above this when inflation is present. Usually this would be simply the result of inflation in both the sales and earnings and not an indication of additional real growth. The real growth potential may be set by available cash flow. A company has to put aside funds to make up for the failure to depreciate at true replacement value and the overpaying in taxes as a result of understated expenses and overstated earnings. A corporation that shows higher growth rates on paper, may be one whose new debt-equity ratio is getting out of hand. Growth and financing for it during inflation will be taken up more fully later in the chapter.

Investment Analysis with Inflation Included

In earlier chapters it was emphasized that each incremental investment—for capital equipment, new facilities, R & D to develop a new product, marketing start-up—should be analyzed by creating the best estimate of the financial consequences built on that incremental investment. With inflation, the matter is changed and made more complex in several respects. For one thing, as we have already shown, the influence of inflation on the cash flow will depend on the way the accounting is done. Cash flow after taxes is affected by the amount of the taxes, which in turn is a function of bookkeeping policies and IRS rules.

Overall, suppose the cash flow back from investment, discounted at the hurdle rate that the corporation decides to use to judge investments, is just equal to the cash investment. This would mean the net P_V at that hurdle rate is zero, and the hurdle rate is then also the internal rate of return. All would then appear to be well with the investment. Unfortunately, however, the returned cash, presumably arriving later, will not buy as much as that same amount of money used to buy, because of the inflation. Perhaps a better way of saying it is that if you have come to expect 15 percent on your investment, maybe you should increase that hurdle rate in view of inflation. Otherwise you will not realistically be on an even basis, because the inflation rate reduces the purchasing power of the return. Put down a dollar and get $1.15 back at the end of the year and you have received a 15 percent return. But now, if there is also 15 percent inflation, what you can buy with $1.15 is just what you were able to buy with a dollar a year earlier. You have held onto your capital, but inflation has eaten up the return. In purchasing power you have no more at the end of the year than you had at the beginning.

This effect is best illustrated by examples. Consider a series of related ones. Table 12–H gives us a five-year history in which an incremental investment of $62,500 in a facility makes possible incremental sales of $150,000 per year which, with a manufacturing cost of $125,000 results in incremental manufacturing earnings (before depreciation and taxes) of $25,000. Depreciation is five-year and straight line at $12,500 per year. The earnings after depreciation, and before and after tax, are as shown in the table. The cash flow and discounted cash flow at 15 percent discount rate are also presented in the table. The net P_V of $370 tells us that the internal rate of return for this investment is very close to 15 percent.

In Table 12–I we assume inflation is present at the rates shown for each of the five years. This inflation is assumed to affect selling price, costs and purchasing power of reinvested earnings equally. When we later invest the returned cash funds, inflation has also decreased our future investment's purchasing power. The same dollars will now buy fewer machines and facilities. Because we have used the historical rate for depreciation, the recorded earnings are higher, and the result is a net present value of $13,659. This is a very substantial improvement; however, we have a right to suspect that it is largely the result of being unrealistic, although legally proper as required by the IRS, in assigning depreciation costs.

What if we were to correct the discounted cash flow to account for the loss of purchasing power, using the same inflation rates that apply to costs and price? That is to say, we now ask, what is the real purchasing value to us of the cash return in terms of being able to provide us with, say, replacement machinery now inflated in price? In the table we correct the actual cash flow generated each year for inflation, after which we discount each figure at the annual rate of 15 percent to give the net present value of those inflation-corrected cash flows. When this is done we find ourselves with a negative net P_V, ($4,599). What this says is that while we have obtained a 15 percent return on investment, the returned cash is less valuable to us as a

Table 12-H No Inflation

Year	0	1	2	3	4	5
Sales		$150,000	$150,000	$150,000	$150,000	$150,000
Mfg. cost		125,000	125,000	125,000	125,000	125,000
Earn., pretax & dep.		25,000	25,000	25,000	25,000	25,000
Depreciation		12,500	12,500	12,500	12,500	12,500
Earn., pretax		12,500	12,500	12,500	12,500	12,500
Net earnings		6,250	6,250	6,250	6,250	6,250
Cash flow	($62,500)	18,750	18,750	18,750	18,750	18,750
Disc. cash flow	($62,500)	$ 16,313	$ 14,175	$ 12,338	$ 10,725	$ 9,319

Total cash flow = $31,250
Total discounted cash flow = $370

Table 12-I Inflation Affects All Factors Equally

Year	0	1	2	3	4	5
Sales		$172,500	$189,750	$201,150	$211,200	$232,300
Mfg. cost		143,750	158,150	167,600	176,000	193,600
Earn., pretax & dep.		28,750	31,600	33,550	35,200	38,700
Depreciation		12,500	12,500	12,500	12,500	12,500
Earn., pretax		16,250	19,100	21,050	22,700	26,200
Net earnings		8,125	9,550	10,525	11,350	13,100
Cash flow	($62,500)	20,625	22,050	23,025	23,850	25,600
Disc. cash flow	($62,500)	$ 17,974	$ 16,670	$ 15,150	$ 13,642	$ 12,723

Total cash flow = $52,650
Total discounted cash flow = $13,659

Inflation Rates Used

		1	2	3	4	5
Prices & costs		15%	10%	6%	5%	10%
PP of reinv. earn.		15%	10%	6%	5%	10%

Purchasing Power of Re-invested Earnings

	0	1	2	3	4	5
Infl. adj. CF	($62,500)	$17,974	$17,431	$17,170	$16,797	$16,527
Discounted @ 15%	(62,500)	15,603	13,178	11,298	9,608	8,214

Total discounted purchasing power = $(4,599)

result of the inflation, and we do not possess the purchasing power to continue our investment pattern into the future on the same basis as before. Gradually our ability to continue to obtain a 15 percent return is being eaten away by inflation. Part of this erosion, we emphasize again, is that we overpaid on taxes, in effect, because we had to use historical costs in figuring depreciation rather than the true, present replacement costs.

Going now to Table 12–J, we alter the depreciation to an accelerated depreciation as shown in the accompanying depreciation chart of Table 12–K. The earnings are affected adversely by this pattern of depreciation, and we pay less taxes. This tells us right away that we are going to be better off as regards cash flow. The figures in the table confirm this. In fact the improvement is so great that when we again correct the cash flow for inflation, then apply the 15 percent discounting to attain a net P_V of the purchasing power of reinvested earnings, it now comes out very close to zero, ($631). Here we have a return on the original investment that will buy almost as much as the same investment would have done five years earlier and a 15 percent return on top of that.

In Table 12–L we go back to historical straight line depreciation and hurt the financial results by assuming that the price increases do not follow immediately upon cost increases, but rather lag by a year as shown in the table. Here we fail to meet 15 percent internal rate of return very badly, even before we account for inflation to reassess the purchasing value of the dollars returned.

Table 12–M gives us a contrast with Table 12–I, only because we reassess the purchasing value of the return using an inflation pattern different from the price-cost pattern as indicated.

To provide an optimistic side to neutralize the pessimistic one of Table 12–M we now assume in Table 12–N that technological developments have made possible higher productivity in the use of investment capital even though a dollar of investment buys less than it did five years before. As the purchasing power of cash return used for further investment decreases with inflation, the productivity factor comes in to neutralize, or in some years even to outweigh, the inflationary effect on purchasing power. Each dollar available for new investment buys less machinery each year, but, because of new inventions, the machinery bought is more valuable in terms of what it will produce for each dollar invested in it. The net real productivity value of any year's cash flow is obtained by applying each factor in turn. The result for the specific rates assumed in Table 12–N is a handsome, positive cash flow of $14,171 to represent the new net purchasing

Table 12–J Inflation Affects All Factors Equally—Accelerated Depreciation

Year	0	1	2	3	4	5
Sales		$172,500	$189,750	$201,150	$211,200	$232,300
Mfg. cost		143,750	158,150	167,600	176,000	193,600
Earn., pretax & dep.		28,750	31,600	33,550	35,200	38,700
Depreciation		31,250	15,625	7,812	3,906	1,953
Earn., pretax		(2,500)	15,975	25,738	31,294	36,747
Net earnings		(2,500)	9,288*	12,869	15,647	18,374
Cash flow	($62,500)	28,750	24,863	20,681	19,553	22,281
Disc. cash flow	($62,500)	$ 25,013	$ 18,796	$ 13,608	$ 11,184	$ 11,073

Total cash flow = $53,628
Total discounted cash flow = $17,174
* Tax loss carrying forward of ($2,500) used here

Inflation Rates Used

	1	2	3	4	5
Prices & costs	15%	10%	6%	5%	10%
PP of reinv. earn.	15%	10%	6%	5%	10%

Purchasing Power of Re-invested Earnings

	0	1	2	3	4	5
Infl. adj. CF	($62,500)	$25,013	$19,654	$15,422	$13,887	$14,384
Discounted @ 15%	(62,500)	21,750	14,859	10,148	7,943	7,149

Total discounted purchasing power = $(631)

Table 12-K   Depreciation Schedule for Table 12-J

Year	1	2	3	4	5
Comput. (50% of)	$62,500	$31,250	$15,625	$ 7,813	$ 3,907
Ann. dep. exp.	31,250	15,625	7,812	3,906	1,953
Cum. dep.	31,250	46,875	54,687	58,593	60,546
Year-end book value	$31,250	$15,625	$ 7,813	$ 3,907	$ 1,954*

* Assume the book value of $1,954 is received in a sale of the asset at the end of the 5th year resulting in added increment of this amount to the cash flow of the 5th year in Table 12-J.

power of the flow in terms of the value to the corporation of the machinery now purchasable with these funds.

Growth and Financing in an Inflationary Environment

We have already pointed out that with the onset of substantial inflation a corporation can get itself into a cash bind. If the corporation is to grow, either to hold its market share or to develop new opportunities, financing during inflation may become a problem. New debt is more expensive. Raising cash by issuing more equity shares, with a low stock market, may be diluting to existing shareholders, and the cost of equity capital will be greater, even without growth. Price rises may lag cost rises causing lower returns on assets employed. The allowable depreciation based on historical costs will not cover replacement, and dividends may have to be raised to try to compensate the inflation's effects on the shareholders' incomes, even as the funds available for them diminish.

Let us illustrate these points by discussing a corporation which, in the absence of inflation, is an absolutely steady nongrowth one. Even though this is idealistic for a technological corporation, it will nevertheless prove useful as a base for discussion. By steady we mean that the corporation produces from year to year the same number of units of the same product. We shall assume this satisfies the constant market demand, and that there is cost-effectiveness to the customer who is satisfied to purchase the products at the given sales price. The sales price in turn is such that after all internal costs and taxes are subtracted the funds available for dividends are also satisfactory and steadily so. More specifically, the depreciation is just sufficient to

Table 12-L Price Increases Lag Cost Increases

Year	0	1	2	3	4	5
Sales		$150,000	$172,500	$189,750	$201,150	$211,200
Mfg. cost		143,750	158,150	167,600	176,000	193,600
Earn., pretax & dep.		6,250	14,350	22,150	25,150	17,600
Depreciation		12,500	12,500	12,500	12,500	12,500
Earn., pretax		(6,250)	1,850	9,650	12,650	5,100
Net earnings		(6,250)	1,850*	7,450*	6,325	2,550
Cash flow	$62,500	6,250	14,340	19,950	18,825	17,600
Disc. cash flow	$62,500	$ 5,438	$ 10,849	$ 13,127	$ 10,768	$ 8,747

Total cash flow = $14,465
Total discounted cash flow = $(13,571)
* Tax loss carry forward of ($6,250) used here

Inflation Rates Used

		1	2	3	4	5
Prices		0%	15%	10%	6%	5%
Costs		15%	10%	6%	5%	10%
PP of reinv. earn.		15%	10%	6%	5%	10%

Purchasing Power of Re-invested Earnings

	0	1	2	3	4	5
Infl. adj. CF	($62,500)	$5,438	$11,336	$14,877	$13,370	$11,362
Discounted @ 15%	(62,500)	4,728	8,570	9,789	7,648	5,847

Total discounted purchasing power = $(25,918)

Table 12–M Same as Table 12–I Except Inflation Rate for Purchasing Power Different From Price/Cost Inflation Rate

Year	0	1	2	3	4	5
Sales		$172,500	$189,750	$201,150	$211,200	$232,300
Mfg., cost		143,750	158,150	167,600	176,000	193,600
Earn., pretax & dep.		28,750	31,600	33,550	35,200	38,700
Depreciation		12,500	12,500	12,500	12,500	12,500
Earn., pretax		16,250	19,100	21,050	22,700	26,200
Net earnings		8,125	9,550	10,525	11,350	13,100
Cash flow	($62,500)	20,625	22,050	23,025	23,850	25,600
Disc. cash flow	($62,500)	$ 17,974	$ 16,670	$ 15,150	$ 13,642	$ 12,723

Total cash flow = $52,650
Total discounted cash flow = $13,659

Inflation Rates Used

		1	2	3	4	5
Prices & costs		15%	10%	6%	5%	10%
PP of reinv. earn.		20%	15%	10%	9%	10%

Purchasing Power of Re-invested Earnings

	0	1	2	3	4	5
Infl. adj. CF	($62,500)	$16,500	$15,978	$15,148	$14,455	$14,066
Discounted @ 15%	(62,500)	14,954	12,079	9,967	8,268	6,991

Total discounted purchasing power = $(10,241)

Table 12-N Technological Advances Improve Productivity of Machinery Purchased with Reinvested Earnings (Other figures from Table 12-I)

Year	0	1	2	3	4	5
Sales		$172,500	$189,750	$201,150	$211,200	$232,300
Mfg., cost		143,750	158,150	167,600	176,000	193,600
Earn., pretax & dep.		28,750	31,600	33,550	35,200	38,700
Depreciation		12,500	12,500	12,500	12,500	12,500
Earn., pretax		16,250	19,100	21,050	22,700	26,200
Net earnings		8,125	9,550	10,525	11,350	13,100
Cash flow	($62,500)	20,625	22,050	23,025	23,850	25,600
Disc. cash flow	($62,500)	$ 17,974	$ 16,670	$ 15,150	$ 13,642	$ 12,723

Total cash flow = $52,650
Total discounted cash flow = $13,659

Inflation Rates Used

	1	2	3	4	5
PP of reinv. earn.	20%	15%	10%	9%	10%
Tech. adv. in prod.	15%	15%	15%	15%	15%

Net Real Productivity Value of Purchasing Power

	0	1	2	3	4	5
Cash flow adj. net	($62,500)	$19,643	$21,000	$23,071	$25,426	$28,132
Discounted @ 15%	(62,500)	17,089	15,876	15,181	14,543	13,982

Total discounted purchasing power = $14,171

374

replace equipment and maintain the facilities at a constant, like-new condition. The cash flow is used in part for this replacement and maintenance, and all the rest is paid out of dividends, since no growth exists to require reinvestment of generated cash. There are no annual incremental retained earnings, since there is no requirement for any.

Again, we shall make some basic points more quickly and clearly if we first imagine this company's costs are entirely its depreciation expenses, T. With no inflation, and a 50 percent tax rate,

$$E = (S - T)/2 \qquad\qquad [1]$$

or

$$S = 2E + T \qquad\qquad [2]$$

The cash flow is

$$F = E + T = V + T \qquad\qquad [3]$$

Now suppose an inflation rate of f sets in and as a result the sales, dividends, and true replacement costs of depreciating assets all increase by the factor $(1 + f)$. If the product being produced steadily has been cost-effective at its price and if there is a constant demand for a certain quantity of the products at that price, it is reasonable to imagine that the price could be raised by the inflation rate without incurring the wrath of the customers or changing their plans.

Let us see what will happen to the earnings and the cash flow in this company that still produces precisely the same number of products as before. More specifically, we shall want to see if the cash flow is sufficient to provide for replacement of the facility that is depreciating.

The reported earnings are obtained as before by subtracting the cost from the sales price. In this instance that reckoned cost, again only the depreciation, is precisely the same after inflation as before because the IRS allows only the historical depreciation rate. Thus, reported depreciation expenses remain T even though replacement costs are higher by the increment fT. After taxes (using the prime superscript to denote the new quantities when the inflation effect is included)

$$E' = (S' - T)/2 = [S(1 + f) - T]/2$$
$$= E + Sf/2 = E(1 + f) + fT/2 \qquad\qquad [4]$$

in which Equation 2 has been used.

By not adequately having covered the true depreciation—we failed to do so by fT—we have recorded more earnings, and have given up more cash to the IRS in taxes.

Now let us look at cash flow.

$$F' = E' + T$$
$$= E(1 + f) + fT/2 + T$$

or

$$F' = E(1 + f) + T(1 + f/2) \qquad [5]$$

We now pay the inflated dividend we shall assume shareholders will expect:

$$V' = V(1 + f) \qquad [6]$$

or

$$V' = E(1 + f) \qquad [7]$$

Comparing with Equation 5 we see that the cash left after the dividend is $T\,(1 + f/2)$. We do not have enough cash to pay for the replacement of depreciating assets which requires $T\,(1 + f)$. We are short $Tf/2$.

This steady company, with the particular pricing policy we have assumed, will have to add to its available cash by increasing debt or selling more equity just to go on continuing the steady output. The company will report higher earnings, but it is unable to finance the continuation of its steady operations out of earnings.

Suppose that more equity is sold to cover the replacement cost shortage. If the original equity is Q, we shall need to sell enough common shares to raise $Tf/2$ to give a new equity

$$Q' = Q + Tf/2 \qquad [8]$$

The reported earnings of the company grow with inflation, and the equity grows as we sell more shares, so it is interesting to ask what will be the reported return on equity.

Before inflation

$$R_{EQ} = E/Q \qquad [9]$$

after the coming of inflation

$$R'_{EQ} = \frac{E'}{Q'} = \frac{E(1+f) + fT/2}{Q + fT/2}$$

or

$$R'_{EQ} = \frac{E[1+f+(fT/2E)]}{Q[1+(fT/2Q)]} = R_{EQ}\frac{1+f+(fT/2E)}{1+(fT/2Q)} \qquad [10]$$

Since E is less than Q and f is positive, then $R'_{EQ} > R_{EQ}$. So, although the company is actually a steady corporation, in true substance of product activities, doing precisely the same things as before and turning out precisely the same number of identical products, the reported earnings grow from year to year as does the equity, and the reported return on equity also goes up.

However, the total dividend rises by only the factor $(1+f)$, that is, directly with inflation. That was the assumption we made in setting the distribution of cash (Equation 6). Since there are now more shares, the total dividend rise has to be spread over them and the dividends per share will not rise adequately to compensate for inflation. This means we can expect the market price of the shares to be adjusted, downwards. Also, it says we shall have to sell proportionately more shares to realize the additional equity required, because our sales of shares will cause the market price to drop. As this situation goes on from year to year, the corporation will develop more and more of a financing problem. It will have to consider raising its price more, to compensate for the inadequacy of cash flow that results from using historical rates of depreciation.

Let us now suppose that the cost effectiveness of the product and the market position of the corporation in this product permits it to raise the price somewhat more than the inflation rate. Specifically, let us make the price rise enough to provide the additional cash flow to fully cover the inflated costs of depreciation. Regardless of what the reported earnings turn out to be, the company now will not have to sell more shares or increase its debt to finance the continuation of its operations.

Having just figured that the cash flow, Equation 5, is short by an amount of $Tf/2$, the extra price increase we require would be twice this, or Tf, to cover also the 50 percent income tax. Thus, the new sales price will be

$$S'' = S' + Tf = S(1+f) + Tf \qquad [11]$$

The reported earnings after taxes will be

$$E'' = \frac{S'' - T}{2} = \frac{S(1 + f) + Tf - T}{2}$$

which, using Equation 2, means

$$E'' = E(1 + f) + fT \qquad [12]$$

The dividend, we shall assume, will be maintained at the previous (inflated) rate but no more (which means that the ratio of dividends paid to newly reported earnings will be lower). That is,

$$V'' = V' = V/(1 + f) = E(1 + f) \qquad [13]$$

The new cash flow will now be

$$F'' = E'' + T = E(1 + f) + fT + T$$
$$= V'' + T(1 + f) \qquad [14]$$

The dividend now is covered, as is the inflated replacement cost for depreciating facilities. Now the steady company, if it can get away with this higher pricing, is at least able to finance its steadiness. But, again, it won't look steady. It will be reporting higher earnings and, with the same equity and number of shares outstanding, a higher return on equity and a higher earnings per share. Inflation defies reporting a steady company's results as steady in financial terms.

Let us consider now another example in which costs other than depreciation will be included, as will other parameters that are influenced by inflation. For the company of this next example the before-tax earnings will be written as

$$E_0 = S - C - T \qquad [15]$$

where C is all costs except depreciation. If

$$C = .6S$$

and

$$T = .2S$$

then

$$E_0 = .2S \qquad [16]$$

and, after tax,

$$E = .1S \qquad [17]$$

Let us now add inflation at the rate of 15 percent in costs, including the true replacement costs for depreciating assets, but only 5 percent in sales prices of the company's products. The before tax reported earnings for the company will now be

$$E'_0 = S' - C' - T \qquad [18]$$

The IRS allowable depreciation charges are again based on the historical costs of the assets. Substituting the figures given

$$E'_0 = S(1.05 - 1.15 \times .6 - .2)$$
$$= .16S \qquad [19]$$

and the inflated, after-tax reported earnings are

$$E' = .08S \qquad [20]$$

Before inflation, the company paid out the earnings in dividends of .1S. Let us assume that the dividend is not raised, despite the pressure to do so to maintain the purchasing power of the shareholders' income against the inflation. After paying this dividend, the cash available previously before inflation for replacement of depreciating assets was

$$F = E + T - V = S(.1 + .2 - .1) = .20S \qquad [21]$$

and, after the inflation, it is

$$F' = E' + T - V = S(.08 + .2 - .1) = .18S \qquad [22]$$

The replacement cash requirements after inflation are

$$T' = 1.15T = .23S \qquad [23]$$

Thus, even without increasing the dividend, the company is short in cash generation for coverage of real depreciation costs to the extent of .05S (from Equations 23 and 22).

However, there is more of this sort of nasty cash problem, the result of inflation. Let us continue. Suppose that the working capital before inflation is

$$W = A/4 \tag{24}$$

and that the assets employed, A, is

$$A = S/3 \tag{25}$$

Thus

$$W = S/12 = .083S \tag{26}$$

Inventories and receivables will typically rise with the inflation (in fact, even more rapidly than inflation, since purchasing agents stockpile somewhat, as well as pay more for materials and parts, and customers become slow in paying of bills). Specifically, assume

$$W' = 1.15W = .096S \tag{27}$$

so

$$W' - W = .013S$$

The total shortfall in cash requirements to fully cover both replacement, .05S, and the needed increment in working capital, .013S, is .063S. Suppose this is borrowed, adding to the company's total debt. If that debt before inflation was

$$D = A/3 = S/9 = .111S \tag{28}$$

the new debt after inflation will be

$$D = (.111 + .063)S = .174S \tag{29}$$

This is a large percentage increase in debt. A year or two of this kind of inflationary effect on the balance sheet and the corporation will be in serious trouble. Unless the management can raise prices it will have to consider extraordinary steps to cut costs. This probably will include withdrawing quickly from marginal products that might have gotten by in the preinflationary period but which cannot rise to the challenge of improvement required for operating in the inflationary environment. The company will take losses in such fire sales, but it will need the cash to pay off excessive borrowings. In addition, the corporation may be forced to do some additional raising of capital by selling shares, despite the higher cost of equity capital that comes with inflation.

Growth with Inflation

It will be helpful now for us to consider the relationship of inflation to the conceived growth rate of a corporation, its dividend policy and its multiple. We recall the equation

$$C_Q = R_V/M + g$$

or

$$M = R_V/(C_Q - g) \tag{30}$$

for a steady growth company. The model of a company that is described by these equations is independent of inflation. The derivation is not concerned with how the growth in dividends arise. Even if the corporation does not grow in real terms, the dividend may grow just because of the general inflation of all of the various numbers that yield the specific dividend for that corporation each year. At any rate, the formula of Equation 30 tells us the relations for a stream of dividends growing steadily. The dividend policy as described by R_V is theoretically still for the corporation to choose, except that in an inflationary environment, because of cash flow problems already discussed, the corporation may be hard-pressed to maintain R_V as high as it might have been had inflation not set in. However, the formula still holds for whatever R_V is set. The cost of equity capital, C_Q, is certain to go up with inflation. At least that we can be certain of.

To illustrate, let us assume that before inflation a steady growth corporation with typically good performance is described for that period by the following figures: $C_Q = .10, g = .08, R_V = .3$. Then

$$M = .3/(.10 - .08) = 15 \tag{31}$$

Now let us postulate an 8 percent inflation. The new growth rate of dividends, we shall assume, will not rise to the combination of the real growth rate plus the inflationary rate or a total of 16 percent. Instead we shall assume it will have to be held disappointingly low, namely only 10 percent. This will result from such problems as: sales prices not going up as rapidly as costs; debt costs being proportionately higher; inventories dealt with conservatively on the balance sheet so no inventory profits are being taken; working capital increasing more rapidly than the inflation rate; and some marginal lines having to be terminated with liquidation losses included in earnings. On the other hand, we shall assume that the cost of capital, C_Q, rises from 10 percent to 18 percent, reflecting the inflation. Further we shall assume that the dividend payout ratio, R_V, remains the same. Putting these assumptions into the equation gives us a new multiple for the common stock of

$$M' = \frac{R_V}{C'_Q - g'} = \frac{.3}{.18 - .10} = 3.75 \qquad [32]$$

This, we can be sure, will be very annoying to the shareholders who held on to their stock instead of selling years before. Again, the answer for the corporation is to try to cut costs and increase prices, to eliminate those lines of activity that are less profitable, to hold down working capital, to turn unused fixed assets into cash as much as possible. All of these considerations represent sound management in general, but the urgency is somewhat greater in an inflationary period.

It will be useful now to rederive the formula for the growth rate through plowback of a steady growth company under a steady inflation. We shall assume that during this inflationary period i, R_{DA}, R_A, and R_V are constant. Also, we shall assume that the annual depreciation cost, T, fails to cover replacement cost by a factor of Tf where f also is constant in time.

The cash flow is, as always

$$F = E + T \qquad [33]$$

This must be reduced by the dividend V and the investment for replacement, $(1 + f)T$, to arrive at the retained earnings increment ΔQ which will finance growth. Thus

$$\Delta Q = E + T - V - T(1 + f) \qquad [33]$$

or

$$\Delta Q = E(1 - R_V) - Tf \qquad [34]$$

Now,

$$E = (R_A - iR_{DA})A \qquad [35]$$

and T may be written as

$$T = R_{TA}A \qquad [36]$$

(Note that T is usually of the order of one-tenth the value of the depreciating assets and these may total around one-half of the total assets A. Thus a typical value for R_{TA} may be .05).

Substituting Equations 35 and 36 in 34 we obtain

$$\Delta Q = (1 - R_V)(R_A - iR_{DA})A - fR_{TA}A \qquad [37]$$

while, as always,

$$Q = (1 - R_{DA})A \qquad [38]$$

which leads to

$$g = \frac{\Delta Q}{Q} = \frac{(1 - R_V)(R_A - iR_{DA}) - fR_{TA}}{1 - R_{DA}} \qquad [39]$$

Problems

12–1. For a few years, in an environment of negligible inflation, a company has been growing at seven percent per year by reinvestment of earnings with a constant R_V of 30 percent and R_{DA} of 25 percent. The seven percent rate applies to the assets, equity, sales, and earnings, since all the operating margins have stayed the same. Looking at the year ahead, the company expects to sell seven percent more units at an increased sales price per unit of eight percent causing sales revenues to go up about 15 percent. Because of inflationary costs, earnings will go up only five percent, but the assets to make possible the sales and earnings will have to rise by 22 percent. Management decides it will adopt a policy of steady R_V. To provide the increase in assets required, it decides to borrow more. What will be the new ratio of debt to total assets, R_{DA}, required for the new year's activity as described?

12–2. Redo Tables 12–A to 12–G for an annual inflation rate of only 10 percent rather than the 20 percent of the chapter example.

12–3. In the chapter example (covered by Equations 11 thru 14), in which a company selling a constant number of units per year adjusted its sales price to cover true replacement costs, assume the inflation factor f is 10 percent. Find the changes in sales price, stated earnings, R_V, and R_{EQ} that result from the inflation if $T = .5S$.

12–4. Suppose a steady growth company in a noninflationary environment when $C_Q = .12$ has a growth rate of 9 percent with $R_V = .2$. This is followed by a long seven percent inflation period during which the company's earnings and dividends again grow steadily, now at a rate of 10 percent. The first year of the inflation, however, the earnings drop 15 percent; thus they start their new steady rise from a lower base. The company maintains $R_V = .2$ in the inflationary period and the C_Q for it then is constant at 16 percent. What is the stock price (as the steady growth model would depict it) and its multiple for the first inflationary year as compared with the preceding year?

12–5. Redo the example in the chapter described by Equations 15 to 29 with everything left the same except the inflation rate is only 10 percent in costs and 4 percent in sales price (rather than the 15 percent and 5 percent of the chapter example) and the working capital required also increases only 10 percent rather than 15 percent.

12–6. In the chapter example described by Equations 15 to 29, what is the effect of inflation on reported R_A, R_{EQ}, R_V, and R_{DA}? Assume $i = .04$ before inflation and .06 during it.

12–7. A steady growth corporation in a noninflationary environment in which annual depreciation expenses equal replacement costs has a growth rate of eight percent and steady operating parameters as follows: $R_V = .25$, $R_{DA} = .25$, and $i = .04$. What is the value of R_A for this company? Assume now that after a few years the company settles down to a new set of steady operating parameters for a period of constant inflation of 10 percent annual rate. Its new steady operation parameters are: $g = .12$, $R_V = .25$, $i = .06$, $R_{TA} = .06$, and $R_{DA} = .35$. What is now its R_A if again the growth is fully financed by plowing back earnings after dividends and full coverage of replacement of depreciating assets?

12–8. Technological advance to create more economical ways to manufacture the same product or to create a product with greater economic effectiveness to the customer is a way to compensate for inflation in labor rates, purchased parts and materials, and other expenses that rise in an inflationary period. Yet, in the United States the apparently permanent, substantial inflation is being accompanied by a drop in the rate of productivity increase. Can you offer some explanation for this coincidence?

12–9. A steady growth company, in moving from a long period with no inflation ($C_Q = .10$) to a period of substantial inflation (during which C_Q rises to .17) manages to keep its dividend growth rate and dividend pay-out ratio constant. If the market perceives these two operating parameters as steady in the long term, what is reasonable to expect would happen to the price earnings multiple of the common stock going from the noninflationary period to the inflationary one?

12–10. The SEC has now required that the annual 10-K reports of corporations show what would happen to earnings if replacement cost accounting for depreciation assets were used. Presumably this requirement of the SEC is to give the shareholders a superior understanding of what is really happening to the financial performance of the corporation. A number of corporations have indicated displeasure with this requirement, arguing that it misleads rather than informing the investor better. What arguments would you use to defend that viewpoint?

12–11. What kind of government policy changes and actions would provide incentives for investment by private industry in cost reduction technology to fight inflation?

12–12. A steady high inflation tends to discourage the founding of companies devoted to radically new, high technology products requiring a long time period from inception to profitable operations. Give three reasons why this tendency should be expected.

12–13. Assume a period of high inflation with limits imposed by the government on allowable salary increases and a short supply (compared with demand) of engineers in certain specialized fields. If there are good opportunities for profitable growth in those fields, explain why the average salaries of these engineering specialists may be expected to rise at a higher rate than the supposedly controlled salary rise rates.

12–14. Assume that the cost of equity capital during a period of inflation is given by $C_Q = C_o + f$ where C_o is the cost of equity capital with negligible inflation and f is the rate of inflation. Show that for a steady growth company that maintains the same dividend ratio as inflation sets in and whose growth rate of dividends is given by $g = g_o + f$, where g_o is the growth rate before inflation appears, the stock multiple (price-earnings ratio) for this company should remain constant regardless of the rate of inflation.

13

INTERNATIONAL OPERATIONS

The Importance of Multinational Activities to a Technological Corporation

To understand why international activities are likely to be very important to a typical technological corporation we should first reflect on the growing importance of science and technology to all nations of the world. Every country—communist or noncommunist, developed or underdeveloped—now perceives a close relation between its status in science and technology and its chances of meeting its national goals. Strength in technological resources is seen to be required for economic strength, high per capita income, military security, and the fulfillment of the material requirements of its people. We observe that even those nations, because they happen to have huge oil supplies could simply live off of the revenues from sales to other nations, are looking ahead to the period when those reserves will dwindle, have concluded that they must be technological nations, and are spending feverishly to elevate themselves to such a category.

Technological resources include many things. There must be a large number of working experts in science and technology. This means a higher educational system must exist and adequate laboratory and experimental facilities must be provided. Technological industry must be present, strong and growing and have substantial versatility in view of the changes that scientific discovery and technological advance bring. Technology advance is important, of course, to the nontechnological industry as well, because the way everything is manufactured and distributed is constantly being altered by advancing science and technology, as is the entire pattern of living.

387

Importance of the World Market

Nations throughout the world aggressively attempt to advance their science and technology base. In some nations this is done almost entirely by government initiative with the free enterprise sector either secondary or nonexistent. In other nations, as exemplified by the United States, West Europe and Japan, the technological resources and the advance of science and technology are influenced very greatly by both government and private policies and activities. There is in those countries a combination of governmental and private market pressure to acquire technology and to develop and sell products and services that are technological in nature to the world at large. Any private technological corporation seeking to maximize the difference between the return on capital and the cost of it and to satisfy to the maximum its various constituents, thus should consider the entire world as its market area. Failure to do so is to give competitors a volume edge and pass up sources of knowledge, ideas and trends concerning technological products and the markets for them.

A United States corporation would be unlikely to develop a new computer with the idea of selling it only in the Pacific coast states. The United States is, admittedly, a spread out nation, and one can list products where perishability or costs of transportation are such important factors that a producer can be well advised to specialize geographically. A small consulting firm, as another example, may serve a city or county government with specialized engineering services and do well. Not so with computers and almost every other technological product. A computer company manufacturing for California would be beaten by a corporation that manufactures for the United States as a whole. The latter is a far larger market, and the company that sets out to serve that market would enjoy numerous advantages.

Many areas of the world contain customers for whom the product of the corporation, if it is successful in the United States, may be equally suitable and superior to those of competitors there. These are sales given away to competitors if operating internationally is disavowed. For many technological products numerous applications exist. The applications are changed with time as the system, of which the product is a part, is altered by further scientific discovery and technological advance as well as changes in the market and in society in general. A corporation that deals with a larger array of different customers in different applications has the advantage of perceiving more trends and possibilities.

Aside from maximizing the return on the corporation's investments, we must emphasize the fundamental competitive situation. A technological corporation usually will be up against competitors who will go out and grab the world market. They then will have the advantages of volume and broader insights for planning, management and investment decisions.

If an American technological corporation has a very large technological lead in its product area, it well may be that exporting from the United States is the best way to exploit the market potential in other countries. The strong patent position that is likely to exist in the United States presumably can readily be extended to other countries with attractive markets, and this approach would inhibit competition there as well as in the United States. If the product line possesses the attribute of high cost-effectiveness to the customer, he will be willing to pay the export price even if higher than the United States price due to transportation and other export costs. Still, it might pay to manufacture abroad in part. This could lower manufacturing costs in the local market being served and hence make possible lower prices and additional applications.

In past decades, United States technological corporations have enjoyed a market advantage in the United States over foreign competitors. The United States market, which they have understood better and were more readily able to anticipate and fill, has been and still is the largest and most affluent technological market. Until recent years it has not been vital to many United States technological corporations that they add the potential advantages of offering their products in the international market as well as domestically. However, the larger, better established companies long ago became international. Now the value of the international marketplace is increasingly appreciated by medium-sized and small-sized technological corporations as well. Increased communications and flow of technological data and decreasing cost of transportation have brought more vigorous competition for the United States market by overseas suppliers and increased opportunities for United States manufacturers outside the Untied States. All technological corporations in the world now face the similar problem of the need to move fast to exploit technological advances, to build a strong position in the world market, and to get as broad a return as possible on investments. These companies must learn how to deal internationally and operate in countries foreign to corporate headquarters.

Another reason for operating in a foreign country is to broaden the technological base for future product extensions by benefitting from membership in the science and technology fraternity of that country.

The United States now does less research and development than the total of all the industrialized nations of the rest of the world. It would seem reasonable to suppose then that more than half of the useful technological ideas are going to appear first elsewhere. These advances can be important to an American firm. The surest way to have adequate intelligence and access and to be adept at forming arrangements for the interchange of technology is to be active technologically in other countries.

The United States lead in technology is slipping. In the United States, R&D, as a fraction of the GNP, is less in the late 1970s than it was 10 years before. In the same period, this ratio has increased in Germany and Japan. The ratio of United States patents issued to foreigners compared with the number issued to Americans has risen by more than two times in the same decade. A survey of the most important innovations in technology to enter the market found 80 percent originated in the United States in the 1950s, but only 60 percent in the early 1970s. An outstanding technological corporation, or one that strives to be, has to put substantial emphasis on playing in the wider world arena of technological change to maximize its chances of knowing what is happening and acting on the perceptions advantageously.

As an example of how operating in a number of countries can provide a broader technological base to a corporation, consider the differences that have existed for years about the role of energy dissipation in technological design. Innovation in the United States has historically been biased toward labor saving and, with energy very cheap, toward the substitution of energy intensity for labor intensity. Continental Europe and Japan have had to live for a lot longer than the United States with scarce and high priced energy. Similarly, densely populated Europe has been coping for many years with pollution and has been interested seriously in materials recycling and waste and sewage disposal under limited area conditions. As sensitivity to pollution and the price of energy rise in the United States, the technology of the Europeans and the Japanese becomes more important. More energy efficient locomotives, energy saving radial tires, electricity saving in smelting aluminum, fuel injection equipment for automobiles—these and many other technologies originated where the payoff was more significant, outside the United States.

A widely disbursed competence in science and technology means that advances will occur in many countries that may be used sooner or later in almost all of them. The difference in the economic-social-political character of the individual countries will provide varying bases for different focuses on specific technologies and cause the locations of leadership in technology to vary as well. Other countries have patterns which make for greater success in some aspects of technological industry and many aspects of innovation than is true of the United States. For example, countries like West Germany have stressed product quality and reliability in their educational systems, and their tax laws encourage innovation, the practical applications of acquired knowledge and industry investment. Japan has shown the way to use export markets to increase the scale of their domestic operations and thus reduce unit costs and increase productivity. Similarly, foreign countries enjoy more cooperation in export promotion between their technological industry and their governments than does the United States.

Other countries have fewer antitrust limitations on their technological corporations compared with the United States. American antitrust laws follow United States based corporations out of the country. A United States multinational corporation must respect these laws even for the setting up of joint ventures and other aspects of relationships with competitors overseas. This is not true of corporations based in foreign countries. Once away from their home country, they can make contracts not to compete and they may engage in mergers and acquisitions that would be illegal by United States antitrust laws.

The World Environment for Technological Corporations

Free Trade versus Isolation

In the economic relationships among the nations of the world a contest is underway between two approaches. One is that of free world trade where materials, investment funds, cash flow from earnings, technology, management know-how and labor move freely across national boundaries. In a free trade world, each nation provides to all what it can best produce and offer as judged by free market competition. It uses its output partially internally and sells the rest to the outside world. One nation may have a plentiful supply of raw materials, another may have cheaper labor, a third greater know-how. These attributes among the nations vary also with the area of endeavor or nature of the resource. The net result is a free market optimization in which all nations enjoy a higher standard of living than they otherwise would, because they obtain their needs at the lowest price and can produce and sell what they have without restrictions.

The other approach to world trade is the opposite of the free motion just described of money, goods and the rest. It is rather an international economic relationship based on nationalism, isolationism and restrictions. Social-political-economic problems in each nation cause its people to demand solutions from their governments. This inevitably includes an attempt by the government to gain economic advantages for that nation over other countries by control of international trade with them. Thus, to protect a local industry from foreign competition, which really means to subsidize it, competitive imports are discouraged. Similarly, each nation tries to handle its inflation and unemployment, the relationship of its currency to that of others, its money transfers, and its balance of exports and imports by numerous measures and countermeasures vis-a-vis the actions of other nations. To seek short-term objectives in response to social-political pressure, governments interfere with free world trade and incur both short- and long-term negatives.

At the present time the second approach may be in the lead. The world certainly is not now progressing with alacrity toward the free trade environment first described. However, despite the local environments of each nation and the consequent government actions to interfere with free trade, there is insistent and powerful pressure for world economic exchange. This results from the simple fact that free trade is a way to raise world economic strength and growth. Free trade gives all nations the benefits of the resources, know-how and overall output of other nations. In addition, each nation is anxious to export, even as it curbs imports, all the while knowing that one goal, if engaged in successfully by all nations, is directly in opposition to the other goal, since an exported item by one nation is an import by another.

The environment in which a technological corporation operates internationally is a constantly changing hodgepodge of logical and illogical actions and controls by the various governments of the world in combination with considerable private, free market activity. This means that in product selection and investment decisions restrictions and complications must be lived with, adjusted to and worked around.

Effects of Inflation Rate Differences

When it operates internationally, it is important for corporate management to realize that, despite the autonomy of the separate nations, there is already such an extent of world trade and monetary exchanges that the economic interdependence among nations is high. In major respects this interdependence transcends the abilities of the governments to control, regulate and maintain economic separatism. Thus, if the economic policy of the government of one nation causes its money supply to grow rapidly and create inflation in that nation, then the products of other nations that inflate less become relatively more expensive and the inflating nation's products become cheaper for those other countries to buy. This condition, if its persists, will create an imbalance in the transfer of funds between the nations. To correct this, revaluations of the currency exchange ratios of the countries will result. As sample figures, note the approximate inflation rates for 1977 shown in Table 13–A, and the currency exchange ratios during the same period shown in Table 13–B, which lists changes in the United States dollar cost of foreign currencies.

A corporation operating in many nations must expect that the financial performance of its various operations will be judged differently in the currency of the local country and in the United States. An American corporation must ultimately do its final accounting and reporting of financial results in American dollars. Its operations in Country A, where a very high inflation rate exists, may appear in Country A's currency to be highly profitable. However, when the funds earned and various balance sheet items are translated into American dollars, it may turn out that the subsidiary has actually had a loss year. The difference is due to a currency exchange loss component in the overall P&L figures.

In the last few years a number of the largest United States corporations have reported annual foreign currency exchange "losses" in the hundreds of millions of dollars and many more multinational corporations with sales exceeding a billion dollars reported such "losses" at the $10 million level. The quotes have been put around the word "losses," because they are not losses in the ordinary sense. We

Table 13–A   Inflation Rates (Annual Percentage Changes)

Country	'73–'74	'74–'75	'75–'76	'76–'77*
United States	9.7	9.6	5.3	6.3
West Germany	6.9	7.1	3.2	3.8
Italy	17.7	17.3	17.8	23.2
U.K.	13.4	28.3	15.4	15.8
Japan	20.7	7.4	6.4	5.2

* As this text is going to press in 1979, the United States rate is rapidly growing to two-digit levels, while Germany's and Japan's rates are being held to a few percent.

Table 13–B   U.S. Dollar Cost of Foreign Currencies (Annual Percentage Changes)

Country	'73–'74	'74–'75	'75–'76	'76–'77
France	12.7	−10.4	− 2.8	3.2
West Germany	5.4	− 2.4	8.5	8.9
Italy	− .2	−20.9	− 6.6	− 2.3
U.K.	− 4.9	−18.5	− 3.6	9.4
Japan	− 1.7	.2	10.8	19.7

shall explain this later in the chapter. For the moment it is only necessary to say that totally nontechnological translations must always be performed to judge the financial performance of foreign based operations. This applies, of course, to evaluating an investment. In addition to all of the factors previously discussed, if an investment being considered is to be made in a foreign country, then the estimate about what return the investment will bring now must include projecting relative inflation rates, possibilities of currency revaluations, and numerous taxes, penalties, and restrictions on money transfers, dividends and imports that do not apply in domestic operations.

Government Restrictions on Money Flow

An especially troublesome factor is restriction on the motion of money. Many countries in which a corporation might otherwise feel it advantageous to operate will make it too difficult to take money out. In most technological operations in foreign countries the objectives, and the probable attainment of something close to those objectives, involve considerable growth. This means the earnings are probably plowed back to maintain the growth and additional investment even may be required from the parent corporation. Under these circumstances, the restrictions on taking funds out of the country are not so important in the beginning. Ultimately, however, as the foreign operations mature, the parent corporation will wish to optimize the use of its total resources and move cash from one country to another. Flexibility to transfer money across national boundaries is of high importance.

It is usually the nation with extraordinarily high inflation that imposes severe restrictions on removing funds. That nation does not want excess currency in its corporations to be changed into dollars and sent back to the United States. Instead it is seeking to accumulate

American dollars. If anything, it would like to have enough American dollars to buy its own currency with those dollars and help keep that currency from falling in exchange ratio relative to the dollar. One way to control the removal of dollars is to put a heavy tax on dividends, since dividends are one common route for the removal of funds from a subsidiary in a foreign country to the parent corporation in the home country.

Not all countries have these restrictions. For example, although income taxes on corporate earnings are high in Germany, they are lower for a corporation that pays dividends. The taxing of received dividends in all countries amounts to a double taxation. The corporation pays the tax on its income and, when it pays dividends out of what is left of the earnings after tax, the receiver of this dividend pays a tax again. Germany has recognized this and, to partially compensate, has eased up on the corporate tax rate on earnings as a function of earnings paid out as dividends.

Most countries encourage exports, seeking a favorable trade balance and a reserve of foreign currency. In this way, the country can exchange currencies to adjust and influence (beneficially, it would hope) the currency exchange rates. Also, the country can be in a position to buy critical items it might need from other countries. The United States has for some years fostered exports by encouraging United States corporations to set up Domestic International Sales Corporations (DISCS) to handle exports and then allowing deferments of income taxes on earnings of these corporations. This is one source of the deferred taxes items appearing on balance sheets of United States multinational companies. These tax deferrals increase cash flow in the near term and aid in financing exports. In addition, the United States in the past has allowed the deferral of income taxes on overseas earnings that are reinvested there. The tax on such earnings is deferrable until the earnings, as cash, are brought back to the United States.

Technology Interchange

The ties among nations are made stronger by technological know-how transfer between them. In the next portion of the chapter we shall discuss this in some detail. Also, noncommunist nations usually grant patent rights to inventors from other countries, and a substantial foreign patent application activity goes on in all countries connecting technological ideas with economic advantages in those various countries. Multinational corporations are very often high technology corporations, and when they set up to produce their products in various countries, they constitute a source for the communication of technological information and the evening out of technological leadership positions among the nations.

All nations tend to be influenced by the technology that arises in the other nations, and the technology transfer activity constitutes a network of economic ties among nations. If Nation A, for example, is behind in computers, it is much to its advantage to attract capital and know-how from corporations based in other nations that possess computer technology. Generally the welcome, warmth and cooperation granted to a foreign-based investment to start corporate activities in a nation are greatly enhanced if it is perceived in that nation that the new activity will elevate the national level of technology.

Another factor which joins the nations of the world to each other, or at least large blocks of nations to one another, is the general world military situation. Thus the United States, Japan and Western Europe are linked through weapon systems technology, and their overall budgets and security policies are connected by joint participation in military pacts and strategies. In a similar way, of course, the Soviet Union and certain other communist countries are connected to one another and have economic, technology and general government policy arrangements.

The military weapon systems relationship among nations is particularly important to technological corporations. This is because such systems are high budget items in all of the nations and involve very new technology. Most of the principal technological corporations, multinational or not, are active in military weapon systems work. Joint bids on major systems by a team of contractors with home bases in different countries often are assembled to supply weapon systems to groups of nations, for example, to NATO countries. Thus, military ties create avenues for technology flow between nations.

Energy, space and the oceans offer additional examples where international corporation and technology flow are required for progress and where international wrangling owing to differences in policies and perceived benefits enter the picture as well. For example, as a factor in the exploitation of ocean resources, technological means exist now to make such sophisticated measurements and computations that could very rapidly advance the understanding of the basic science of ocean phenomena. This augers well for accelerating utilization of such basic data to make ocean resources available. New sources of minerals, food and energy and improved transportation and weather forecasting are among the many possibilities that are now just over the horizon.

These scientific and technological potentials are more than matched, however, by the difficulties of world government cooperation.

To cite only one point, who owns what is taken from the deep ocean bottom as raw materials? Private know-how and private capital will not be available to any great extent until there is clarity on this issue and such clarity is, as this book is written, far beyond the horizon. The governments of the world have been meeting in Law of the Sea negotiations and getting nowhere. Still, as the years go by, what with the ocean resources being so vast and with the increasing future world need for these resources, many of the problems will be resolved, at least sufficiently so that private investment from the noncommunist countries probably will enter the picture in a substantial way. The point here is that technological corporations dealing with ocean resources must take into account international government relationships as a major factor when they try to understand the potential return on investment.

In energy resources, numerous international government relationship issues dominate return on investment analyses and the judging of the markets for various technological products. Thus a corporation seeking to exploit special know-how, experience and facilities in the nuclear reactor field must consider the world market and not merely that of a single nation. In addition, worry about potential energy shortages and general concern about nuclear safety and proliferation are forcing a pattern of international activity that is the biggest single factor in determining the use of nuclear reactors. The rules for control of the motion of fissionable matter, nuclear waste and nuclear technology, as well as the delivery of actual nuclear hardware, vary from one nation to another, because each nation perceives differently its role in the nuclear field and what it believes is good for its own nation and the entire world society. No technological corporation could embark intelligently on a nuclear energy program without great attention to what is going on in this field in many nations. With nuclear energy the nations of the world have become highly interdependent and the technological industries' decisions have become dependent on more than one government's policies.

Something similar can be said about every other aspect of energy and the effect on decisions of technological corporations dealing in any way with energy. Of course, energy availability is a ubiquitous parameter affecting all activities of man. However, we speak here of technological corporations whose activities are specifically in the energy field. Thus if the United States were to create an adequately ambitious program to utilize coal much more fully, success in such a project would have an enormous effect on energy utilization, sourcing and pricing everywhere and on the overall economic health of the world. What the United States does in this area affects the rest of the world, since we are the largest energy user. The pertinence of this to the point we are making in this chapter, however, is not the solving of the energy crisis but rather the way in which the economics of the world become interdependent and dependent in part on the movement of technology among nations. In this instance, energy is one of the dimensions of that interdependence.

A large technological corporation, or a team of several of them, intending to make great advances in the use of coal, would have to consider, before making the investment, not only the United States economy and the policies of the United States government but also those of other nations. Economic demand and government policies everywhere would have a controlling effect on the return-to-risk ratio for such a contemplated project.

Increasing Control By Governments

In continuing to discuss the environment for technological corporations on a world basis, we must now speak of one special deterrent to private investments in foreign countries. In a number of nations takeovers of private industry by the government have occurred. When this has happened, there has sometimes been an effort at compensation and sometimes not depending upon the degree to which social conditions have driven governments to extraordinary steps about the private enterprise sector of the economy. A United States corporation, for example, must include in its consideration of the future that in many countries of the world the government may at some time in the future nationalize the industry.

How serious is this for technological industry in view of the point we made earlier that all nations desire the advanced technology of other countries and such technology transfer often accompanies investments by corporations based elsewhere? The problem is a complex one and a simple answer will not suffice. For example, the making of steel is a highly technological activity. The world now seems to have an oversupply of steelmaking facilities. In each nation the problem exists of what to do about its steel industry and its threatened underutilization and consequent high unemployment. Most nations regard steel-making as fundamental and cannot imagine going out of this business. If their steel industry appears to be in sufficient financial trouble, then for some nations a government takeover is almost the only step, since neither bankruptcy nor zero local production of steel is an acceptable political option.

In a similar way the aircraft industry has been nationalized in the U.K. In France the government has purchased all or portions of computer, automotive and other companies. In some of these instances the government's analysis has told them that these industries, when they consist of only medium-sized corporations, are not strong enough to compete on a world scale. They then decide that only if the government puts together a combination of private industry know-how with liberal government support can it be hoped the industry will survive and prosper.

Small, specialized technological corporations are relatively safe from takeovers by government. Very large foreign owned entities and joint ventures of multinational corporations are somewhat more vulnerable to eventual nationalization.

Government regulation and control, as distinct from government takeover, may be expected on an increasing scale in countries all over the world. A corporation operating in a foreign country will have especially to be aware of the peculiar regulations and restrictions that will apply to such a foreign owned activity. In Japan it is very, very difficult to arrange for 100 percent foreign ownership of a technological activity. A non-Japanese corporation wishing to exploit the Japanese market, or to use Japan as a base for whatever reason to expand in additional markets, almost always requires Japanese partners. In most of South America and Asia, and in some European countries such as France, an American corporation would not receive government approval to purchase a local corporation, but only a part of it, a fraction below control. Exceptions are conceivable, exceptions that are derived from governments need for the highly advanced technology that might be brought by the foreign-based corporation.

Because to the normal problems of securing a favorable return on investment one must add operating regulations, restrictions on the flow of funds and the possibilities of government takeovers, many technological corporations prefer to realize overseas exploitation of their product activities through license and royalty agreements. If an American corporation with a desirable and economically cost-effective technological product of high originality wishes to broaden its markets in foreign countries, it can license a company that already exists there and is a national in that country to distribute, market, assemble, or even manufacture the products en toto. A common way to receive a return is a first payment (up front) for the general license and privilege and then a royalty as a fraction of sales for all of the products made and sold in those additional countries. If all goes well, direct investment in foreign operations often pays off better than the royalty approach. However, because of the complications and the risks involved, it is very difficult to generalize. Instead, the management of a technological corporation should consider all routes for the use of its know-how on a world basis.

Technology Transfer

The fullest use of scientific and technological advance on behalf of the world's society would appear to require the know-how of which these tools are comprised to be freely transferable about the world. Just as world trade is enhanced by free movement of money, manufactured products, manpower and raw materials, so the mobility of science and technology affects the utilization and benefits to be obtained from these tools. To a technological corporation the greatest return on available technological resources would appear to come from that corporation's having the total privilege of moving its technological ideas, stored wisdom and actual products among its various operations in various countries, to other companies in negotiated deals, and even to governments in those countries where the governments have control of the technological applications.

Government Restrictions on Technology Flow

Governments restrict technology transfer at both the transferer and transferee ends of the transfer process. In the United States, apprehension, delay and indecision characterize the government effort to determine what should be the proper rules and controls for technology transfer, whether in the form of products or data, to other countries. The United States government is in the act because technology is judged to be an important asset whose shift to other countries can affect the general health and security of the nation. Some of the advanced technology is, of course, directly a result of classified research and development supported by the government in the interest of providing a base for United States security and, more specifically, for the design of United States military weapon systems. The government must be the arbiter about what is or is not classified and who, even within the body of U.S. Citizenry, has a need to know and should be permitted access to the technology. It almost goes without saying that the government would virtually ban the transfer of such technology to other nations, except as part of deliberately planned military cooperation, and then only under strict government control.

The problem is more complex for those aspects of technology that bear on national security but that are not classified. The specific technology may not in fact have arisen from government sponsored military effort. The question is whether the interest of security of the United States would be impaired by allowing the technology to leave the country. This question in turn suggests others. For example, does not any technology shift to other nations have the chance of aiding potential enemies? Thus, should we not stop all exports of advanced technological products and try to put a barrier on any leakage of new science and technology information from the United States?

An extreme, total limitation would obviously be ridiculously impractical to police. What constitutes a transfer of technology is in many instances virtually impossible to define. If the United States were to seek to deny giving any advanced knowledge we may have to others for fear it will somehow be used against us by any enemy, then we would in effect have to take ourselves out of world trade. For instance, semiconductors and computers might all be banned as export candidates, and we could not sell commercial jet airplanes to foreign-based airline companies. Restrictions, even if less than a total ban, put a handicap on American technological corporations in world trade. Almost everything that takes place in the United States on the technology front will find its way to other countries in time, if indeed we start out ahead. We would have to create a crazy pattern of living to restrict the ability of foreigners who come to the United States to observe what we are doing, to purchase, study, take apart, and become acquainted with our nonmilitary, commercially available technological products. We would have to deny to our scientists and engineers the privilege of educating each other at their professional society meetings, and thus put a critical constraint on the functioning of the entire scientific and engineering establishment in the nation.

Still, if we are highly advanced in certain critical technology items, why should we allow a potential enemy to save even a year or two? Should not some advanced aspects be withheld, at least partially? Thus, why should the Soviet Union be allowed to buy the fastest and largest computer ever built in the United States, if we know that the only application we have ever been able to find for that computer is to aid in the design of nuclear bombs? Or if we develop techniques for forging materials of such unusual composition that they make possible higher temperatures, efficiencies and thrust-to-weight ratios in our jet engines—why should we allow the details of this process to be in the hands of a potential enemy? The answer is that the denials of specific transfers may well be wise and justified, but they can only be temporary. As new techniques find a place in commercial product applications, it is eventually impractical to control and halt the export of such technology. Even on a security basis we must take some risks and allow the work of the technological world to go on.

Technology Transfer and Job Export

But there are other concerns that cause control of technology transfer to be constantly considered in the United States with similar situations applying to other nations as well. Despite many attempts at objective analysis there remains a difference of opinion in the United States whether the transfer of technology to other nations in effect transfers jobs and creates unemployment in this country. In theory a technological corporation in the United States may have a choice about whether to export its products overseas or to make those products there by setting up an operation that to some extent duplicates the American operation. If the total world market for an American technological product could be filled just as readily by manufacturing it in the United States and exporting it, then perhaps the choice would not be an issue. Most often, however, the corporations have reason to believe that if they do not manufacture their products in other parts of the world, then local manufacturers in those areas will soon commence the building of very similar products and will succeed in doing so with advantage there over exports from the United States. In other words, American technological corporations believe that their lead is most often not great and that they must prepare for and, in a timely way, execute the obvious and inevitable next step of spreading out manufacture geographically to meet the world market for their products.

Sometimes American corporations will go overseas to manufacture a product because of lower labor costs. This is usually because they already face foreign competitors with low labor costs and are engaged in, or in imminent danger of, losing not only the world market but the United States market as well. For example, radios and some TV sets of top quality based on the best technology are being made more cheaply out of the United States than they can be made in the United States. Thus there is an influx of such manufactured products into the United States and there has been virtually a halt to the manufacture of equivalent products here. The jobs have not so much been exported by American technology transfer as they have been taken over by other nations willing to produce them with a lower standard of living. It is argued by some that the ability of other nations to do this is the result of a technology transfer from the United States that took place years ago and that containment of existing American technology will make for a better situation in some years to come for the American worker. Of course, the American worker is also the American consumer, and he gains when he goes to buy goods that are produced more cheaply elsewhere.

Regardless of the various arguments, the transfer of technology from America, including its transfer by American corporations setting up operations overseas, is a political issue that is undecided and that will probably remain in dispute for years. The managements of United States technological corporations should assume that what they might seek to do to optimize the exploitation of the corporations' technologies in the world markets will be partially controlled and regulated by the American government. One reason why the issue will be with us is because it is a good political issue. With substantial antibusiness sentiment in the United States some politicians can make points with their constituencies by arguing that what American technological corporations do in technology transfer must be carefully watched and regulated or else the American citizens' interests will be impaired as the corporations pursue a path that selfishly optimizes only their shareholders' benefits and not those of the nation as a whole.

Two-Way Flow of Technology

Restrictions on technology transfer work in both directions, and an American technological corporation must consider the attitudes and controls of the governments of all of the nations where it chooses to operate and not that of the United States alone. It must be recognized that while the United States may lead the science and technology olympics on overall points, we cannot win every contest today. In a number of technological areas, other nations of the world will make the discoveries, do the inventing, or create the proper follow through to application and market development ahead of United States corporations. We have already said that one reason why an American technological corporation should plan to operate elsewhere in the world is because it can in this way benefit from technological developments and market understandings that exist outside of the United States and which if understood could usefully affect the American corporation's management of its overall affairs. It is also true that a multinational corporation becomes a participant in the scientific and technological life of the various areas where it operates. Its employees in those areas make, or certainly have the potential to make, important contributions. The parent corporation would like it to be true that it can move the technology wherever it arises to wherever in its family of world operations it may be put to advantage.

In this connection the proper operation of a multinational technological corporation includes attention to utilization of the wise perceptions of the market and applications that can arise in those operations. Suppose a corporation manufactures a high technology product in the United States and decides that it ought to be made also, say, in Western Europe for sale there as the optimum plan to exploit the investment in the product. The corporation should do more than merely put a duplicate manufacturing operation into Europe. That would not fully utilize what Europe has to offer. It should see that adequate strength in marketing, application engineering and possibly R&D should be built up also in its European operation. Recognizing that the technology changes and the applications are somewhat different from one nation to another, the product and its extensions must constantly be surveyed. The European operation, if it has strength beyond a simple copying ability, will add to the quality of this survey. Ideas that are useful to exploit, perhaps even on a worldwide basis, will likely originate in the European subsidiary.

Now that we have brought up the idea of the value to the technological corporation in moving technology's about for full utilization no matter where it originates, we should not be surprised that the governments of the various countries where the technology originates will, for the same reasons we listed above for the United States, want a say in the transfer of that technology. For economic competitiveness or security reasons or protection of jobs at home, those other countries will present obstacles to the all-out, free movement of technology.

The LDCs

The lesser developed countries (LDCs) offer some special problems and opportunities for technology transfer. On one hand, those countries are the most zealous in their desire to bring advanced technology activities into their countries. On the other, many of those countries argue that technological know-how, being merely wisdom, belongs to all, like the sun and the skies. Many of those nations are accustomed to receiving financial aid grants from the developed nations. If money itself can come for free, then surely any kind of knowledge one nation

possesses that could help another should be granted as a simple philanthropic act of civilized society.

Unfortunately, to a private technological corporation, the technological know-how it possesses is one of its most important assets.
Giving it away is pure charity and is no different from such a corporation's contributing funds, products, or machinery without pay. The
act would not be popular with shareholders who would feel at the least
that they ought to vote on each such gift and be able to take a personal
charity income tax deduction for it, if they approve.

In addition, in LDCs there is a constant tendency for government
leaderships, pressed as they are with impossible social problems to
solve, to find a scapegoat. The multinational corporation is often used
for that. An attack on a locally based, foreign-owned company for
seeking a profit is generally popular with the public. The LDC government, on one hand, wants to have foreign corporations come in and
bring technology and jobs. It seeks to make entry attractive for the
corporation, often providing special tax advantages for a period of time
and low interest loans to provide some of the facility construction. On
the other hand, it creates an atmosphere that makes it difficult for
the corporations to be successful in their relationships with the local
population.

Management must deal with these problems when operating in
lesser developed countries. Each project or arrangement must be negotiated on its own merits. The return-to-risk ratio must be assessed.
Either the nation is sufficiently interested to have the entry of the
technological corporation from outside, or it is not, and the operation
is launched or not in accordance with the details of the deal and the
assessment of risk and return. Sometimes these problems are lessened
by setting up joint ventures with local businesses sharing in the ownership and responsibility.

Risk in Foreign Operations

We have already mentioned that when an American technological
corporation sets up operations in other countries, it should include in
its list many risk possibilities for the future that are decidedly negative, including government takeovers and over-control on movement
or resources. Of course, we have problems in operating a technological
corporation even in the United States. The risks of not understanding
adequately the external environment—the market, government,

labor—exist everywhere. For technological corporations an additional risk stems from unpredictabilities on the science and technology front. However, foreign investments are riskier and more difficult for an American corporation to manage, because of the differences in culture, language, business practices, and detailed social and political trends. Put another way, the management of a technological corporation in the United States has enough to worry about and enough things to try to understand beyond its own internal operations. If it operates in foreign countries, it has a whole host of new and harder to understand issues to be concerned with as well.

Exploiting advanced technology internationally usually involves the following steps for a United States corporation: the first is to manufacture and market in the United States as quickly as possible to create a head start in the market place and to prove the technology. Next, an effort is made to export the products overseas, thus to begin developing a market for the products and a position for the corporation there. This export activity involves little risk but is usually handicapped by the higher price of the product to cover shipping, tariffs, and other added expenses of operating remote from the home base. Also, the acceptance of the new product overseas may be slow without relatively expensive marketing and application engineering indoctrination.

When the overseas market appears to be large enough, then the United States corporation typically will consider the big risk of investing in a plant abroad. It will usually seek total ownership but often will find that only partial ownership is permissible within the laws or practices of those foreign countries. The risks usually are greater than investing in a United States expansion, but if the technology is really advanced and cost effective, the American company can find itself with a commanding lead in foreign markets. The volume in foreign markets grows more rapidly when shipping and tariff barriers are bypassed through local manufacturing, or at least local assembly of the product. Such manufacturing and assembly usually requires some components from the United States and, as the foreign operation builds up successfully, this may increase United States exports en toto over what they would have been had no foreign manufacture been undertaken. Another reason for the foreign plant is that foreign competitors will find a way in time to surmount the original lead in technology. Then the United States company will find it virtually impossible to export, and it may also be too late to enter the foreign markets through local operations.

Licensing to foreign companies is also a permanent or long-term possibility, continually involving less risk, but with severe market penetration limitations compared with local manufacturing by an American dominated subsidiary. The difficulty in getting a good return from licensing starts with the long required time and the high cost of R&D. A substantial period is also required to arrive at a high foreign sales volume and with it a high licensing fee flow. By the time the technology is thoroughly debugged, the product totally accepted and the sales substantial, enough years may have elapsed that the license may be about to run out.

In creating new technology, there are failures as well as success. This is a principal reason why the overall R&D expenses of a technological corporation can be high. When a foreign company purchases a license for a specific product, the license fee they pay covers only the successful products' R&D, not that of the failures. Moreover, it is difficult to create license agreements which are adequately broad and binding for improvement technology. Of course, this is especially important in advanced products because of the rapid change of the technology. Thus, it is not just that license agreements may run out too near the beginning of the profitable period. Equally important, extending the license period substantially and making available to the licensee all improvements may give far too much to the licensee (or, from his standpoint, far too little). Neither party knows ahead of time how overwhelming or trivial the impact of subsequent improvements may be on the overall success of the product area.

The United States government helps and hinders exports in a number of ways, and these actions require consideration in gauging risks, so familiarity with pertinent government policies is important to the management of a technological corporation. For instance, the government has established the export-import bank with billions of dollars of backing for loans to foreign customers of big-ticket items such as aircraft, nuclear plants and the like. For a while, as already mentioned, the United States government also encouraged exports by allowing American corporations to set up DISCs to market exports, book the earnings and defer taxes on these earnings in order to use the generated cash to finance further exports. The Commerce Department maintains export promotion programs to help United States exporters enter foreign markets. The government also uses diplomatic efforts to urge foreign countries to reduce their barriers to United States goods and to influence their economic policies to increase their purchase of such goods.

However, the government is inclined to do such things as disallow certain income tax deductions for Americans abroad, who typically have higher expenses in undertaking such assignments. This raises the cost of keeping United States sales and service personnel overseas and discourages export sales. The government has also chosen to interpret our antitrust laws in ways that prevent United States companies from bidding jointly on major foreign projects, even though foreign governments typically do not handicap their companies in the same way. It also requires the export-import bank to assess the impact of United States exports on the environment in foreign countries even though those countries may not have environmental restrictions comparable with those we have.

In foreign operations, part of the risk is associated with the greater difficulty of finding the appropriate market strategy. A mere extrapolation of a strategy that has worked in the United States is dangerous. For instance, in international operations, the importance of market share and the strategy that this importance suggests can often be accentuated. A typical entry by an American company with a technological product in a foreign country may be a direct result of a head start in a new product area that has a substantial market potential in that foreign country. Because the product has an initial advantage, it may offer the United States company an opportunity for a high price and a high margin. If a local distributor is used, which is also quite common, then a high price and a high gross margin are needed in order that the distributor will be able to handle the product profitably, considering the need for educating the customer and developing the market. If the product is accepted, then the market presumably will grow. However, the market potential and the high profit margins do not go unnoticed by potential local competitors. A local company may enter with a product that is not nearly as good but, protected by the high profit margin of the American company, that company may nevertheless be able to get by, gradually move in, and perhaps even take over the market.

Clearly, the United States company must not take the risk of relying on a strategy of getting the highest earnings in the near term. It must lower the price and accept somewhat lower margins in order to maintain a controlling position in market share. This reasoning admittedly applies to the United States market as well. But the company presumably manufactures in the United States while initially it does not do so overseas. During the exporting phase, the best pricing strategy thus may be quite different in the two situations. When setting up strategy overseas, at some point the company has to consider shifting to local manufacture of the product. At all times, however, market share is the dominant factor in deciding when to commence foreign manufacture unless, of course, the technology moves so rapidly and the U.S. company is so advanced in it that it keeps a very large technological lead over potential competitors for a very long time. Even so, it may turn out that a somewhat lower price will increase volume and develop the market faster and provide the greatest insurance against the risk of a local competitor's entering the market.

When it operates in foreign countries, the parent corporation must recognize that some fundamentals of the market, like the ability of the industry and consumers to appreciate, accept and realize economic benefit from the product, may be substantially different from the situation in the United States. It is necessary to do market surveys suited to that nation and its technological status, industrial position, and economic prospects. All of these factors may bear heavily on the nation's ability to accept technological change. This analysis is very difficult to perform well without competent understanding of the area involved, including the ability to assess potential competition.

It is not easy for management to acquire adequate sophistication about the foreign environment. For a small technological corporation the risk of failure is such that it may not even be advisable to try. It might do better to turn over the fullest exploitation of its product endeavors to other larger corporations. In doing so the smaller corporation accepts a lower return but gains a much higher probability that it will achieve that return, with essentially no dilution of its limited management strength. The larger corporation presumably is operating in enough different countries to be able to afford the hiring of the expertise required to integrate, manage, and assess investments and strategy.

Minimizing Risks

Generally, the external environment for high technology corporations operating outside the United States in the future appears to be ideally suited to forcing an ever widening departure from perfection in management decision-making. Whether one looks at political, social, economic or technological factors the scene is characterized by rapid change, instability, unpredictability, and confusion, with high probability that the running of the corporation is going to be more difficult and less rewarding. Most noncommunist countries of the world, including the United States, have worsening social problems which dominate their politics and universally are being tackled by more pervasive government control. The elected leaders talk increasingly about less government, while creating more. Be it inflation, unemployment, economic competitiveness, shortages of critical resources, perceived or actual security problems, urban decay, hunger, safety, environmental degradation, consumer protection, health, rights, sex life, birth rate, or death rate, increased government control is everywhere encouraged by public demand. Deeper government involvement appears to guarantee over-spending, inflation, high consumption to investment ratios, price controls, increased shortages, unemployment, nationalism, protectionism, lowered public esteem for private business, less public appreciation for corporate profits. All of these ills are mutually reinforcing and lead to more restrictions on a business entity's management. This not only decreases return on investment but increases risk.

Sophistication in adjusting to this general political-social-economic environment on a world basis includes an ability to sense, interpret and discriminate about every aspect. There will not be a total homogeneity of these evils throughout the world. For some technological corporations and some segments of technology and product areas there will be opportunities that exceed the problems. The well-run technological corporation will be able to emphasize these, accentuating the positive, while not entirely eliminating the negative.

Among the risks difficult to assess are those involving labor. Strikes are more common in foreign countries than in the United States, although there are some exceptions such as Japan and Germany. But each of these nations have their own problems with labor. In Japan, for example, the culture makes it necessary to regard labor as a fixed cost, because it is not proper or acceptable to lay off workers when there is a turndown in product demand. In Germany labor shortages in the past have been handled by bringing in temporary foreign workers. However, when unemployed they choose to regard that situation as temporary and will not go home. This creates special problems. In Italy workers can act in a manner totally unacceptable in the United States. If fired they can appeal to the government for reinstatement and recovery of back wages with a very good chance of being sustained by the government administrative unit that does the judging regardless of the circumstances.

In short, the risk of having an unstable labor situation is much too high for an American technological corporation setting up to operate in some foreign countries unless it takes some special steps to equip itself with adequate expertise. The risks of having labor difficulties can be made lower by hiring experienced managers who are citizens of those countries. Some risks of a political-social kind can be minimized by skill in working with the government to interpret regulations. Other risks can be cut by setting up a joint venture with an established local company in that nation rather than having the operation fully owned. This, of course, adds a new risk even though it may lessen the others. The added one is the risk of not getting along well with the partner.

There are many legal risks which can be kept under control by adequate legal advice within the country of operation. The laws are often so different from those of the United States and so differently interpreted by the courts that every activity and commitment, every major change in policy or relationships with the community, government, partners or employees must be reviewed from every legal angle by experts in the local legal patterns.

A technological corporation operating in a foreign country will probably find itself with many contacts in the banking and investment community there. It may borrow money locally, seek to list its stock in foreign securities exchanges, or wish to get the benefit of financial analyses which commercial and investment banking firms can produce. They are also sources of intelligence on mergers, acquisitions, timings on investment and the like. American banks are also helpful. Most of the large ones have foreign branches that are particularly able to aid American based corporations. Astute management of the foreign operations of an American based technological corporation includes having good working relationships with both American and foreign banking establishments.

In making foreign acquisitions an American corporation will have to deal with risks of every kind that have been mentioned. Such an acquisition is very often a good way for an American corporation to get started overseas. To an appropriately acquired foreign company, an American corporation can add new products and technology to give that unit a possible edge on its competitors. However, the assimilating of a foreign acquisition into an American based corporate entity is not as easily accomplished with high benefits as with an American acquisition. The foreign corporation acquired will have substantial differences in its historical way of operating and in the way it sees opportunities and problems and reacts to them.

Very often an American corporation will make a foreign acquisition heavily weighted by the expectancy of getting and retaining the experienced foreign management when the company there is acquired. Almost equally often there will be some aspect of incompatibility between the American corporation and the management leadership of the acquired foreign entity. There is the risk, in other words, that a new management may be needed. Again, the risk of bad repercussions after such a management change, if it must be made, will be diminished if the new management is professional and experienced in operating and living in that country.

Accounting for Foreign Operations

If an American technological corporation is presented with a balance sheet and P&L statement for the period just ended for a foreign subsidiary, it has the task of translating all of the figures to American dollars. This may at first appear to be a straightforward task in which each figure is simply multiplied by the same factor, the exchange ratio of the currencies on that date. It is not that simple, There are rules in the United States for this process, not all arbitrary and nonsensical (although here and there the opposite may appear to be true). They result from an attempt to describe the situation so that the financial condition and the performance for the period reported on will be accurately displayed by the balance sheets and the P&L statements.

To a first approximation, all debt on the liability side of the balance sheet and working capital on the asset side together take the brunt of the currency revaluation adjustments. Thus for neutrality about changes in currency exchange ratios, arranging that the sum of debt and working capital be zero will achieve a first approximation to that desired result. However, before we get into further discussion of this translation process, let us discuss some rules applying in foreign countries that set the basis for the way the balance sheet and profit and loss statements are constructed there, in their currency.

Foreign Accounting Practices

We have already seen that we can obtain a variety of earnings reports and statements of present value of the shareholders' investment depending upon what depreciation rules are used in a period of inflation. The way inventory is accounted for is also a factor. The rule on depreciation is the same in foreign countries as the rule set by the IRS in the United States, namely, that historical figures must be used and not the inflated replacement figures. This means that in the inflationary environments of foreign countries (and many have inflation rates exceeding that of the United States) the actual depreciation that appears on the books will be undervalued and the cash flow from depreciation will not be sufficient to provide for replacement. In some countries, say, Brazil, where the inflation has been in the 30 percent range or higher for years, this understatement can be very substantial. This leads not only to overstating the earnings but to paying out more taxes than would have occurred had the depreciation been based on replacement value.

As to inventories, recall that the United States practice is to permit either LIFO or FIFO as long as the corporation is consistent and does not shift from one to the other for a short-term reporting advantage. For all practical purposes, in most foreign countries LIFO is not permitted. This means that companies include inventory inflation as part of their earnings and also pay taxes on those inflated earnings.

U.S. Accounting Practices for Foreign Operations

Let us now turn to the accepted practices in the United States for the translation of figures from the balance sheet and the P&L statement into American dollars. The United States rules for translation are set by the Financial Accounting Standards Board (FASB). In its so-called regulation No. 8, an attempt is made to report on an up-to-date basis the value in dollars of both the current assets and the debts of a foreign operation. In each quarterly report a dollar figure is set on these two items by applying to the foreign currency figures the currency exchange ratio applicable on the date of the report. However, it is more complicated than this and we had best break up the assets base into parts for a more careful statement of what FASB No. 8 requires.

For current assets and current liabilities, excluding inventories, the current exchange rate is used, and the translation is indeed simple. Inventories are translated, not at replacement value translated at current ratios and not at historical values translated at current ratios, but rather at the (historical) actual dollar cost, the price paid at the earlier date when the purchase was made. (In theory inventories can be carried on the foreign balance sheet at current replacement value and translated at the current exchange rate. However, and here is the rub, this is allowed only if the translated value is below the historical dollar cost. In an inflationary environment this will never be true.)

It is worth pondering this matter of inventory translation for a moment by discussing as an example a unit in Germany operated by an American corporation. Using the historical value instead of the replacement value for inventory, as we have already noted, swells stated profits on the books, as in FIFO generally. To make matters worse, since the American dollar has depreciated steadily against the Deutschemark for years, when we translate the already understated inventory, as part of translating the balance sheet into dollars, an out-of-date currency exchange ratio will be used. (Recall, the exchange ratio when the inventory was bought is the one the rules require be used and not today's ratio.) Thus the inventory might have cost a million Deutschemarks when it was purchased. Its market or replacement value today might be two million Deutschemarks. On the date of the purchase a million Dms might have been the equivalent of $300,000; today a million Dms is the equivalent of $500,000, and two million Dms is equivalent to $1,000,000. The translation of the German operation, in other words, provides us with two cumulative distortions (away from replacement reality) for the inventory as we view the American translation of the balance sheet. That sheet will show the inventory as $300,000. To replace it today would cost $1 million.

The first distortion is a function of German accounting rules and the second is the fault of our American translation accounting board practices. Can the second factor be justified for any reason? There is a rationale. If we are going to value in America the inventory that we bought a few years ago in Germany, we should value it at precisely the dollars it took to buy it at that time; otherwise we are not using historical rates. What it is worth now in American dollars to replace it is not relevant to the balance sheet once the use of historical values for inventories have been agreed upon. After all, suppose there were a deflationary, instead of inflationary, economy and America deflated more than Germany. Then American accounting rules would permit using the current replacement figure, because that would be more conservative, being lower.

For fixed assets the exchange rate on the date of acquisition is again used. Related depreciation is also translated at those same historical figures and exchange rates. The conservative approach, in other words, is used as with inventories. This means though that, compared with replacement value expressed in American dollars there again are two distortionary effects, the failure to use replacement depreciation in Germany and the use of the out-of-date exchange rate. These again are cumulative, adding up to understate the balance sheet's fixed assets compared with the real replacement cost today of those assets in American dollars. For sales and all costs, with the exception of the depreciation costs already discussed, each figure is translated using the present average exchange rates that were applicable during the period being reported (year or quarter).

Long-term debt, according to FASB rules, is translated (surprisingly?) at the current rate of exchange. A debt may have been incurred 10 years before and is still on the books, let us say, because there is no requirement or intent to repay that debt for yet another 10 years.

Nevertheless the debt figure on the balance sheet is retranslated at every reporting period, using the then new current rate of exchange. The German debt is constant, of course, constituting as it does a set contract to repay the lender, to which contract such things as the relative rates of German and American inflation are irrelevant. Yet, each time the balance sheet is reproduced in dollars that constant debt goes up or down (and the U.S. company must report gains or losses) all depending upon whether or not the United States currency has gone up or down with respect to the currency of Germany.

Suppose in Germany 10,000,000 of Deutschemark debt was committed years ago and was then the equivalent of $3,000,000. At current exchange rates it might be about $5,000,000. This would mean that the stated book value of the entry on the balance sheet, expressed in American dollars, would have had to rise by $2,000,000 and the German subsidiary's net worth would have to be lowered by $2,000,000 because the book loss would have to be reported even though the loss had not happened in actual fact, the loan not paid off. This unrealized loss would affect the descriptions of the financial performance of the German entity when translated. It would be expressed in American dollars and integrated with the other operations to form the total financial report for the American corporation for the period.

Transfers of funds from a German operation to the parent are translated as to their value in dollars at the current exchange rate. The transfer is usually in the form of a dividend.

Apart from dividends, the German company will have on its balance sheet a retained earnings figure. This also must be translated to produce the American balance sheet and must be at the historical exchange rate, that is, at the rate that applied when those earnings were attained and reinvested or accumulated. Each increment to the shareholders' equity in the German entity, when shown in the American-made balance sheet, accordingly does not go up and down with the exchange rates when translated to dollars. These increments instead stay fixed at the dollar values they had when they were first booked in Germany. When a dividend is paid, which draws out funds from the retained earnings, a realized exchange gain or loss will occur, since the dividend, unlike the retained earnings, is translated at the exchange rate applicable on the date of the dividend.

Suppose, for example, that the German company accumulated some earnings during a period some years ago and the dollar equivalent of those earnings was $1 million. Time and again after that, the translated balance sheet will continue to show that million dollars ignoring the changes taking place in the currency exchange rate, this in accordance with the rules. Suppose we now move those retained earnings to America, turning in the Dms for dollars at the present exchange rate. To our glee, because the Dm has risen relative to the dollar since those funds were earned and booked, we find ourselves with $2 million and we correctly list that. What is the reasoning behind the rule? It is sensible to use the current exchange rate because the $2 million is actually what we now hold in our fists. Once we have it, we suddenly lose interest in how big that pile of dollars would have been instead had we taken it out when it was originally earned and began to be held by our German subsidiary.

Tax Differences

This completes our recital of how key figures on the balance sheet are translated. In addition to translation rules and variations in accounting practices between the United States and other countries, there are also differences in taxes.

The income taxes in foreign countries vary. In 1977, with the United States rate then 48 percent, other figures were: 56 percent in West Germany, 52 percent in the U.K., 50 in France, 40 percent in Sweden, 30 percent in Japan, and 25 percent in Italy. Each nation has a welter of other taxes to add to these that affect the net profitability of operations and also the flexibility to transfer funds out. While some countries tax dividends (back to the parent corporation) heavily, others lower the income tax on earnings if dividends are paid. For instance, in Germany the combination of corporate income and trade tax actually totals 64 percent, if all earnings are retained in the business and only 46 percent, if all earnings are distributed to shareholders, with a sliding scale between if partial dividends are paid. This tax reduction is helpful to our German subsidiary's P&L statement, giving it higher earnings after tax. Unfortunately, the recipient of the dividend, namely the parent American corporation, must pay a 15 percent income tax in Germany upon receiving that dividend. The parent company, having obtained the dividend, must also pay a tax in America on that dividend as income received. However, a United States tax credit is allowed (up to a point) recognizing the tax on the dividend in Germany.

In Germany, because of the strength of the economy, the general prosperity, the modest inflation and a determination by the German government to control inflation, companies are encouraged to pay dividends. Most successful American subsidiaries in Germany are likely to be earning enough to have available cash above what is required for business growth, since essentially no additional working capital must be assigned to cover the modest inflation. In fact, a company is penalized by a higher income tax rate if it does not pay dividends. It is not sensible to borrow in Germany, if there is no need for the funds, even though the interest rate is low as befits a low inflation country, because no beneficial hedging is likely, it being probable that the past record will extrapolate well for a time with the United States having a higher inflation rate than Germany. Currency revaluations affecting the working capital item on the balance sheet in that case will increase earnings when they are expressed in the U.S. in dollars.

In Brazil, to discourage the withdrawing of money from the country, the income tax to be paid there on earnings is increased if generous dividends are paid. The corporate income tax is modest to begin with. However, only around 12 percent of invested capital can be removed before the income tax becomes extremely penalizing—a minimum 40 percent tax on dividend distribution above the 12 percent of invested capital, rising quickly to 60 percent.

All in all, the various adjustments for accounting practices, the effects of inflation, the currency exchange gains and losses, the various taxes on earnings and on the movement of money, and the various credits allowed on those taxes constitute an adequate workload for a staff of expert accountants in multinational corporations. There are many decisions for management for which the accountants provide the settings with their figures on the cost of alternative approaches. For instance, we may or may not elect to extract a dividend or pay off debts. In some countries where we suspect there will be substantial inflation and the currency will fall against the dollar we can elect to borrow locally as a means of hedging on the inflation, this depending upon what the interest rate is that we will be charged on the debt. In the U.K. the interest is not prohibitive. In Brazil, the interest rate is set by the government at much greater than the sum of normal interest plus the anticipated inflation and the government totally controls interest rates. It is not a market phenomenon. It puts the interest rate on borrowed money so high that it forces foreign companies to bring money in for expansion and not to borrow it in Brazil. Hedging can be done in Britain but not in Brazil.

Suppose, as an example, that we have subsidiary in Britain with a total of $10 million in working capital and also a $10 million debt in local currency (British pounds) according to the balance sheet at year end. Assume that these items remain constant, expressed in pounds, for the ensuing year. However, a change in the currency exchange rate of 10 percent favoring the dollar, we shall further suppose, takes place during the year. In dollars, the subsidiary's current assets will fall to $9 million—assume the inventory turns over rapidly—and that represents a loss. However, we now owe only $9 million on the debt, and that is a gain. By the FASB rules, these two items will continue to neutralize, whichever way the currency exchange rates fluctuate and the American corporation will not show the peculiar gains and losses due to currency exchange. Note, had we borrowed the $10 million in dollars we would have missed the gain and had only the loss. If any foreign loan is a long-term one that we have no intention of paying up immediately, then the ups and downs of the currency exchange rates yield only accounting gains or losses in the interim. No real gain or loss on the loan will occur until the loan is paid, and who can say what the exchange rate will be then?

If we have an opportunity to grow profitably in a country, and have use for generated funds to finance the growth, then we are less likely to want to bring money back and pay additional taxes in the process. On the other hand, our desire to broaden the activities in a country may be tempered by our concern over inflation. We may feel that if we do not bring funds back now, we may find they will not amount to very much (in American dollars) later.

Investment Analysis

To illustrate further some of the factors that enter into the analysis of the financial performance of foreign operations, let us consider a quantitative example, an incremental investment analysis. Suppose that in 1968 an investment of $240,000 (Dm 960,000) was made to bring on stream a new product in a company's West German subsidiary. Initial investment was composed of $140,000 (Dm 560,000) of machinery having a seven-year useful life and $100,000 (Dm 400,000) working capital. In addition, the parent company transferred $10,000 per year in added working capital to the German subsidiary. We assume no new fixed assets were required during the period. Now, in 1976, it is necessary to replace the old factory equipment to continue production.

As justification for the new investment, the subsidiary's management representative in the United States cites the high past growth rate of sales (15 percent) and the high returns the product has been generating, exceeding the company's 10 percent cost of capital. As shown in Table 13–C which details all of these facts, the net present value, at the company's cost of capital of 10 percent, is $41,932. For

Table 13-C Investment Analysis in U.S. Dollars

Year	Sales US $	Earnings After tax 8% Sales	Investments	Depreciation	Cash Flow	Disc. Cash Flow
1968	—	—	(240,000)	—	(240,000)	(240,000)
1969	250,000	20,000	(10,000)	20,000	30,000	27,273
1970	288,000	23,040	(10,000)	20,000	33,040	27,305
1971	331,000	26,480	(10,000)	20,000	36,480	27,429
1972	380,000	30,400	(10,000)	20,000	40,400	27,596
1973	437,000	34,960	(10,000)	20,000	44,960	27,925
1974	503,000	40,240	(10,000)	20,000	50,240	28,384
1975	578,000	46,240	160,000	20,000	226,240	116,020
						41,932

the above analysis it has been assumed that the equipment was depreciated on a straightline basis with a seven-year life, that all working capital, $160,000, is returned in the eighth year without any additional taxes and that the after-tax income is eight percent of sales each year.

We know that during this seven-year period the currency exchange rate has been changing between the Dm and the dollar and that there has been inflation in Germany, albeit modest compared with most nations, including the United States. Table 13-D shows these ratios. Suppose we translate Table 13-C back into Dms first, and then into constant Dms, taking out first the effect of the changing currency exchange ratio and, second, the German inflation. This yields Table 13-E. We see the picture is far different from that disclosed in Table 13-C. About half of the subsidiary's growth was in currency translation. Practically all of the balance can be accounted for by the inflation in Germany.

Now let us redo the investment analysis of Table 13-C in the local currency. We will assume that tax ratios are the same in Germany and the United States. Thus, as shown in Table 13-F, the German subsidiary receives the $240,000 initial investment from the parent company in equipment and working capital, expressed now in Dms. For the next six years it receives the annual additional $10,000 working capital contribution, which though constant in American dollars varies when expressed in Dms because of the varying currency exchange rate. Using 10 percent as the cost of capital we obtain a net P_V of 40,507 Dms. At 1975 currency exchange ratios this P_V is less than 40 percent of the $41,932 figure for P_V when the financial results were

110 Table 13–D German Inflation

Year	Wholesale Price Index	Exchange Rate Dm/$
1968	100	4.0
1969	101.8	3.94
1970	107.5	3.66
1971	112.1	3.49
1972	115.3	3.19
1973	123.14	3.67
1974	139.7	2.59
1975	146.2	2.46
1976	151.9	2.52

Table 13-E Investment Analysis in Deutschemarks

Year	Sales Dm	Earnings After tax Dm	Sales in Constant 1968 Dm	Earnings Constant 1968 Dm
1968	—	—	—	—
1969	985,000	78,800	968,000	77,410
1970	1,054,000	84,326	980,000	78,440
1971	1,155,000	92,415	1,030,000	82,440
1972	1,212,000	96,976	1,051,000	84,110
1973	1,167,000	93,343	948,000	75,800
1974	1,302,000	104,222	932,000	74,600
1975	1,422,000	113,750	973,000	77,800

expressed in dollars. This means the same investment and performance, which when examined in United States dollars yields one internal rate of return, yields a different and lower rate of return when figured in Dms.

For judging whether the investment worked out well, the calculation in American dollars is what counts with the American corporation. However, we must be aware that the investment looks as good as it does because some substantial profit was made by the company being inadvertently involved in foreign currency exchange speculation that worked out well. It should also be noted that a company averaging a low internal rate of return on investments in Germany may be satis-

Table 13-F Investment Analysis in Constant Deutschemarks

Year	Earnings	Investment (current exch. rate)	Depreciation	Cash Flow	Disc. Cash Flow
1968	—	(960,000)	—	(960,000)	(960,000)
1969	78,800	(39,400)	80,000	119,400	108,534
1970	84,326	(36,400)	80,000	127,726	105,502
1971	92,415	(34,900)	80,000	137,515	103,273
1972	96,976	(31,900)	80,000	145,076	99,087
1973	93,343	(36,700)	80,000	136,643	84,855
1974	104,222	(25,900)	80,000	158,322	89,293
1975	113,750	605,400	80,000	779,150	409,964
					40,507

factory to an American with a higher hurdle rate here. The cost of capital in Germany is lower than in the United States because the inflation in Germany is lower.

If the parent company desired to bring back the cash flow, it would have to declare a dividend and pay a tax to the German government of about 15 percent at present rates on that dividend. The declaration of the dividend would bring the tax that the German subsidiary has to pay on its operating income to the government down from around 64 percent to 46 percent. Also, the parent corporation would receive a credit in paying its overall income tax to the American government for the 15 percent paid. Taken as a whole we were justified in this specific example in assuming that the overall percentage tax paid on income was approximately the same whether the analysis was made in Dms or dollars.

Participating in Currency Exchange Speculation

This example helps to emphasize that, whether a corporation likes it or not, when engaged in foreign operations, it is automatically engaged in investing in currency speculation. It is gambling, playing the market, on international rates of exchange. Part of its P&L performance will encompass its success or lack of it in such activities. This may be especially painful for a technological corporation which thinks of itself as being engaged in developing, producing and marketing substantive things, not in currency speculation.

Of course, we should recognize that even if a company operates in the United States alone, inflation provides almost the equivalent of currency speculation. Foreign operations add a new dimension to the handling of the inflation by injecting the need for paying attention to differences in inflation between countries. More than any other factor, it is the variations in inflation rates that cause the variations in currency exchange rates. With a very high inflation rate a country's currency will devalue against that of a country with a lower inflation rate. On a short-term basis money may move between those two countries in anticipation by speculators of differences in inflation rates that are thought to be coming, either improvements or more rapid degradations. Also the governments may be expected to intervene from time to time. The government treasuries have reserves of foreign currencies that they can use to buy and sell and thus affect the free market motion of funds. Money transfer in denominated currencies (and occasionally in gold) goes on to correct for the varying degrees of inflation or the varying perceptions of what the inflation rates will be in the future.

A corporation, particularly a technological corporation, may try to stay aloof from this inflation and currency exchange rate oscillation, but it cannot do so because it has to have working capital. A certain amount of hedging or insurance is possible. Thus, as we discussed earlier if the company has current assets in a foreign country, it may seek to borrow a comparable amount there. If the assets then go down, expressed in American dollars because of what happens to the exchange rate, then so does the loan obligation expressed in American dollars. Also, the parent corporation can make constantly updated analyses of its options in moving money in and out in an attempt to anticipate changes that will be distorting of what might be called the basic and substantive financial performance. Of course, the reported earnings have to include these nonoperational currency exchange contributions. As the rates fluctuate with time, the appearance is created of oscillations in the performance of the company operations. Actually, the substantive operations may be quite steady, or growing in a steady fashion.

A corporation that carries on operations in a number of countries must make estimates into the future of inflation rates and currency exchange ratios. It must use these to influence its estimates of interest rates on loans, costs of capital, and appropriate hurdle rates for measuring the attractiveness of investments in foreign countries. The problem of judging performance and the potential of performance as influenced by further investment is basically the same in foreign countries and in the United States; it is merely complicated by these added factors, and the hurdle rate of return must be heightened to account for the added risks.

Problems

13–1. Make up what you think might be a representative, simple balance sheet of assets and liabilities for an imagined foreign division of an American company, expressing everything in dollars and including the following items explicitly: fixed assets at acquisition value, less accumulated depreciation; cash, current receivables and current liabilities; inventories at cost of acquisition; long-term debt in the local currency; initial investment by the parent and accumulated earnings. Also, construct a P&L statement for the preceding period, including sales, costs, and net earnings after taxes (assuming no dividend). Then redo both statements assuming that a sudden currency exchange ratio revaluation takes place in which the foreign currency falls 10 percent against the dollar. Repeat this with the assumption that the currency rises 10 percent.

13–2. The financial manager of an American company with a foreign subsidiary has some excess cash in that subsidiary. He considers bringing that cash back to the parent company expecting that he can earn interest of 10 percent before and 5 percent after taxes on it at home during the coming year. The dividend and other taxes and fees involved in this transfer will consume 35 percent of these funds, however. He has the option to leave the excess funds in the foreign country and to loan it out at an interest rate of 18 percent in the foreign currency. He expects the devaluation to be 24 percent against the dollar by the end of the year. Compare the two alternatives, both quantitatively and qualitatively. Explain why it is conceivable that the financial manager could be right by going either way, depending on varying circumstances not included in the above description.

13–3. A technological corporation is seen to be marketing its American made and domestically well established product in European countries A, B, and C but not in adjacent D. What could be good reasons for this?

13–4. Select from the annual reports of technological corporations two that make or sell a substantial fraction of output in other countries as well as in the United States. From clues in the annual report, speculate on why the particular countries in which the company is active have been selected and why others apparently have been excluded.

13–5. A small company with an outstanding new product does not have the financial means to exploit it in foreign countries. A large company with foreign distribution capabilities is considering acquiring the foreign rights to the small company's products but knows this will not be sound unless the small company's overall financial stability is ensured. Hence, the large company buys some new equity stock in the small company, this at possibly overvalued price, to add to the small company's equity. Discuss as quantitatively as is reasonable, and in general terms qualitatively, the degree of overpricing that the large company should be willing to accept in relationship to the earnings it might expect on the sale of the product in foreign countries.

13–6. A foreign subsidiary of an American technological corporation needs additional funds beyond the cash it is generating internally to cover a major R&D program that is seems advisable to carry on in that subsidiary. It is anticipated the currency in the foreign country will fall substantially against the dollar during the next two years while these funds will be used. After that, the cash flow of the subsidiary will be ample to take care of its needs. The parent company is considering various ways of providing the financing. One is to buy additional common shares, sending dollar payments to the subsidiary to be used as required. Another is to borrow the dollars in the United States and loan the money to the subsidiary. A third is for the parent company to borrow dollars in the foreign country at a somewhat higher interest rate and then to loan those in turn to the subsidiary. A fourth is for the subsidiary itself to borrow local currency at a substantially higher interest rate—higher because of the relatively high inflation in the foreign country, inflation which is also the prime reason for the expected devaluation of the currency. Compare these approaches and suggest which in your opinion would be the correct one to use.

13–7. A wholly owned subsidiary in Germany has earnings before taxes of approximately $1 million and does not need this cash in the operation. The taxes on these earnings to be paid in Germany depend on dividend policy: a minimum of 45 percent, if all earnings are paid out in dividends; a maximum of 65 percent if no dividends are paid; a straight line formula between the two extremes for partial dividend payment. Further assume that after various transfer, withholding and United States income taxes are paid, the net after-tax cash received by the parent will be 50 percent of the dividend. If retained by the German subsidiary, the cash will be loaned out to earn the local interest rate before tax of 5 percent. If the dividend is received by the parent, it will earn 10 percent after tax during the next year. Compare the parent corporation's increment of reported dollar earnings after taxes (next year) that result from the German operations for (1) the full cash transferred as a dividend at the beginning of the year versus (2) no cash transferred as a dividend. Assume a currency revaluation of 10 percent during the year in favor of the Deutschemark.

13–8. For Problem 13-7, shift the country to Brazil and assume a corporate income tax of 22 percent and a combination of withholding, distribution, and penalty taxes on dividends of 90 percent including the United States income tax effect. Assume that the cash is not needed by the Brazilian subsidiary and, if kept there, would be loaned out at the local interest rate of 50 percent. Compare the increment in the net earnings that the parent United States company would add to its profit and loss statement for the two cases: (1) all the excess cash is transferred to the parent as a dividend and (2) the cash is kept in the Brazilian economy. Assume a 20 percent revaluation during the year in favor of the dollar.

13–9. A young, high technology company has a unique position in a new, profitable, proprietary product growing so rapidly that the company is hard-pressed to meet customer requirements. Owing to the priority of filling the United States market demand, a lack of experience and competence in international operations and no resources or time for the required effort, the company is doing nothing to market its product overseas. Describe three ways in which, with minimum effort, the company might exploit its product internationally.

14

THE START-UP OF A NEW CORPORATION

FILLING A CONTEMPLATED NEED

Unless its founders plan deliberately to take advantage of those to whom they offer shares of stock in their new corporation, it makes no sense to launch it unless it is thought to fill a need. For a technological corporation this often means that a novel or superior product is planned to be put on the market by the new corporation. This is not always the case, of course. The product may be relatively mature, not very different from that of competitors, but one where it is envisaged that either new techniques of manufacture or of distribution and marketing will cause the product to be favored over a competitors'. More generally, then, we should say that the new corporation, if it is to have a reasonable chance of success must offer something that is not now available, a new product or simply better customer service on an old one.

But perhaps we should question this generalization for a moment. Could there not be a situation at times in which the total market for a product area is not being filled adequately by existing competitors? Without offering anything new or better in any aspect—product performance, manufacturing methods, or relationship with the customer—an additional corporation conceivably can then enter the field and enjoy its share of the market. This is a theoretical possibility, of course, but those who form a new venture on this basis should ask themselves what it is that deters the existent, established producers from expanding to fill the market. Only if they are convinced that the present suppliers all have permanently backward managements (or perhaps some special limitation, say, in financing or location that precludes their meeting the demand) should they form a new corporation. Those circumstances will be relatively rare. As a first approximation it is well to answer the question, "Who needs you?" before seriously starting the process of creating the corporation and all that it entails.

An obvious product that will be significant probably already will be under development by the established companies, even if it has not been announced. New companies, and entrepreneurs to start them, are more suitable for those products that are not so obvious. The founders are not likely to be successful if the best they can think up to do is launch companies to work in precisely the same fields as companies started long ago. Some old companies have lost out and become problems, mainly due to poor management. Most have prospered and become large and well established. The products of the latter are now mature and their product development capabilities sharply tuned. So they are not likely to have overlooked an attractive product opportunity in their specialty. To compete with them in their areas takes an inordinate amount of capital and a rather improbable assembly of extraordinary talent in every function, engineering, manufacturing and marketing. Basically, the entrepreneur should look for fields in which the existing companies either cannot perform well or have good reasons for choosing not to compete. The best product choice for the new company is outside the major track for established companies, either an activity entirely new or a very new way to engage in something old.

It has been common for technological corporations to be started based on an invention, a new technological approach, an idea whose time is believed to have come, a means of doing something useful not previously do-able, a new way of performing some task customers need, something cheaper or faster or more reliable or of lighter weight or simpler or easier to use and repair. This line of thought should usually dominate in the decision to start a technological corporation.

Risk

Small technological corporations seem to contribute benefits in innovative technology out of proportion to their size, but the rate of launching of such businesses in the United States has fallen drastically in recent years. In the decade of the mid-1960s through the mid-1970s, new stock issues to start small high technology companies dropped from the hundreds to only a few a year. In fact, during 1975, which combined recession and inflation, not a single public issue of new common stock appeared for a small, high technology company. Although the situation recovered somewhat in 1976-78, it is no longer easy to attract investors for new technological corporations. The big reason is risk, or, more accurately and completely, it is the ratio of risk to return. Thus, the promoter of a new company must have a strong case to propose, one in which ideas about marketing, product technology, and/or manufacturing seem highly novel and practical, and exceptionally profitable.

Regardless of the foundation for confidence of the founders of a new corporation in future success, objective analysis leading to a sound decision to start the corporation must begin with an understanding of the market, the demand for the products or service of the contemplated new company. If the product itself is very new, if no precedent for its application and no readily extendable data exist about similar products and applications, then the assessment of the demand for the product may be very difficult. The difficulty then needs to be matched by intensity of effort. In the end it may be that it is simply impractical, well nigh impossible, to gauge the market. The only action that could disclose the true facts about market acceptance might be the experiment of creating the corporation. Launching a corporation becomes a bigger gamble, the risk gets higher, as inability to understand the market increases. If the corporation is started based on such a risk, it should be with full knowledge thereof, a calculated risk, even though the back-up investigations are very sketchy.

Some high risk activities succeed, but the word risk is applied aptly only if it is accepted that more high risk ventures fail than succeed. We tend to hear later only about those that make it big. Less often are the more frequent results, the failures, disected in detail and made known to us. Documentation of all the facts and considerations in the past formations of corporate failures leaves much to be desired by those looking for general principles. If a corporation based on some new and untried approach is a success, a passionate desire will be found in some for documenting the evidence of it and heralding the founders as men of genius. If the operation is a failure, it is often fortunate for the founders that the historical evidence of what lead them to start the corporation in the first place is of skimpy availability. If you become a founder of a new corporation and it is a bust, the last thing you need in addition is to have it recorded in great detail. The exercise has little appeal.

Venture capital organizations were polled recently about the factors they believed most dominant in the success or failure of new technological companies. Management ability was rated first, market acceptance of the products second, the technical feasibility of the product third, and the availability of capital fourth. The idea is that if a new company rates high in the first three categories, then capital will generally be found.

The Market

Returning now to a sensible, generally sound starting of a new corporation, let us be more specific about this matter of understanding the market. The founders should gather data on the requirement for what it is that they expect to supply. Before worrying about competitors, they should prepare their estimates of the total market for a long time ahead. The pertinent time period should commence not from the moment the analysis begins but rather from the instant the new offerings to the market from their corporation will commence. This timing distinction is a trap for the naive who tend to overlook it.

Quantitative descriptions of the market are inextricably bound up with many qualitative considerations. We are speaking of technological corporations and technological products and services. So again we must emphasize that the technology constantly changes, as does the system for which the products of the new corporation may constitute a deviation. By the time the new corporation is really ready to deliver its products the market may change. New applications for the general product concept may evolve, of course, and any manufacturing or marketing leads that the new company is expected to be able to exploit may become applicable in time perhaps for related products as well. All of this needs to be established for a substantial period.

The quantitative considerations about the market will involve not only the size of the market in terms of units sold but also the price at which the products will be cost effective and attractive to customers. Since the price of a product is related to volume, the market estimates must involve more than specific numbers versus time, but rather a range of volumes for a range of final prices.

Among the qualitative considerations to be included in a description of the market are those special features beyond cost effectiveness that will cause acceptance of the product. If a substantial amount of detailed application engineering is needed or if maintenance is a complicated procedure involving considerable interaction between the producer and the customer, then this must be carefully noted. If the field is one where technological obsolescence is expected to be rapid, then this greatly affects the nature of the market, because it affects the customers' reaction to making investments by buying those products.

Now, all of these issues have been discussed in earlier chapters on product selection and marketing. However, there is one big difference in the way the results of these analyses are judged for a new corporation. It has no initial position, no organization, nothing to extrapolate from. Thus the value of the new product to the customer has to appear extraordinary. Is the product something that provides exceptional benefits for the customer for the price paid? Is there a big margin in its value to him over costs that can lead him to higher profit margins? If so, then there is a basis for investment to produce the article. If, in addition, a high growth rate should be expected as the product and its extensions begin to affect what customers can do with the product and how they can improve their operations, then a foundation starts to develop for the next step for consideration of starting the corporation. (In contrast we have only to cite the extreme of considering entering a field where there is a substantial market but where it is expected the market will decrease in a relatively short time because the benefit to the customer is not great and entirely different ways of meeting the customers' requirements are coming to take over the market. At some point in automotive history a very much cheaper, longer lasting, and better looking buggy whip was no longer an attractive product for the starting of a corporation.)

In examining the market for the novel product of a fresh technological corporation, it is especially important to take account of the distinction between initial and continuing demand referred to earlier in the text. This difference, if ignored, can be especially injurious to the plans of a new company. For a few years, the annual sales forecast may be based on filling a demand that will not endure at anywhere near the same level. Thus, a totally original and unusually effective medical equipment item may enable hospitals to perform a valuable service they could not previously render. The result may be that virtually every hospital will buy one of the instruments as soon as possible. The process of manufacture and distribution to fill the first wave of demand may take, say, three or four years. After that it is only the expansion of hospitals, or the replacement of worn out equipment, or selling to the less well funded hospitals that provides the continuing annual volume. The new corporation might look good for a few years while it is filling the original demand. Then it will be discovered it has a relatively small and disappointing business.

The Competition

Now we must come to consideration of competitors. In founding a new corporate entity to fill a market demand, it is the total potential competition that must be assessed. The present competition is only a part of what the new corporation may have to contend with. Here the founders would do well to make several lists.

One is of those corporations that are already in the business and have some of the market or are in almost the same field and could easily spread out to produce directly competitive products. Then there must be a list of those companies that are not at the moment in anything closely related, but who if they chose could enter the field and be tough competitors. Every very large technological corporation could presumably decide to enter almost any technological field, but only a fraction of these possibilities will have a substantial probability of actual occurrence. We do not mean to suggest dreaming up a theoretical group of competitors as broad as possible. Such a list would not be very useful and the founders could accept some risk from remotely conceivable competitors. Serious potential competitors are companies that have considerable understanding of the pertinent market and already possess a significant portion of the required skills for product design, manufacturing or marketing.

A new corporation has to be considered initially as possessing only unproven competence and resources. An established corporation has many advantages in expanding to cover new products, even if it does not initially encompass every dimension required to meet the product's needs. Thus IBM could be listed as a potential competitor for almost anything that has to do with computers even though at the present time there is much computer related equipment that IBM does not manufacture or market.

When you attempt to list potential competitors not now engaged in supplying the market with products similar to those of your proposed new company, it is useful to ask which companies now deal with the same customers you expect to sell to with any kind of product. They know the customer well and have a head start, even if they do not yet have your product. Also it is helpful, if the contemplated product line of the new corporation is sufficiently new, to ask what systems will be affected by the comtemplated new product line. What products of some existing corporations will be put out of date by your new products? Those companies that have a lot to lose are candidates to become competitors. They presumably already have a position with the customer and an understanding of his operations. In those regards they have a head start. They may move rapidly to provide an adequate alternative to the proposed new products. Years ago, IBM, a punched card mechanical tabulator company, not then an electronics company, did exactly this and beat out GE and RCA, two electronics companies, in electronic computers. IBM, not GE and RCA, was an old hand at dealing with accounting departments.

Every consideration just mentioned applies when an existing company ponders putting a new product on the market. But a new company starts everything from scratch and every competitive problem is heightened by that fact.

Still another list of potential competitors must be studied. These are companies, perhaps brand new ones such as yours, who seeing the same market opportunity you have discovered will decide to enter it to compete with you. Such new entities could be newly formed divisions of existing companies that have embarked on a diversification program. It may not be that these other new entries are simply jumping in to copy you after you have pointed the way, although that could happen. Rather, the same line of reasoning that caused you to start a new company may have independently appeared in their minds as well. If you see a market opening not now being filled as a basis for starting a new corporation, why should not others make the same observation and think up the same product entry without necessarily telling you about it ahead of time? If you have a technological innovation, why should not others with large and competent technical staffs be engaged in developing precisely that advance or one very similar to it? If you invent something novel in marketing or manufacturing technology that you think will give you an edge and enable you to take over a share of an existing or a developing market, why should not other corporations with specialized skills be expected to come up with the same appreciation of the potential?

All business investment involves risk, but it is paramount before launching a corporation to have made an adequate attempt to understand the market, list the potential competitors, have a convincing rationale for your ability to hold your own against them and then to set down a strategy for actions versus time to achieve success. This story of how the future will unfold should include milestones for reevaluation, for pauses to take readings of the market, the technology, the competitors' actions, and all other factors, A scenario in very substantial detail is important not only to provide an adequate rationale for starting the corporation but also it is a necessary step in estimating the capital requirements and cash flow. We are now ready to discuss these financial items.

Arranging Financing

With a detailed schedule of market-based requirements versus time, it becomes possible to create an accompanying schedule of financial requirements. A successful corporation based on new technology at some time, say 5 to 10 years ahead, will reach a period of activity characterized by a profit position, a reasonable volume of activities and a satisfactory growth rate. The start-up activity is a period of expenses, losses rather than profits, and very little revenue. In earlier chapters we described scenarios for development of a new product, from conception and start-up costs to maturity and positive cash flow. The context of those descriptions was that of a new product being added as an increment of activities to a going, successful corporation. In starting from the beginning of the corporation, the same transition periods should be expected and should be estimated for start-up costs, capital requirements and the build up of sales, earnings and cash flows.

The new corporation, if formed around a single product, is projected financially no differently from our previously recommended forecasting techniques, except that we must add now the start-up costs and period for the corporation as a whole, its organizing and launching. The corporation may not involve one product alone but rather an array of products with different timings as to their development. Or the corporation may be engaged only in marketing and not in product development or manufacture at all. The corporation may provide technical services such as consulting, planning or analysis and be in a profitable position from the first day, if it has an initial contract for services. The corporation may be put together to handle a government project under a cost-plus contract. For these varied circumstances the financial scenarios will differ greatly. What is common is the need for such a scenario with enough depth that the cash requirements can be usefully estimated and the potential return on investment gauged.

At this time it is well to emphasize the need for adequate safety margins for a technological corporation's start-up activities. One of the most often repeated experiences in starting a new technological corporation is the failure to be realistic about the time and cost to develop products. It is common to underestimate the time for organizing and manning a company, manufacturing start-up, and the marketing and establishment of the product with the customers. Equally often underestimated, and not surprisingly, is the amount of financing required. Remembering also that we are in an inflationary world, any specific dollars set down for, say, a manufacturing facility required a few years hence, or labor and material costs to estimate the price of the product, and almost every other expense, must be put down with a realistic assumption of continued inflation.

Given enough insistence on adequate safety margins, no corporation would ever be started because the funds required and the time to get to a satisfactory return on investment is almost certain to appear discouraging. Perhaps this is just as well. More often than not new technology corporations soon get themselves into financial trouble. They either fail entirely or they have to be rescued before failure with very disappointing financial results for those who made the investment. There have been periods in the past when the founders and initial investors in almost any new high technology corporation were able to sell off what they had after a few years of mediocre or worse financial results to large corporations that overestimated the value of the technology the small corporation may have created. Those days of over-paying and over-appreciation of technological starts are probably behind us. At least this approach to gain financial success should not be counted on. Instead, those contemplating starting a corporation should try to establish realistic estimates of what their start-up and growth costs will be and what returns will be generated for the investors. Then, with an integrated package, they should ask whether it makes sense from the standpoint of the founders, the managers and the investors.

Suppose now that a group of entrepreneurs have what they consider to be a competently drawn description of the company's activities versus time, including all of the important financial quantities that should be in the forecast. Suppose also that when the whole story or prophesy is looked at from the standpoint of return on investment, it appears favorable. This means it offers the investor a reasonable probability of enough return that he can justify taking the risk, remembering that the risk for a new corporation will be regarded by the investor as greater than that of an extrapolation of an existing corporation's successful history.

There is an element of risk taking or gambling that works in favor of some fledgling technological corporations. High technology is intriguing to certain investors. The extent of the attractiveness for a gamble of funds on the future is related by those investors to the degree to which the technology appears to be advanced over the existing art. The harder it is to pinpoint the market size, the product's cost effectiveness and hence its price structure, and the length of time and amount of funds it will take to develop salable equipment and systems, then the more irresistible the corporation is to some as an investment opportunity.

Even if the founders and managers of the new corporation were to persevere far beyond the average in attempting to research, analyze and articulate all of the potentials for profit, and the correlated possibilities for loss if things do not go as hoped for, the future of the corporation will remain rather vague. An honest description, and that is the only kind the SEC encourages and (within their abilities to judge) permits, must make clear to the potential investor that he is putting his funds behind something with limited visibility about the future outcome.

Raising Launching Funds

It has turned out that R&D effort has generally paid off well for those who invest in it. The economic base of any technological country today exhibits a tremendous growth in man-made resources, which can in substantial part be traced back to investment in scientific research and technological development. The same is true of corporations that have invested in R&D—on the average, that is. However, for most investors in a new enterprise the odds based-on the mass results of the past are not sufficient. They are likely to be very fussy. They will pass up investments in a new technologically oriented corporation that does not disclose ample evidence the intended activities are decidedly beyond minor departures from existing ones. They will probably be skeptical about whether the new corporation is really needed and will be inclined to argue that it is unlikely a new corporation can engage successfully in operations little different from the corporations already possessing established market positions and proven technological resources. The promoters of the new company should not look to such general investors as a source of financing unless their proposed products are excitingly innovative.

At any rate, if the detailed projections look good to the corporate founders, a detailed plan for providing the capital is next needed. Numerous patterns should be considered with the issuance of common stock, preferred stock, convertible preferred, and the use of long- and short-term debt all as possibilities in various combinations. It is quite common in the start-up of a new corporation to have a small number of private investors, and go public later, greatly increasing then the number of investors when the corporation has provided evidence it is on the right track. A capitalization changeover occurs when the initial products have had some acceptance and where large-scale funds compared with the beginning investment are now needed to provide for a larger manufacturing facility and a build up of volume for full exploitation of the market.

Certain companies known as venture capital firms specialize in providing initial financing. Such companies often assemble funds from generally high-income individuals who are looking for capital gains rather then long-term investments. They examine candidates for new corporations on the basis of their potential for making an adequate showing in a few years, then going public with an enhanced market value of the initial shares. Other sources of venture capital are large corporations with a cash flow problem—too much cash accompanied by too few ideas within their company deserving the application of the cash. For diversification and superior investment potential, such companies may be willing to take equity positions in new high technology corporations.

When a new, and hence small, high technology corporation obtains its financing from a large corporation, there is the potential advantage of the new corporation's obtaining more than funding. Presumably the financing corporation is very interested in the new corporation's success, and the large corporation has available much expertise that can help to ensure it. In addition, it can provide certain services (legal, accounting, public relations, manufacturing technology, market growth data) at no charge or a modest charge. In contrast, the new corporation usually finds it very difficult to buy the expertise it needs on occasion to supplement and enhance its small staff.

Perhaps the worst way to get financing is to borrow from relatives, mortgage the house for the second time, and try to make it on a shoestring. We all read about great industrialists who started this way, but the odds of success are lower these days. Those who finance in this fashion might also be the very entrepreneurs who badly underestimate the start-up costs and the time to attain a breakeven point.

The plan we have discussed for thinking out the starting of a company, that begins with marketing research and develops detailed financial projections, is not independent of the way in which the financing is arranged. For example, suppose the financing comes from a venture capital group and the corporation is launched as a private one with the intention of going public in, say, four years. Then the plan needs to maximize the probability of the company's ability to go public at that time. What might appear to be an optimum plan for the future in the absolute sense has to be changed to incorporate this particular important step of going from private to public, even if at some later point the corporation is a bit less successful by objective ways of judging than it would have been with different financing steps.

Similarly, if the financing comes from a large corporation, that corporation may have in mind the possibility of merging the new corporation into the large one at some later point. That also makes a difference in the detailed plan. There is, accordingly, a chicken- and -egg problem in producing a plan and, at the same time, a strategy for attracting the capital to implement it.

We must not overlook the founders of the new corporation and its initial group of principal executives, scientists, engineers, and manufacturing and marketing experts as we discuss optimum plans and strategies. The relatively small number of individuals who set out to create a new high technology corporation may have their inherent strengths, but they also have weaknesses. An adequate team is needed to cover all the facets required for success. Part of the organizing of the team goes to the motivation of these individuals. Part of the motivation in turn may depend on the plan for financing, because some approaches will have a much higher potential for providing for high eventual remuneration for the original team than other plans. If the founders try to hold on to as much first-issue common stock as possible, they may become richer if the corporation is an outstanding success. On the other hand, they will find it more difficult to finance the company. Limitations on the amount of capital they can raise, if they overdo arranging for their later rewards, may lead to failure. Thus, the founders have some optimizing to do of their own, and some gambling, as they attempt to work out a balance between their own potential for financial gain and the chances of success of the corporation. For the future of the key employees who put together a new corporation there is a risk-to-return ratio just as much as for the investors who furnish the money.

Special Management Requirements for a New Venture

The most critical requirement for a new high technology corporation is overall management—not R&D, or production, marketing, or even finance. If the general management of a new corporation is not strong enough, then the corporation had best not be launched, no matter how brilliant a scientist or outstanding an idea it has and how much its product may be needed. Experts must be available in all of the pertinent aspects and functions in which the corporation is engaged. But as to top, integrating management, there must be an adequate amount of experience accompanied by determination and ambition. In fact, although this was not true in the 1950s and 1960s to the same extent it is today, it is difficult to arrange financing for a technological corporation, even if it creatively proposes to get into some exciting new areas, if those who are slated to manage it—often the founders and commonly the inventors of the new product—have not had experience in managing successful technological enterprises.

The management of the new technological corporation must enjoy the confidence of the financial backers. Sometimes those who possess venture capital and think the new company merits their support, believing also that those who propose to run the new corporation lack necessary breadth of competence, will help in the process of finding experienced talent to inject into management.

Even if the new corporation is managed by individuals of experience in running technological corporate operations, some special requirements in managing a start-up operation must be emphasized. The call on management talents is different from what is required to operate an established corporation successfully. Because the corporation is newborn, it has no history and working-in of management. The team, although it may consist of proven hands in all of the required aspects, is still a new team. The products are inclined to be novel, and the relationship with customers is decidely at square one. It can be expected in a new technology corporation that every dimension—marketing, manufacturing, R&D, customer relationships, and relationships with financial backers—requires a process of learning, education, compromise and adjustment. Finally, it is also true that the products of a new technology corporation are not established in the same sense that the products of an existing technology corporation are. There are likely to be false starts. The absence of background means more guessing has to be done, and unusual flexibility and alertness are required to make rapid adjustments to the facts of life as they develop. Although we have emphasized the need for detailed plans, we must equally emphasize the need for detailed changes in these plans as the true history of the activities unfolds. Of course, some of the embryonic company's executives may have worked with each other for years, and some may have been very close to customers the company proposes to deal with. Such head-starts are very important.

Many people who can operate with skill, coolness and logic, and can put all of their experiences quickly to bear on a new situiation, lose their ability to do so if the situation is too unstable. We cannot use the word stable realistically in a new technology corporation until things depart from the total start-up condition that describes a new corporation on day one.

In a corporation that has been in business for many years, a general recognition will have developed of the degree of control that is necessary. Watching everything in detail and comparing actuals against plan is a never-ending process. There is always something else that could be drawn to the attention of management to give it an opportunity to optimize further, correct more ills, and ferret out reasons for the existence of problems. A mature corporation has worked out satisfactory balances. When a corporation is newly formed, that pattern of the degree to which everything must be watched has not yet been established. The interplay of judgments of individuals in relationship to one another and to the actual situation has not yet been worked out. This means a danger of over-control exists, as all conscientiously try to be sure they are on top of everything, but where the everything that they are on top of is not going well. Or, on the other hand, at the beginning everyone may operate with a looseness of control that almost amounts to a lack of it.

Also, the degree of risk-taking involved in day-to-day decisions in the running of a new corporation is different from that in the monitoring and managing of an old one. Take for example the ordering of material ahead of time. Particularly in an inflationary environment this is not a trivial matter. It is one thing to gauge the extent of inventory requirements for a going operation with years of background, including experience with recessions and booms. It is another situation entirely to create all of these estimates from ground zero. A good manager will know it is possible for him to badly underestimate or overestimate many factors. Should he hire labor ahead of time and start the training process, or should he wait to be sure how the marketing will go and whether the product is going to work well in the field? To what extent should there be an overlap of R&D, manufacturing and marketing? These are questions far more difficult to answer in a new operation. Many managers are uncomfortable when high risks are attendant to every decision. Such people are less suitable for the launching of a new corporation then they would be for the continuing of a stabilized operation on the road to success.

Acquisitions and Mergers of a New Venture

It is sometimes a very sound approach for a new technology corporation to consider merging with an existing corporation. The new corporation will have an immediate need for management, specialized expertise, and facilities. Sometimes it can find an answer to these needs in an existing corporation with the right size and composition to form a good team. We are speaking here of using the acquired company to augment and enhance the new corporation, so that our emphasis is still on the new corporation and its management. It is thus pertinent to list a few points that the management of the new technological corporation should consider very seriously as it contemplates the acquisition of an existing corporation.

First of all, we are assuming the new company is not engaged in some kind of major stock manipulation stunt. We rule out, for example, the idea of the small new technological corporation acquiring a very large existing corporation because that would constitute some kind of management takeover move directed by large financial interests. Presumably the corporation being acquired is a specialized, small- or medium-sized corporation, and, although not necessarily highly successful, has had substantial beginnings and development of at least part of its potential, It is being acquired as a way to save time and to enhance the probability of a new company's success by adding in what it has.

This means the plan should be that the management of the new technology corporation will take control of the combination. Certain of the principal executives of the acquired corporation may find themselves with principal positions in the new, augmented corporation. On the other hand, some may find themselves no longer appropriate in the new organization, and will need to be separated. In a similar way some of the lines of activity and some of the facilities will not meet the requirements of the new corporation, and the plans should include divesting or terminating these activities. When we establish these requirements about people and operations of the corporation to be acquired, we may find it difficult to arrange the acquisition.

Any acquisition discussion rests on a way of financing the acquisition. Either the new corporation is adequately financed, or perhaps we should say generously financed so that it can buy the acquired company for cash at a price that will interest the owners of that corporation, or the new corporation needs to issue additional stock. That stock, though brand new, must interest the shareholders of the existing corporation that is a candidate for acquisition. Ordinarily, for the new company's stock to be acceptable enough to effect the acquisition, the new high technology corporation's prospects must appear extraordinarily attractive, its shares already treated with great respect, with substance behind this early image. Although this is certainly not likely to happen in every instance of a relatively new company, sometimes it can occur. This would be particularly true where the corporation to be acquired appears to have little promise for stock appreciation if it continues on its own; the stock may even be regarded as in danger of going down to lower values. Also, the leaders of the new entity would have to be people of considerable reputation.

In any case, the acquisition of a substantial corporation will require a restructuring of the financing of the still relatively new corporation that does the acquiring. Its balance of equity and debt, and its entire projection of activities and financial make-up will have to be changed. The potential acquisition itself, if there is a strong rationale for it, may cause the new high technology corporation to be more highly valued in the market. In this sense the acquisition's new financing tends to be somewhat automatically taken care of, since it will be easier to sell more common stock to finance the acquisition than it might have been to sell additional common for continued activities.

Let us now consider a merger or acquisition the other way around. The new high technology corporation is acquired by, merged into or becomes a part of a larger, older corporation. This is not very likely as a strategy when the new corporation is first formed—at least not a strategy for early implementation, or there would be little reason for starting the new corporation. It could well be part of the plan scheduled for some years after the inauguration of the new corporation. This could occur especially when an older, larger corporation acts as the original financial backer. It is also a route to be considered by a new high technology corporation, when and if it appears to be heading for failure. At the other extreme, it may be, as time goes on and the new high technology corporation begins to develop successfully, that an opportunity for it to be acquired by a large established corporation with which it is compatible comes up, and the proposition is too good to turn down.

Of course, if the new corporation is having difficulties, this may portend a poor return for its original investors, even if it gets out of those difficulties. The company may be seen to need more time and more funds to get itself established than was thought necessary early on. This means its cost of capital will now rise. The original shares will probably be diluted by the need to sell more shares at a lower price to raise capital. Or perhaps the higher cost of added debt will impair earnings or delay the corporation getting into a profit position, both of which will have a negative impact on the market price of the common shares.

If the corporation is having enough difficulties, it may become too weak to survive or attain anything like the position its founders had in mind. As has been stated throughout the text, a broadly based diversified corporation of large size has certain inherent advantages in holding its own against competitors in a technological world of rapid and unpredictable change. A small technological corporation is going to have to be on the way to becoming a larger one, if it is to be successful. If it does not appear to be in a position to grow sufficiently after enough years of trying, it may be that it never will be able to make it, and ought to consider becoming part of a larger entity.

If the small corporation appears successful, or at least is moving on the original plan that was thought to be one road to success, it may still happen that the advantages of larger size are clear to its management. The company may find, for example, that it has numerous good opportunities it cannot begin to exploit. In principle, it could go out and raise still more venture capital to follow up each of those ideas. However, the management of the small corporation may have its hands full and be unable to take on more. Also, attempting too many start-ups at once may hurt the credibility of the management in the eyes of the investment world. The full exploitation of what the new, small high technology corporation may be into and the promising product lines it may have uncovered may add up to the small corporation possessing a greater worth to a large corporation than it has to its existing shareholders. A corporation with 10 ideas, of which it can only exploit three, may be worth less than a division of a large corporation with 10 good ideas, all of which the larger corporation is able to exploit.

A number of disadvantages in putting together any two corporations were discussed in a previous chapter. Particular problems arise when a large established corporation acquires a small entrepreneurial one run by its founders. If the entrepreneurs are particularly suited for the start-up phase, they may be much less appropriate for running a division of a large corporation. They would no longer be the bosses and would have to adapt their managerial style to the patterns of operation and the judgment of the executives of the larger corporation. Anyway, it is not always true that a corporation is best managed in its more developed phases by the same individuals who are ideally suited to creating the corporation as a new venture activity. It may be that, as it grows and settles down, the corporation needs a different management slate for best results. Continued adaptation of organization and changes of executive assignments are part of the natural progress and motion of all corporations as they go from start-up to maturity. However, in the technological corporation the additional dimension of the dynamics of the changing technology adds speed and complexity to the motion.

The ideal combination of the large established corporation and the new smaller corporation occurs when what each brings to the partnership greatly strengthens the other's contribution. Thus, the older, established corporation may need the new ideas and pioneering product endeavors that have been the basis for the creation and at least the partial, if not complete, success of the new corporation. The older and larger corporation may have the cash for investment and full utilization of the ideas and resources of the smaller corporation, and may have experience and established teams for marketing and manufacture, as well as much other expertise, such as in labor relations, public relations, international operations, law, and patent matters.

Problems

14-1. You wish to start a new company based on a patented product. You see a market of $10 million sales a year that should grow steadily for a long time. Your general plan will be to issue common stock to raise an initial $1 million of equity capital to cover fixed and working capital requirements as well as start-up operating losses. Assume: the assets employed are always split equally between depreciable fixed assets and working capital, the tax rate is 50 percent, losses will be carried forward on tax returns, and the interest rate before taxes is 10 percent. Draw up a 10-year forecast of the important balance sheet and operating profit and loss items incorporating the following estimated figures. First year: total assets employed, $175,000; no income from sales; securities income on invested excess cash, 8 percent before taxes; operating costs (including depreciation), $225,000. Second year: assets employed, $300,000; sales zero; operating costs, $310,000. Third year: assets employed, $300,000; sales, $225,000; operating costs, $410,000. Fourth year: assets employed, $300,000; sales, $480,000; earnings from operations before taxes, $100,000. All years following: a continuation of the fourth year's return on assets employed in operations and a steady sales growth rate of 12 percent. If all goes according to this plan, when might you sell more common stock if you are willing to borrow as required up to a level of $R_{DA} = .20$? When might you start paying a dividend? If the market sets a cost of equity capital, C_Q, for your venture of 20 percent, does your forecast net out to a return on investment that will meet this figure? If not, then suggest how your performance would have to be improved to have consistency with your plan for attracting the capital.

14–2. A company was started fifteen years ago to produce and market a new proprietary, high technology product. For two years, privately raised money sufficed for development and pilot production. At the start of the third year, a public stock issue furnished funds for full production and marketing. At the beginning of the fourth year, the company began to report profitable results which have continued to the present date. In the sixth year the company started paying dividends, a practice it has maintained. In each of the sixth and tenth years more common stock was sold to add to the equity base and provide more capital for expansion. In the twelfth year the product line was expanded and marketed overseas as well as domestically. Describe the various changing goals over the years, noting particularly where a conscious change of objectives might have been expected to be in the minds of the management as it looked ahead.

APPENDICES

A

BALANCE SHEET OPTIONS

Corporations publish lists of assets and liabilities in many different forms. The variations result from differing, though equally acceptable, accounting practices and the broad range of purposes for which the balance sheets are drawn up from time to time. One of the common alternatives has already been described in the text in which Working Capital, the net of current assets less current liabilities, is expressly shown on the assets side and is the result of subtracting the current liabilities from both sides (Table 1–B). This form is advantageous for study of return on assets employed because it distinguishes those sources of capital committed long term to the financing of the business from the short-term capital available merely because bills due and payable have not yet been paid and the funds meanwhile can be employed. In a similar way, on the assets side of the balance sheet, the working capital category separates clearly the liquid assets, such as cash, receivables, and inventory being readied for shipment, from the fixed assets of buildings and equipment.

Balance sheets sometimes contain items not readily put in the category of long-term debt and shareholders' equity on the liability side and working capital and fixed assets on the assets side. Of course, we can always lump these additional items into "other assets" or "other liabilities". However, since in this text we develop many concepts by using only a simplified balance sheet, it might be useful to mention one or two examples of these additional complicating items.

On the liability side, we might occasionally see on a balance sheet an item labeled minority interests. Very often corporations will be involved in joint ventures and other forms of partnerships with others. The assets shown on the balance sheet may include some assets of

449

such activities; these are not totally owned by the shareholders of the corporation the balance sheet represents, since various other partners in jointly owned operations have a partial claim on those assets. If, in the joint activities involved, the outside partners are majority owners, then the assets would not be shown on the corporation's balance sheet (though properly on the balance sheet of those partners). Then their ownership would not be recognized on the liability side of the corporation's balance sheet either and no minority interest item would appear there. In those circumstances, the corporation would be the minority holder and the assets side of the corporation's balance sheet would then show an item listing the value of such investments labeled as investments in affiliated or other companies.

Deferred taxes sometimes can be a substantial item on the liability side of the balance sheet (or the equivalent, a negative item to subtract from other assets on the asset side of the balance sheet). For growing technological corporations of substantial size this item may reach a figure amounting to five percent or so of the total liabilities. It usually arises from the privilege the government allows corporations under certain circumstances to accelerate depreciation of particular facilities and equipment. For tax purposes, that is, the IRS will allow a company to expense a specific capital item rapidly, showing relatively high depreciation expense in the first few years of its use. By taking a large fraction of the eventual total depreciation early, the corporation's stated earnings on its income tax report are lowered and the income tax paid to the government is then also decreased. When it reports earnings to the shareholders, the company will take only the regular (and smaller) depreciation charge against its earnings. Thus, the reported earnings to the shareholders will be greater than the reported earnings to the IRS, with the IRS's full approval. The extra cash available to the corporation by this deferring of taxes is available to the corporation and appears on the asset side of the balance sheet. On the liability side, this is balanced by and recognized by deferred taxes.

The work deferred is appropriate. With the bulk of the total depreciation taken early, the annual depreciation expense, as reported for tax purposes, will become modest in later years. So, in those years, the income tax to be paid will become relatively higher. When all the annual depreciation charges have been listed and the history of that depreciating asset is complete, the IRS will have received its total required taxes, the payments only having been deferred in the early years.

If a corporation is growing and continues to be active in areas of endeavor in which the deferring of taxes through accelerated depreciation is proper, then the deferred tax category will remain on the balance sheet. Specific items included in it will decrease in value but will be replaced by other new items. Thus, deferred taxes on the balance sheet becomes, for all practical purposes, a permanent listing. By allowing the deferring of certain taxes, the government becomes, in effect, a source of financing for the corporation. Some accountants believe this is made clearer by lumping deferred taxes with long-term debt as a new, higher debt equivalent on the liability side of the balance sheet. Others believe it more meaningful to put the deferred taxes together with the shareholders equity into a new total equity. For the purposes of this text, we will regard the deferred taxes item as not of prime importance. Admittedly, in some of the analytical developments and problems in the text, such quantities as debt-equity ratios would be modified by a few percent depending on how we group deferred taxes with other liabilities, but this would not change the basic concepts that the text discussion or the problems are meant to cover.

B

OPERATING PARAMETERS FOR SELECTED TECHNOLOGICAL CORPORATIONS (1978)

Glossary of Symbols

S = Sales or revenues [millions of \$]
C = Costs (includes depreciation + taxes + interest) [millions of \$]
E = $S - C$ = Earnings [millions of \$]
D = Debt (long term) [millions of \$]
Q = Equity (common and preferred shareholders' original investments + retained earnings) [millions of \$]
A = Net assets employed (total assets less current liabilities) [millions of \$]
T = Depreciation [millions of \$]
W = Working capital = current assets − current liabilities [millions of \$]
F = Cash flow = $E + T$ [millions of \$] (may include also write-off of intangibles)
V = Dividends (common + preferred) [millions of \$]
R_{ES} = Sales margin = E/S
R_{SA} = Turnover = S/A
R_{DA} = Debt-assets ratio = D/A
R_{EA} = Return on assets employed = E/A
R_A = Return on assets employed before interest charges = $(E + iD)/A$
R_{EQ} = Return on equity = E/Q
R_V = Dividend ratio = V/E
N = Millions of common shares outstanding

Data taken from the Compustat Data Bank of Standard & Poor's Compustat Services, Inc., current as of June 1979 except for R, R_{RE} AND R_{RS}, which are from "R & D Scoreboard: 1978," *Business Week* (July 2, 1979). NA − not available. ''1977 data.

453

Q_S = Book value of common share = Q/N

P = Market value of common shares outstanding

P_S = Market value of common share = P/N

E_S = Earnings per common share = E/N

M = Price-earnings multiple = P_s/E_s

g_E = Average annual growth in net income (1968–1978)

R = Research and development expense [millions of $]

R_{RE} = Ratio of R & D expense to income = R/E

R_{RS} = Ratio of R & D expense to sales = R/S

R_{PQ} = Ratio of preferred to common equity

Name	S	C	E	D	Q	A
AT&T	40,993	35,721	5,273	34,501	42,719	91,683
ARCO	12,298	11,494	804	3,300	5,508	10,411
BECKMAN	338	316	22	52	152	204
BENDIX	3,626	3,496	130	343	931	1,305
BOEING	5,463	5,140	323	91	1,474	1,717
BURROUGHS	2,422	2,169	253	193	1,901	2,170
DEC	1,437	1,294	142	342	905	1,263
DOW	6,888	6,312	575	2,937	3,395	6,838
DUPONT	10,584	9,797	787	1,099	4,760	6,512
EASTMAN-KODAK	7,013	6,111	902	76	4,858	5,238
EXXON	60,335	57,572	2,763	3,749	20,229	29,490
FAIRCHILD	534	509	25	69	206	288
FLUOR	2,866	2,787	78	17	421	508
FORD	42,784	41,195	1,589	1,145	9,686	12,823
GEN DYNAMICS	3,205	3,253	−48	71	704	1,007
GEN ELECTRIC	19,654	18,424	1,230	994	6,587	8,861
GM	63,221	59,713	3,508	979	17,573	20,548
GTE	8,723	8,096	627	5,805	4,304	12,650
GOODYEAR	7,489	7,263	226	1,418	2,108	3,845
HP	1,728	1,575	153	10	1,002	1,047
HONEYWELL	3,548	3,366	182	317	1,387	2,006
IBM	21,076	17,966	3,111	286	13,494	14,961
ITT	15,261	14,599	662	2,872	5,507	9,705
MacD'L-DOUGLAS	4,130	3,969	161	76	1,200	1,276
MERCK	1,981	1,674	308	211	1,455	1,779
MMM	4,662	4,099	563	362	2,592	3,209
MOTOROLA	2,220	2,095	125	198	886	1,141
NCR	2,611	2,417	194	348	1,300	1,782
POLAROID	1,377	1,258	118	0	915	915
RCA	6,601	6,322	278	1,118	1,599	3,261
ROCKWELL	5,669	5,460	209	463	1,355	1,896
SPERRY-RAND[a]	3,649	3,473	177	524	1,434	2,159
TI	2,550	2,410	140	19	845	881
TRW	3,787	3,613	174	431	1,033	1,535
UNION CARBIDE	7,870	7,475	394	1,483	3,639	6,250
UNITED TECH	6,265	6,031	234	757	1,773	2,710
WESTINGHOUSE	6,663	6,352	311	371	2,439	3,198
XEROX	5,902	5,437	465	908	2,786	4,239
ZENITH	980	957	23	53	273	342

Name	T	W	F	V	R_{ES}	R_{SA}
AT&T	5,540	−3,988	10,812	3,201	.129	.447
ARCO	798	1,039	1,602	289	.065	1.181
BECKMAN	10	126	32	3	.065	1.661
BENDIX	72	505	201	51	.036	2.778
BOEING	96	921	419	83	.059	3.181
BURROUGHS	220	726	474	61	.105	1.116
DEC	50	887	192	0	.099	1.137
DOW	562	1,165	1,137	236	.084	1.007
DUPONT	776	2,350	1,563	358	.074	1.625
EASTMAN-KODAK	344	2,437	1,246	376	.129	1.339
EXXON	1,678	4,328	4,441	1,472	.046	2.046
FAIRCHILD	23	123	47	4	.046	1.854
FLUOR	42	−40	121	20	.027	5.642
FORD	1,314	3,093	2,903	417	.037	3.336
GEN DYNAMICS	96	232	48	158	−.015	3.182
GEN ELECTRIC	576	2,580	1,806	570	.063	2.218
GM	3,036	7,949	6,544	1,726	.055	3.077
GTE	902	−385	1,530	364	.072	.690
GOODYEAR	214	1,496	440	93	0.30	1.948
HP	56	537	209	14	.089	1.650
HONEYWELL	248	612	430	442	.051	1.768
IBM	1,824	4,511	4,935	1,763	.148	1.409
ITT	424	1,935	1,086	293	.043	1.572
MacD'L-DOUGLAS	60	657	221	22	.039	3.238
MERCK	75	667	383	132	.155	1.114
MMM	203	1,574	766	234	.121	1.453
MOTOROLA	83	620	209	32	.056	1.945
NCR	186	966	380	27	.074	1.465
POLAROID	43	620	161	30	.086	1.504
RCA	364	1,146	642	110	.042	2.024
ROCKWELL	120	771	329	81	.037	2.989
SPERRY-RAND[a]	134	795	311	39	.048	1.690
TI	131	278	271	40	.055	2.894
TRW	99	582	274	68	.046	2.468
UNION CARBIDE	417	1,621	811	181	.050	1.259
UNITED TECH	111	1,125	345	103	.037	2.312
WESTINGHOUSE	149	749	460	84	.047	2.084
XEROX	664	1,228	1,129	161	.079	1.392
ZENITH	16	209	39	19	.024	2.868

Name	R_{DA}	R_{EA}	R_A	R_{EQ}	R_V	N
AT&T	.376	.058	.087	.123	.607	670
ARCO	.317	.077	.114	.146	.359	112
BECKMAN	.253	.109	.143	.146	.139	16
BENDIX	.263	.099	.140	.139	.392	22
BOEING	.053	.188	.193	.219	.258	64
BURROUGHS	.089	.117	.134	.133	.242	41
DEC	.270	.113	.130	.157	0	40
DOW	.430	.084	.126	.169	.411	181
DUPONT	.169	.121	.142	.165	.455	48
EASTMAN-KODAK	.014	.172	.176	.186	.417	161
EXXON	.127	.094	.108	.137	.533	444
FAIRCHILD	.240	.086	.111	.120	.174	5
FLUOR	.033	.154	.163	.186	.258	16
FORD	.089	.124	.139	.164	.262	120
GEN DYNAMICS	.070	−.048	−.031	−.068	−3.278	26
GEN ELECTRIC	.112	.139	.164	.187	.463	228
GM	.048	.171	.188	.200	.492	285
GTE	.459	.050	.094	.146	.580	142
GOODYEAR	.369	.059	.106	.107	.411	72
HP	.010	.146	.152	.153	.092	29
HONEYWELL	.158	.090	.117	.131	2.438	21
IBM	.019	.208	.212	.231	.567	146
ITT	.296	.068	.111	.120	.443	112
MacD'L-DOUGLAS	.059	.126	.132	.134	.138	37
MERCK	.119	.173	.187	.211	.430	76
MMM	.113	.175	.191	.217	.415	117
MOTOROLA	.174	.110	.134	.141	.257	31
NCR	.195	.109	.136	.149	.137	26
POLAROID	0	.129	.136	.129	.250	33
RCA	.343	.085	.120	.174	.395	75
ROCKWELL	.244	.110	.140	.154	.387	34
SPERRY-RAND"	.243	.082	.118	.123	.220	35
TI	.022	.159	.169	.166	.286	23
TRW	.281	.114	.145	.169	.392	29
UNION CARBIDE	.237	.063	.089	.108	.460	65
UNITED TECH	.279	.086	.103	.132	.440	41
WESTINGHOUSE	.116	.097	.110	.128	.271	86
XEROX	.214	.110	.139	.167	.346	81
ZENITH	.156	.068	.088	.085	.807	19

Name	Q_S	P	P_S	E_S	M
AT&T	63.80	40,441	60.40	63.80	7.67
ARCO	49.33	5,061	45.33	49.33	6.29
BECKMAN	9.25	395	24.00	9.25	17.82
BENDIX	41.92	807	36.30	41.92	6.22
BOEING	23.00	3,045	47.53	23.00	9.43
BURROUGHS	46.41	2,989	73.00	46.41	11.80
DEC	22.69	2,133	53.50	22.69	15.00
DOW	18.74	4,475	24.70	18.74	7.78
DUPONT	99.03	6,057	126.00	99.03	7.70
EASTMAN-KODAK	30.10	9,442	58.50	30.10	10.46
EXXON	45.60	21,781	49.10	45.60	7.88
FAIRCHILD	38.20	34	6.40	38.20	1.39
FLUOR	26.85	521	33.20	26.85	6.65
FORD	81.03	5,033	42.10	81.03	3.17
GEN DYNAMICS	26.65	838	31.76	26.65	−17.44
GEN ELECTRIC	28.88	10,741	47.10	28.88	8.73
GM	61.60	15,291	53.60	61.60	4.36
GTE	30.31	4,019	28.30	30.31	6.41
GOODYEAR	29.47	1,152	16.10	29.47	5.09
HP	34.54	2,602	89.70	34.54	17.01
HONEYWELL	64.69	1,488	69.40	64.69	8.20
IBM	92.54	43,510	298.40	92.54	13.99
ITT	49.09	3,029	27.00	49.09	4.58
MacD'L-DOUGLAS	32.23	1,236	33.20	32.23	7.67
MERCK	19.25	5,102	67.50	19.25	16.59
MMM	22.12	7,394	63.10	22.12	13.13
MOTOROLA	28.49	1,234	39.70	28.49	9.86
NCR	49.66	1,581	60.40	49.66	8.16
POLAROID	27.85	1,695	51.60	27.85	14.31
RCA	21.40	1,951	26.10	21.40	7.01
ROCKWELL	39.30	1,220	35.40	39.30	5.84
SPERRY-RAND[a]	41.30	1,264	36.40	41.30	7.16
TI	37.13	1,822	80.00	37.13	12.99
TRW	36.17	1,028	36.00	36.17	5.90
UNION CARBIDE	55.93	2,212	34.00	55.93	5.61
UNITED TECH	43.19	1,589	38.70	43.19	6.78
WESTINGHOUSE	28.43	1,416	16.50	28.43	4.55
XEROX	34.59	4,284	53.20	34.59	9.21
ZENITH	14.51	239	12.70	14.51	10.25

Name	g_E	R	R_{RE}	R_{RS}	R_{PQ}
AT&T	.097	841	.160	.021	.052
ARCO	.177	65	.080	.005	.114
BECKMAN	.181	27	1.215	.079	0
BENDIX	.137	51	.391	.014	.020
BOEING	.269	276	.855	.051	0
BURROUGHS	.193	143	.563	.059	0
DEC	.360	116	.814	.081	0
DOW	.210	232	.402	.034	0
DUPONT	.055	377	.479	.036	.052
EASTMAN-KODAK	.081	389	.431	.055	0
EXXON	.099	290	.105	.005	0
FAIRCHILD	.295	50	2.023	.094	0
FLUOR	.243	NA	NA	NA	.129
FORD	.076	1,464	.921	.034	0
GEN DYNAMICS	.341	41	−8.42	.013	.044
GEN ELECTRIC	.149	521	.424	.026	0
GM	.087	1,633	.466	.026	.017
GTE	.113	127	.203	.015	.098
GOODYEAR	.025	152	.671	.020	0
HP	.241	154	1.007	.089	0
HONEYWELL	.110	187	1.031	.053	0
IBM	.144	1,255	.403	.060	0
ITT	.104	371	.561	.024	.449
MacD'L-DOUGLAS	.031	169	1.048	.041	0
MERCK	.136	161	.525	.081	.002
MMM	.115	204	.362	.044	0
MOTOROLA	.163	133	1.066	.060	0
NCR	.257	138	.713	.053	.001
POLAROID	.052	87	.730	.063	0
RCA	.058	141	.505	.021	.092
ROCKWELL	.111	61	.290	.011	.099
SPERRY-RAND[a]	.116	195	1.105	.053	0
TI	.180	111	.791	.044	0
TRW	.093	54	.307	.014	.350
UNION CARBIDE	.129	156	.395	.020	0
UNITED TECH	.175	440	1.879	.070	.256
WESTINGHOUSE	.075	152	.488	.023	.007
XEROX	.134	311	.669	.053	0
ZENITH	−.092	NA	NA	NA	0

INDEX

461

474 INDEX